How to Design
Electrical Systems

How to Design Electrical Systems

A complete manual on practical design and layout of electrical systems for power, light, heat, signals, and communications in commercial, industrial, and residential buildings

JOSEPH F. McPARTLAND and the Editors of
Electrical Construction and Maintenance

 McGRAW-HILL BOOK COMPANY

New York   San Francisco   Toronto   London   Sydney

Foreword

This work was originally outlined to provide an up-to-date guide to electrical systems design practice for the subscribers to *Electrical Construction and Maintenance*. In exploring the task, the editors found that the subject was covered briefly in handbooks and academically in textbooks, and that trade literature was devoted primarily to product application. While these sources were valuable and authoritative, each in its own scope and objective, the task of bringing together basic data and considerations leading into practical systems design evidently had not been achieved on a sufficiently comprehensive scale.

There was obvious need for such a work. The crucial importance of good system design is recognized today in every segment of the electrical industry. But what is good design? For any one job there are probably several satisfactory systems. The choice more often involves judgment than formula. Therefore, there is a distinct and useful place for a practical, interpretive, published work setting forth the criteria of good design in the context of actual current practice.

There are many engineers well qualified to prepare such a project. But it takes large resources, much time, and expert help to reach the printed page. Our editorial staff had several distinct, even unique advantages: an unexcelled file of source literature, expert service facilities, and almost daily first-hand contact through broad travel with actual and current electrical work in all parts of the United States.

The project was assigned to Joseph F. McPartland, Managing Editor, who produced all but two sections of this volume and richly deserves the by-line. Berlon C. Cooper and William J. Novak, Associate Editors, contributed the sections on lighting design and electric heating, respectively. Information, data, and guidance were provided by other staff members from their extensive experience and contact with the industry and its technology. These included Senior Editors August Eckel and Hugh P. Scott; John H. Watt, Associate Editor; and Alice McMullen, Consultant.

W. T. STUART, *Editor*
Electrical Construction and Maintenance

Preface

This book contains new and revised material on electrical systems design and was preceded by three volumes on the same subject: two editions of "Electrical Systems Design" followed by "Electrical Systems for Power and Light." The title for this book, "How to Design Electrical Systems," more accurately describes the purpose and contents of the book.

Although phases of electrical design are covered in many books, booklets, and magazine articles, this report is a treatment of the complete art of electrical design. The presentation goes into design of complete electrical systems for a wide range of industrial, commercial, and institutional buildings. From specific electrical loads and the circuits to serve them, down to connection to main power supply lines, this book incorporates the many design considerations and relates all parts to the whole. It has been prepared as a guide and reference source.

Aimed at the ever-increasing need for modern electrical design data, the book covers accepted practice and emphasizes design trends which have particular merit. Over and above sound engineering principles and intelligent conformity to the safety provisions of the National Electrical Code, the basis for this report includes due recognition of substantial spare capacity as an essential element of modern electrical design.

The material is presented in the normal order of design procedure. First, general considerations are stated for the contemplated system design. Then detailed design of the system begins with provision of the branch circuits to supply the loads directly. From the nature and extent of branch circuiting, the required system of feeders and subfeeders can be determined. Then the overall distribution scheme can be developed. Finally, the details of energy supply for the entire system are developed.

Separate sections are devoted to certain specific areas of design which can be considered apart from the bulk of commercial and industrial wiring. These include residential wiring design, selection and layout of lighting equipment, application of electric heating, and design of signal and communication circuits and layouts.

JOSEPH F. McPARTLAND, *Managing Editor*
Electrical Construction and Maintenance

Contents

Planning for electrical design

Design of an electrical system for any building or outdoor area is basically a matter of providing an arrangement of conductors and equipment to safely and effectively transfer electric energy from a source of power to lamps, motors and other functional devices which operate on electricity. This simple task is readily reduced to three basic steps which set the outline for detailed electrical design of any electrical system:

1. Select basic wiring concepts and configurations which will supply electrical power of the required characteristics at each point of electrical utilization.
2. Implement the electrical circuiting concepts with actual conductors, apparatus and hardware, selecting types, sizes, models, characteristics, appearances, ratings and other specifics of the required equipment.
3. Account for the installation of the overall electrical system, as determined from the first two steps, within the physical dimensions and structural makeup of a building, showing, as clearly as possible, locations and details of equipment mountings, raceways runs, connections to main power supply lines and whatever elements require special attention.

Of course, these three steps are necessarily interrelated, and particular decisions made within any one step will affect corresponding elements within either or both of the other steps.

As can be seen from the three steps, design of an electrical system is expressed in the form of electrical plans. All phases of a design, including design of subsystems within the major system, should be reduced to a set of blueprints which present schematic wiring diagrams, single-line diagrams, full-wiring hookups, riser diagrams, isometric and other sketches, detail drawings and equipment schedules—all as necessary to convey a clear picture of the system to the installer.

But before the actual design work begins, there are many factors which must be considered and understood in their relation to the contemplated design of an electrical system.

Approaching the design task

Successful electrical design for all types of modern buildings depends first of all upon the right approach. The electrical designer must be thoroughly familiar with all of the background factors of design. He must, of course, have depth in engineering ability. But over and above this, he must also fully understand the relation between pure technology in an electrical system and such considerations as safe application, capacity for load growth, flexibility in use of the system and effective layout. From such understanding, the right approach to electrical design is inevitable.

Then the right approach must be correlated with modern standards. Because electrical design is a dynamic thing—the continually evolving product of years of accumulating technology—the electrical designer must learn the new techniques and follow the promising trends. Electrical design is not a mechanical procedure for merely filling in formulas and adding parts together. It involves clear understanding of old, accepted techniques and the reasons why those techniques survived the test of years of application. It requires combinations of old and new wiring techniques and the ability to devise original circuits and layouts for new or special equipment applications. In short, it demands that the designer be as dynamic as the art and science he practices. Only from an all-around grasp of the subject can a designer exercise judgment in selection of circuit and feeder arrangements, equipment types and ratings and installation methods.

Every electrical system must provide power and light without hazard to life or property, with sufficient extra capacity to meet foreseeable load growth, with ready adaptability to load modifications and revised layouts and with all necessary accessibility in the distribution arrangement.

Safety is basic

Compliance with the provisions of the National Electrical Code can effectively minimize fire and accident hazards in any electrical design. The code (throughout this manual, the word "code" refers to the National Electrical Code) sets forth requirements, recommendations and suggestions and constitutes a minimum standard for the framework of electrical design. As stated in its own introduction, the code is concerned with the "practical safeguarding of persons and of buildings and their contents from hazards arising from the use of electricity for light, heat, power, radio, signalling and for other purposes."

Although the code assures minimum safety provisions, actual design work must constantly consider safety as required by special types or conditions of electrical application. For example, effective provision of automatic protective devices and selection of control equipment for particular applications involves engineering skill of the designer, above routine adherence to code requirements. Then, too, the designer must know the physical characteristics—application advantages and limitations—of the many materials he uses for enclosing, supporting, insulating, isolating and, in general, protecting electrical equipment. The task of safe application based on skill and experience is particularly important in hazardous locations. Safety is not automatically made a characteristic of a system by simply observing codes. Safety must be designed into a system.

The NE Code is recognized as a legal criterion of safe electrical design and installation. It is used in court litigation and by insurance companies as a basis for insuring buildings. Because the code is such an important instrument of safe design, it must be thoroughly understood by the electrical designer. He must be familiar with all sections of the code and should know the accepted interpretations which have been placed on many specific rulings of the code. He should keep abreast of official interpretations which are issued by the NE Code committee. He should know the intent of code requirements—i.e., the spirit as well as the letter of each provision. He should keep informed on interim amendments to the code. And, most important, he should keep this code book handy and study it often.

In addition to the NE Code volume itself, the electrical designer should have on hand and be familiar with other standards and recommended practices made available in pamphlet form by the National Fire Protection Association, 60 Batterymarch St., Boston, Mass. 02110. These cover such special subjects as: Hospital Operating Rooms, Municipal Fire Alarm Systems, Garages, Aircraft Hangars and similar special applications with great potential hazards due to improper design.

Every electrical designer must also be familiar with insurance company regulations and all local codes which affect a particular installation. He should know in detail where and how local codes depart from the NE Code. Again he must understand the basis for special provisions to assure most effective conformity throughout a system. Often, a local condition which requires special code rulings has a significant effect upon the entire design.

Still another measure which a designer can take to enhance the safety characteristic of his work is regular use of literature issued by the Underwriters' Laboratories, Inc. The UL examines, tests and determines the suitability of materials and equipment to be used according to code regulations. Each year, the

UL publishes three volumes which are essential as references for electrical designers. These are listings of commercially available electrical products which have been found acceptable with reference to fire and accident hazards and in conformity with the application and installation requirements of the code. The three volumes are entitled as follows:
1. "Electrical Construction Materials"
2. "Electrical Appliance and Utilization Equipment"
3. "Hazardous Location Equipment"

The UL also has other literature on special equipment involving hazard to life or property, such as "Gas and Oil Equipment" and "Fire Protection Equipment."

Capacity for present—plus

In general, every electrical system should have sufficient capacity to serve the loads for which it is designed, plus spare capacity to meet anticipated growth in the load on the system. In particular, this means that conductors and raceways must be sized liberally for computed loads; substations, transformers and switching and protective devices must have the needed capacity and ratings. And spare capacity throughout the branch circuiting should be reflected back through the entire electrical system to the point of power supply.

Allowance for load growth is probably the most neglected consideration in electrical design today. Although the code contains an almost obscure recommendation that electrical plans and specifications include "allowances for future increases in the use of electricity," experience with current electrical modernization practice indicates that lack of spare capacity plagues existing systems. In all types of buildings, conduit risers are filled to capacity and the conductors in them are either loaded fully or overloaded. In most commercial and institutional buildings, the entire electrical system is at or near saturation—in branch circuits, feeders and service. And in the majority of these buildings, modernization of the existing electrical system to handle increased load demands is impeded by absence of space in which new risers and circuits might be run. It is obvious that overall design of these electrical systems did not account sufficiently for future load growth.

Modern electrical design, therefore, must carefully plan for future increase in electrical utilization. Depending upon the particular conditions in any installation, mains, switchgear, transformers, feeders, panelboards and circuits should be sized to handle considerable load growth. Conductors should be selected on the basis of carrying capacity, voltage drop and estimated future requirements. Conduit, wireways, troughs and other raceways should be sized to allow future increase in occupancy. And space used to house electrical equipment—electric closets, switchgear rooms, substation cages, riser and pipe shafts, etc.—should also be able to accommodate the addition of more equipment at a later date.

Every design must consider—

Flexibility: Depending upon the type of building—industrial, commercial or institutional—the electrical system must be designed to provide required flexibility in distribution and circuiting. Layout and type of equipment should readily accommodate changes in locations of motors and other utilization devices. Feeders, distribution panelboards and circuits should be suited to a wide range of utilization patterns, allowing full and efficient use of power capacity for activities in the building's various areas.

Accessibility: Every electrical system should rate high in accessibility. In its final form, design of the system must provide ease of access to equipment for maintenance and repair and for any possible extensions, modifications or alterations in the system. The system of conductors, raceways and equipment must allow for full use of its power handling ability.

Reliability: Depending upon the nature of activities in a building, continuity of electrical supply and overall reliability of the wiring system itself can be a more or less important consideration. Where electrical utility companies have a good record of supply continuity and temporary loss of power would not be a direct life or property hazard, special provisions for a separate emergency power supply are usually not necessary. But in many industrial plants, hospitals and buildings with essential equipment electrically powered, standby power plants or multiple services must be used for absolute reliability of supply.

Analyzing a specific system

Based on full recognition and appreciation of the foregoing system characteristics, electrical design for a specific building begins with analysis of the type of building, its loads and the source of supply. This involves careful determination of all usual and special electrical requirements for the type of building. Consideration must be made of the activities performed in the building and the nature of electrical usage by the occupants. Whether the building is a school, an office building, an industrial plant, a hospital—the designer must know the history of electrical application in the type of building and must be well informed on current trends and practices.

What kind of building?

The general design approach to any contemplated electrical system takes into account characteristics of the building—small or large, single-story or multi-level industrial plant; high office building; apartment house; single- or multi-level school; hospital; etc.—as this gives insight to types of electrical utilization, need for flexibility, accessibility of the system and the duty cycles of various load devices. The many and varied considerations for hazardous locations also serve to give direction to design approach. From the general approach, the mind of the designer should have selected many design possibilities which suit the particular building and have rejected all methods and techniques which are immediately not applicable.

In general, planning for design of an electrical system should begin with determining and studying the size and nature of the total load to be served. This means approximation of lighting loads on the basis of watts/square foot, analysis of number and sizes of motors served in various areas of the building and determination of amount of other utilization loads and their concentrations throughout the building. Full understanding of all loads—their values and points of application—is essential to selection of the best type of distribution system.

Standardizing equipment

Maximum standardization in equipment type and ratings should always be a design objective. Selection of standard supply voltage and standard values at all voltage levels is a significant economy factor in that standard rated transformers, switchgear, motors and other equipment cost less than special equipment for nonstandard voltages.

Lack of standardization in an electrical system com-plicates maintenance in that replacement parts are not easy to get, inventory of parts and equipment is high and the efficiency of maintenance personnel is reduced. And the use of special, nonstandard equipment and voltages may seriously impair expansion or alteration of the electrical system at a later date. However, where special, nonstandard equipment is necessary for the particular functions required in a building, such equipment must be carefully selected and integrated into the system.

Providing system power supply

Another preliminary consideration which fundamentally affects design procedure involves the characteristics of the power supply which will serve the building's electrical system. The power supply may be either the distribution system of the electric utility company or a private electric generating plant.

A utility power system is the most common type of supply to buildings and plants. Purchase of energy usually represents decided economy over the cost of private generation of electric energy within the building or plant. Of course, there are certain cases, such as paper and pulp mills, in which requirements for large amounts of process steam make possible the use of excess steam for economical generation of energy. In such cases, the generating plant may be operated independently of a utility supply to the building or in parallel with it.

If the local generating plant operates independently, part of the total electrical load may be connected to it and part to the utility system. Use of a generating plant in parallel with a utility supply must be checked with the utility company engineers.

If power is obtained from a utility line, the characteristics of the supply must be matched to the requirements of the building. Depending upon the voltage and capacity of the supply, one particular type of distribution is often best suited to carrying the electrical loads in the building.

Purchase of power at utilization voltages indicates certain types of distribution; higher voltage services and primary supplies also indicate their own types of distribution systems within the building When several different supply voltages are available, each should be appraised in relation to the various distribution methods which might be used.

Consultation with the utility company about the relation between different services and interior distribution systems should precede any decisions.

CHECKLISTS OF MODERN

INDUSTRIAL PLANTS

Varying with the particular type of industrial operation, electrical load density can run well over 20 watts per square foot. Typical modern elements of industrial electrical systems include the following:

- ☐ Primary distribution to load center substations.
- ☐ Interlocked armor cable feeders rated for 5-kv or 15-kv circuits.
- ☐ Extensive use of 480-volt power and 277-volt fluorescent and/or mercury vapor lighting.
- ☐ Busway and/or interlocked armor cable for secondary voltage feeders.
- ☐ Cables troughs and/or racks carrying suitably protected cables, for maximum system flexibility and accessibility.
- ☐ Rigid non-metallic conduit in corrosive locations.
- ☐ Underfloor power ducts for flexible circuiting to machine loads throughout widespread plant areas.
- ☐ Plug-in busway for ready tapping to power and light loads.
- ☐ Careful attention to hazardous location installations.

- ☐ Thoroughly engineered protection against system faults.
- ☐ Adequate interrupting capacity in all devices which interrupt current flow—both control switching and protective equipment.
- ☐ Coordinated application of short-circuit and overload protective devices to effectively isolate faulted sections of the system without interrupting service to other sections.
- ☐ Modern switchgear—totally enclosed, dead-front for maximum safety; designed for easy maintenance.
- ☐ High power factor operation with excellent regulation of voltage at all levels in the plant.
- ☐ Use of high frequency (over 60 cps) electric energy for power applications and for maximum-efficiency fluorescent lighting, with reduced heat load.

OFFICE BUILDINGS

Typical load densities for modern office buildings can run over 15 watts per square foot where electrical usage is at a maximum for light and power facilities. General area lighting may account for eight or more watts per square foot; power loads, for four or more watts per square foot; and the balance of small machines and incidental loads, up to 2 watts per square foot.

- ☐ Primary supply to two or more unit substations widely spaced vertically within the building.
- ☐ Adequate interrupting capacities and coordinated protection.
- ☐ Distribution at 480/277 volts, 3-phase, 4-wire for power and general area fluorescent lighting.
- ☐ High frequency distribution system for high-level, high-efficiency fluorescent lighting.
- ☐ Busway risers.
- ☐ Aluminum conduit risers.
- ☐ Air-handling luminaires to provide lighting and air conditioning from single unit for module layouts.

- ☐ Step-down local transformers for 120/208-volt, 3-phase, 4-wire supply to incandescent lighting and convenience receptacle circuits.
- ☐ Underfloor raceway systems for power, light, telephones and signals in large office areas with shifting loads or layouts.
- ☐ Effective alarms, signals and communication facilities—fire alarms, burglar alarms, watchmen's systems.
- ☐ Remote-control switching.
- ☐ Carrier-frequency relay switching without control wires.
- ☐ Raised floors for underfloor circuiting to computers in data processing centers.

DESIGN TECHNIQUES

HOSPITALS

Typical electrical demand for modern hospital facilities can range up to 3,000 watts per bed where maximum use is made of electrical equipment.

☐ Use of load center distribution where possible.
☐ Careful provision for electrical supply continuity in case of failure of normal supply: two separate services, a special emergency service, an emergency standby power generator or standby dc supply for essential lighting and other essential facilities.
☐ Modern lighting throughout the hospital.
☐ Engineered application of modern signal and communication equipment: call and register systems, paging systems, intercom, closed-circuit television, radio program distribution.
☐ Modern wiring of laboratory facilities, X-ray equipment.
☐ Careful compliance with all code requirements on wiring in operating rooms (ungrounded circuits and ground detector and alarm system) and in hazardous (anesthetizing) areas.

SCHOOLS

Lighting loads for modern schools vary with the type and layout of buildings and the extent to which daylighting is utilized in classrooms. Typical load densities range from 3 to 7 watts per square foot, depending upon type of lighting—incandescent or fluorescent—and luminaires used. Power loads may include air conditioning, electric heating, ventilation, compressors and elevators.

☐ Distribution at 4160 volts (or higher where direct utility supply requires) to two or more load centers in large-area, multi-building school layouts.
☐ Use of on-site electric generation for air-conditioned schools.
☐ Use of 480/277-volt distribution for power and lighting loads.
☐ Electric heating throughout school buildings for maximum comfort and effective climate control, minimizing maintenance and eliminating the hazards of combustible fuels.
☐ Modern, high-level lighting with maximum visual comfort.
☐ "Showcase" wiring and equipment application in laboratories and craft shops, providing integration in the teaching of electricity and its use.
☐ Modern gymnasium lighting, electric scoreboards, effective use of public address equipment.
☐ Engineered lighting and power facilities for auditoriums, including programmed, dimmer control of stage lighting and house lights.
☐ Intercom and paging systems.
☐ Closed-circuit television systems for instruction purposes.
☐ Clock and bell program system.
☐ Modern fire alarm system.
☐ Vandal alarm system to protect school against vandals and other intruders during closed hours.

SHOPPING CENTERS

Lighting load densities vary widely for the different areas of shopping centers—from 3 to more than 10 watts per square foot. Actual figures depend upon the sizes and types of stores, the relative amounts of fluorescent and incandescent lighting, light used for decoration and the amount of outside lighting. Power load densities depend upon the facilities selected.

☐ Primary distribution to load center subs.
☐ Use of 480/277 volts among and within buildings.
☐ Use of contactors and split-bus panelboards for time clock control of large blocks of sign, display and outdoor lighting.
☐ Modern store lighting.
☐ Music distribution, intercom and paging systems.
☐ Modern parking lot lighting: fluorescent, mercury-vapor and/or quartz-iodine luminaires.

Branch circuits to utilization devices

A branch circuit is that part of a wiring system extending beyond the final automatic overload protective device which is approved for use as branch-circuit protection. Fig. 1. Thermal cutouts or motor overload devices are not branch-circuit protection. Neither are fuses in luminaires or in plug connections, where used for ballast protection or individual fixture protection. Such supplementary overcurrent protection is not a substitute for branch-circuit protection. See NE Code Section 240-30. But Fig. 2 shows a common case of bridge and highway circuits in which a number of large lamp loads are fed by a feeder with individual fusing for each fixture which does make the tap circuits become the branch circuits of the system.

In its simplest form, a branch circuit consists of two wires which carry current at a particular voltage from protective device to utilization device.

Although the branch circuit represents the last step in the transfer of power from the service or source of energy to utilization devices, it is the starting point for modern design procedure. First, the loads are circuited. Then the circuits are lumped on the feeders. Finally, the distribution system is connected to one or more sources of power.

FIG. 2—Common variation from standard branch-circuit layout

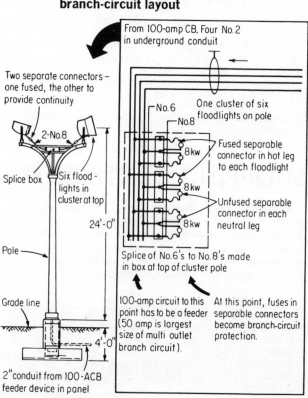

From 100-amp CB. Four No.2 in underground conduit

Two separate connectors – one fused, the other to provide continuity

2-No.8

Splice box

Six flood-lights in cluster at top

Pole

24'-0"

Grade line

4'-0"

2" conduit from 100-ACB feeder device in panel

No.6

No.8

One cluster of six floodlights on pole

8kw

Fused separable connector in hot leg to each floodlight

8kw

Unfused separable connector in each neutral leg

8kw

Splice of No.6's to No.8's made in box at top of cluster pole

100-amp circuit to this point has to be a feeder (50 amp is largest size of multi outlet branch circuit).

At this point, fuses in separable connectors become branch-circuit protection.

FIG. 1—Definition of a branch circuit

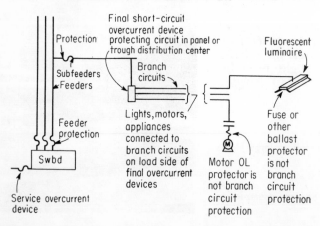

Protection

Final short-circuit overcurrent device protecting circuit in panel or trough distribution center

Subfeeders Feeders

Branch circuits

Fluorescent luminaire

Feeder protection

Swbd

Lights, motors, appliances connected to branch circuits on load side of final overcurrent devices

Motor OL protector is not branch circuit protection

Fuse or other ballast protector is not branch circuit protection

Service overcurrent device

Each and every branch circuit—whether for power or lighting load, in commercial, industrial or residential buildings—should be sized for its load, with spare capacity added where possible load growth is indicated, where necessary to reduce heating in continuously operating circuits and/or for voltage stability requirements. Design should also provide for economical addition of circuits to handle future loads. Each circuit must assure required power capacity at full utilization voltage at every outlet.

Accessibility and flexibility are two important characteristics of effective branch circuiting. In commercial and industrial buildings, shifting of load devices as a result of tenant changes, rearranging of office layouts, changes in production schedules or relocation of production lines are common. Circuits in such areas must readily accommodate these changes and must allow extensions.

Safety provisions in branch circuits are, of course, essential. Adherence to the provisions of the code will assure basic safety. In providing circuits for special or unusual utilization devices or for devices not covered in the code, the designer must call upon his own engineering skill and perception in providing effective control, grounding and protection for maximum safety.

Selecting branch-circuit voltage

In general, modern branch-circuit design has developed from the trend toward high distribution voltages, incorporating the favorable economic and operating characteristics of loadcenter layout. As a result, branch circuits are short runs from strategically located panelboards or transformer loadcenters instead of long circuits from a central distribution panelboard. The high voltage is delivered to the loadcenter where it is reduced to utilization levels. Or in the one-voltage system, the feeder is carried to the approximate physical center of a load concentration area before it is subdivided into branch circuits. The use of loadcenters and resulting short branch circuits provides better-regulated voltage supplies to utilization devices and minimum circuit disturbances to load changes.

Modern electrical systems use four basic voltage configurations (or systems) for branch circuits to supply utilization voltages at light and power outlets. These are derived from the common secondary distribution systems, as follows:

SINGLE-PHASE, 3-WIRE SYSTEM

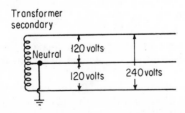

This is a commonly used system in individual residences, small apartment and commercial buildings. Both lighting and single-phase motor loads can be served. Two-wire, 240-volt branch circuits can be used for power loads; 3-wire, 120/240-volt circuits for lighting outlets, split-wired duplex receptacles and

some power devices such as electric ranges; and 2-wire, 120-volt circuits for lighting and receptacle outlets.

3-PHASE, 4-WIRE WYE SYSTEM

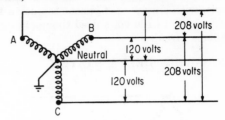

This is the most widely used 3-phase secondary distribution system. The most common use of this configuration is the 120/208-volt, 3-phase, 4-wire system with the neutral grounded. With this system, a variety of circuits is available: 4-wire, 120/208-volt circuits; 3-wire, 120/208-volt circuits; 3-wire, 208-volt circuits; 2-wire, 208-volt circuits; and 2-wire, 120-volt circuits. Such a system can serve a combination of power and lighting loads and offers flexibility for circuit layout and application of required utilization equipment.

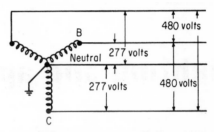

Another 3-phase, 4-wire, wye-connected system which has gained rapidly in acceptance and application is the 480/277-volt wye-connected system (also called 460/265-volt system, due to the voltage spread). Under certain conditions, this system offers more advantages and economy in commercial building applications than the 120/208-volt system. The system makes available three types of branch circuits: 480-volt, 3-phase for motor loads; 277-volt, single-phase for fluorescent or mercury vapor lighting; and 120-volt, 240-volt or 120/208-volt circuits from stepdown transformers for receptacle circuits and miscellaneous loads.

3-PHASE, 3-WIRE SYSTEM

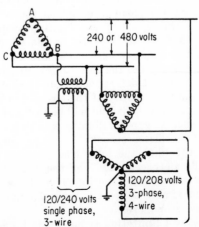

This is the common delta-connected secondary system with phase-to-phase voltage of 240, 480 or 600 volts between each pair of phase conductors. This system is used where the motor load represents a large part of the total load. In some such systems, 3-phase, 3-wire circuits at 480 volts feed individual motor loads, with single- or 3-phase step-down transformers from 480 to 120 volts used to supply lighting and receptacle circuits.

3-PHASE, 4-WIRE DELTA SYSTEM

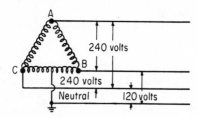

This is a variation on the 3-phase, 3-wire delta system above and is commonly called a "red-leg" delta system because the phase leg with higher voltage-to-ground than the other two phase legs is commonly painted red to differentiate from the other two phase legs. One of the transformer secondary windings supplying the system is center-tapped to derive a grounded neutral conductor to the two phase legs between which it is connected. Motors are supplied at 240 volts, either 3-phase or single-phase with single-phase 120-volt branch circuits taken from the grounded, center-tapped conductor and its associated phases.

In some areas, electrical systems are supplied from two coexisting services—a 3-phase, 3-wire system for power loads and a separate 120/240-volt, single phase or 120/208-volt, 3-phase grounded system for lighting and appliance loads.

Other system configurations are commonly used to supply branch circuits, but they are derived from the basic systems above. Particular local conditions and/or requirements for load balance throughout an overall system frequently dictate the use of less common derivations of branch circuits. Such arrangements include 120/208-volt, 3-wire feeds to branch circuit panelboards, open-delta 3-phase supply to light and power branch circuits and other special transformer hookups supplying branch-circuit loads. Motor branch circuits may be served directly from high-voltage supplies.

Lighting and appliance branch circuits

Design of a lighting layout for any commercial, institutional or industrial area includes determination of the required footcandle intensity of lighting, selection of the general type of lighting—incandescent, fluorescent, mercury vapor or some combination of these, number of lamps per luminaire, number of luminaires, types of luminaires, mounting details, wiring methods and other specifics covered in the section of this manual which describes the lighting design. As a result of the lighting design for a particular area, a known value of required watts of circuit capacity is obtained. This value is used in determining the number and type of lighting circuits needed.

How many circuits?

The number of branch circuits required to handle the general lighting load is based on the total load to be served, the layout of the lighting system and outlets, the amount of load to be placed on each circuit and the capacity of the circuits to be used. According to the code, the number of circuits shall be not less than that determined from the total computed load and the capacity of the circuits to be used.

Where a branch-circuit load will be in "continuous" operation—such as general illumination in large office areas, private offices, schools, hospitals, industrial plants and the like—the total load on each branch circuit shall not exceed 80% of the rating of the circuit. The code defines "continuous load" as "A load where the maximum current is expected to continue for three hours or more."

This 80% load limitation is not made because the conductors cannot carry full load. It is made to limit the heat load on the equipment to which the conductors are connected—the fuses, circuit breakers, switches and busbar connections in the panelboard. This particular code limitation on circuit loading is set forth in three different sections of the code—Section 210-23(b), Section 220-2 and Section 384-16(c).

Section 210-23(b) says that the maximum load on a branch circuit "shall not exceed 80% of the rating" of the circuit when the load operates for three hours or more. But there are two exceptions to this rule, as follows:

"**Exception No. 1.** When the assembly including the overcurrent device protecting the branch circuit is approved for continuous operation at 100% of its rating, the total load may equal the branch circuit rating."

"**Exception No. 2.** Where branch circuits are derated in accordance with Note 8 of Tables 310–12 through 310–15 the derating factor for continuous loading shall not apply."

The wording of these new rules of the 1965 NE Code poses a number of serious practical problems in application:

First: As shown in Fig. 3, the correlation of this rule to Note 8 poses a difficulty because the basic rule of Section 210-23(b) is concerned with limiting load to 80% of the *circuit rating* which is set by the rating of the overcurrent device, whereas the basic rule of Note 8 actually changes the maximum allowable current-carrying capacity of conductors. Section 210-23(b) does not change the current rating of conductors. The use of the words "derating factor" in

FIG. 3—1965 NE Code poses adequacy conflict (NE Code Section 210-23b)

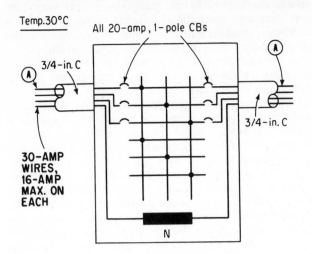

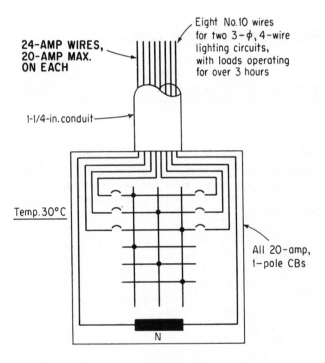

Temp. 30°C

All 20-amp, 1-pole CBs

3/4-in. C

3/4-in. C

30-AMP WIRES, 16-AMP MAX. ON EACH

(A) Four No. 10 wires for 3-φ 4-wire lighting circuit, with loads operating for over 3 hours

24-AMP WIRES, 20-AMP MAX. ON EACH

Eight No. 10 wires for two 3-φ, 4-wire lighting circuits, with loads operating for over 3 hours

1-1/4-in. conduit

Temp. 30°C

All 20-amp, 1-pole CBs

N

Case 1—Load on 30-amp rated wire is limited to 16 amps, with limited heat load on 20-amp CBs.

1. No. 10 wires are used for 20-amp circuits to limit voltage drop in long home-runs.
2. The maximum continuous current rating of each No. 10 is **30 amps**, because there are not more than three current-carrying wires (exclude neutral) in each ¾-in. conduit.
3. In accordance with NE Code Section 210-23(b), the load on each No. 10 wire must be limited to 80% of the branch circuit rating (.8 x 20) or **16 amps.**

Case 2—Same size wires and same size breakers. Load on 24-amp rated wire may be up to 20 amps, with breaker loaded to 100% of its rating and subjected to increased heat loading in same panel.

1. No. 10 wires are used for 20-amp circuits to limit voltage drop in long home-runs.
2. Because there are six current-carrying wires (exclude neutrals) in the 1¼-in. conduit, the maximum continuous current rating of each No. 10 has to be derated to only 80% of the value it has when not more than three wires are in a conduit. The continuous current rating of each No. 10 is then **24 amps** (30 amps x 0.8). See Note 8 to Tables 310-12 through 310-15.
3. But because the branch-circuit wires are derated in accordance with Note 8, the 80% load limitation does not apply and the circuit could be loaded up to 100% of the CB rating. A load of **20-amps** could be used on each CB.

Exception 2 is inaccurate because the 80% limitation on load does not change the ratings of either the wire or the protective device.

Second: The use of the words "shall not apply" in Exception 2 have the effect of making it mandatory that a derating not be applied. It is surely not the intent to imply a violation if a load limitation is applied.

Third: In Exception 1, use of the phrase "approved for continuous operation at 100% of its rating" is not clear inasmuch as the word "approved" is defined in the code as "acceptable to the authority enforcing this code." The wording could be inter-

preted to mean that the local inspector will decide on the need for the 80% limitation of load as required in Section 210-23(b).

These questions should be checked out with the local inspector to avoid conflicts with local interpretations.

Basic rules

As shown in Fig. 4, the code gives definitions in Article 100 covering three types of branch circuits. The framework of lighting and appliance branch circuit design is given in Articles 200, 210 and 220 of the code. As set forth in Section 210-1, the scope of this article covers "branch circuits supplying lighting or appliance loads for combinations of such loads. If motors, or motor-operated appliances, are connected to any circuit supplying lighting or other appliance loads, the provisions of both this article and Article 430 shall apply. Article 430 shall apply if branch circuit supplies only motor loads."

A branch circuit is rated according to the setting or rating of the overcurrent device used to protect the circuit. Branch circuits with more than one outlet may be rated at 15, 20, 30, 40 or 50 amps.

That is, the protective device must have one of those ratings for multioutlet circuits and the conductors must meet the other size requirements of Article 210.

It is important to note that it is the size of the overcurrent device which determines the rating of any circuit covered by Article 210, even when the conductors used for the branch circuit have an ampere rating higher than that of the protective device. In a typical case, for example, a 20-amp circuit breaker in a panelboard might be used to protect a branch circuit in which No. 10 conductors are used as the circuit wires. Although the load on the circuit does not exceed 20 amps and No. 12 conductors would have sufficient current-carrying capacity to be used in the circuit, the No. 10 conductors with their rating of 30 amps were selected to reduce the voltage drop in a long home-run. The rating of the circuit is 20 amps because that is the size of the overcurrent device. The current rating of the wire does not enter into the ampere classification of the circuit.

Although multioutlet branch circuits are limited in rating to 15, 20, 30, 40 or 50 amps, a branch circuit

to a single load outlet (for instance a branch circuit to one machine or to one receptacle outlet) may have any ampere rating. For instance, there could be a 200-amp branch circuit to a special receptacle outlet or a 300-amp branch circuit to a single machine.

A "branch circuit" as covered by Article 210 may be a 2-wire circuit or may be a "multiwire" branch circuit. A "multiwire" branch circuit consists of two or more ungrounded conductors, having a potential difference between them, and an identified grounded conductor having equal potential difference between it and each of the ungrounded conductors and which is connected to the neutral conductor of the system. Thus, a 3-wire circuit consisting of two opposite-polarity ungrounded conductors and a neutral derived from a 3-wire, single-phase system or a 4-wire circuit consisting of three different phase conductors and a neutral of a 3-phase, 4-wire system is a *single* multiwire branch circuit. This is only one circuit even though it involves two or three single-pole protective devices in the panelboard. This is important because other sections of the code refer to conditions involving "one branch circuit" or "the single branch circuit." See Sections 250-24 and 410-26.

Branch-circuit color coding

Code rules on color coding of conductors apply only to branch-circuit conductors and do not directly require color coding of feeder conductors. For branch-circuit conductors, color coding is required only when the conductors are: 1. installed in raceway (rigid or thinwall conduit, flex, surface raceway, underfloor duct—see definition in Article 100 for word "raceway") ; 2. installed as aluminum sheathed cable; 3. installed as open work; or 4. installed as concealed knob-and-tube work. It is not required that conductors used in armored cable or nonmetallic sheathed cable be color coded, but such cables are made with color coded conductors.

Color coding shall be as follows: 3-wire circuits— one hot leg—black, one hot leg—red and the neutral —white; 4-wire circuits—one black, one red, one blue and the neutral white. Where more than one multiwire branch circuit is installed in a single raceway, other colors *may* be used to differentiate the additional wires.

In many modern systems using both 120/208-volt and 480/277-volt, 3-phase, 4-wire circuits, a separate color code—such as brown, orange, yellow and white —is used for safety purposes for the 480/277 circuits to distinguish these higher voltage circuits from the 120/208 circuits which are coded black, red, blue and white. To use such color coded 480/277 circuits in their own conduits is technically a code violation, because the code only recognizes black, red, blue and white for a 4-wire circuit in a conduit by itself. The violation actually increases the safety of the system from a maintenance standpoint in that the higher voltage is indicated to maintenance personnel.

Any conductor used solely for equipment grounding purposes must be color coded green or it may be bare. Green colored conductors must not be used for any purpose other than grounding.

In Fig. 5, an important requirement of code color coding is shown in detail. This concerns the rule that all conductors of multiwire branch circuits and two-

FIG. 4—Types of branch circuits

GENERAL PURPOSE BRANCH CIRCUIT

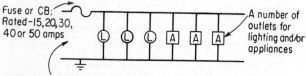

Fuse or CB:
Rated—15, 20, 30, 40 or 50 amps

A number of outlets for lighting and/or appliances

Circuit voltage shall not exceed 150 volts to ground for circuits supplying lampholders, fixtures or receptacles of standard 15-amp rating. For fluorescent, incandescent or mercury lighting under certain conditions, voltage to ground may be as high as 300 volts. In certain cases, voltage for electric discharge lighting may be up to 500 volts ungrounded.

APPLIANCE BRANCH CIRCUIT (RECEPTACLE CIRCUITS)

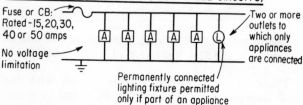

Fuse or CB:
Rated—15, 20, 30, 40 or 50 amps

No voltage limitation

Two or more outlets to which only appliances are connected

Permanently connected lighting fixture permitted only if part of an appliance

INDIVIDUAL BRANCH CIRCUIT

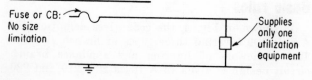

Fuse or CB:
No size limitation

Supplies only one utilization equipment

FIG. 5—Consistent color coding of phases

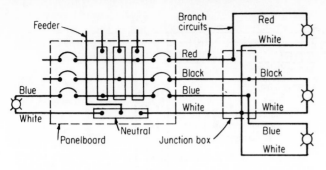

wire branch circuits connected to the same system must conform to the color code. And the code further says that "All circuit conductors of the same color shall be connected to the same ungrounded feeder conductor throughout the installation."

This means that all branch-circuit conductors connected to a given busbar in a panelboard must be of the same color. In a 3-phase panel, for instance, all red wires must connect to only one of the busbars; all black wires must connect to another busbar; etc. And if the red wires in one panel are connected to a busbar fed by, say, phase A of the feeder, all red wires in all other panels throughout the entire wiring system must also connect to busbars fed by a phase A feeder conductor. It can be readily seen that compliance with these code rules on color coding branch-circuit conductors would require that the various phases of feeder circuits be identified. Because of this, the code can be said to *indirectly* require color coding of feeder conductors.

It should be noted that, with the exception of aluminum sheathed cable, the code does not require color coding of conductors in cables. In general, color coding is limited to conductors pulled in raceways. If cables had to meet color coding rules, 2-wire cables would have to be made in three different color combinations—red and white, blue and white, and black and white—to provide for 2-wire circuits from the different busbars in panels and for 2-wire taps from multiwire circuits.

Voltage limitations

Voltage limitations for branch circuits are presented in Section 210-6. In general, branch circuits serving lampholders, fixtures or receptacles of the standard 15-amp or less rating are limited to a maximum voltage rating of 150 volts to ground. Exceptions to this rule are as follows:

a. In industrial occupancies, or in stores where the conditions of maintenance and supervision assure that only competent individuals will service the lighting fixtures, branch circuits supplying only mogul-base, screw-shell lampholders or other approved types of lampholders may be operated above 150 volts to ground, but not above 300 volts to ground, provided the lighting units are mounted at least 8 ft above the floor and do not have switch control within the unit itself. Fig. 6.

b. In industrial, commercial and institutional occupancies, branch circuits serving only ballasts for mercury vapor or fluorescent lamps may be rated over

150 volts to ground, but not above 300 volts to ground, provided the ballasts are in permanently installed fixtures, the lampholders are not of the screw-shell type, and the fixtures do not have manual switch control as an integral part of them. When electric discharge lamps are used with screw-shell lampholders, the fixtures must be installed not less than 8 ft above the floor. Fig 7.

Both of the above exceptions permit installations on 480/277-volt, 3-phase, 4-wire wye systems—with equipment connected from phase to phase (480-volt circuits) or connected phase-to-neutral (277-volt circuits). In either case, the voltage to ground is only 277 volts and therefore does not exceed the 300-volt maximum. In any such application, it is important that the neutral point of the 480/277 wye be grounded to limit the voltage above ground to 277 volts. If the neutral were not grounded and the system operated ungrounded, the voltage to ground, according to the code, would be 480 volts (see definition "Voltage to Ground," Article 100) and lighting equipment could not be used on such circuits.

On a neutral-grounded 480/277-volt system, incandescent, fluorescent and mercury vapor equipment can be connected from phase to neutral on the 277-volt circuits. If fluorescent or mercury vapor fixtures are connected phase to phase, some code authorities contend that under certain conditions autotransformer type ballasts cannot be used. (See Section 410-76.) On such connection they would require use of 2-winding, electrically isolating transformers for ballasts.

The exceptions noted above would also permit use of lighting equipment on 2-wire or 3-wire circuits derived from 240-volt, 3-phase, 3-wire delta-connected systems—of either the corner-grounded or the ungrounded type, inasmuch as the voltage to ground would be only 240 volts (under the 300 volt maximum) in either case. Fig. 8. Lamps rated at 240 volts and 240-volt ballasts would be used. Again, however, there might be objection to use of autotransformer ballasts between the ungrounded phase wires of the grounded delta system; and, in some cases, there would be definite objection to their use on the ungrounded system because that would be a clear violation of Section 410-76, which requires that autotransformer ballasts be supplied from a grounded system when they raise the voltage to more than 300 volts.

FIG. 6—Incandescent lighting at 300 volts to ground

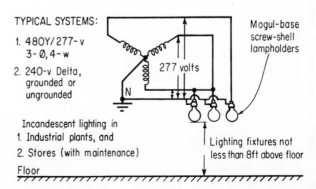

FIG. 7—Fluorescent or mercury vapor lighting at 277 volts to ground

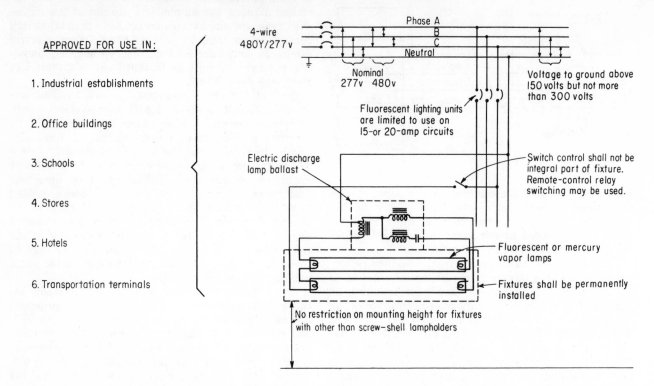

APPROVED FOR USE IN:

1. Industrial establishments

2. Office buildings

3. Schools

4. Stores

5. Hotels

6. Transportation terminals

4-wire 480Y/277v

Phase A
B
C
Neutral

Nominal 277v 480v

Voltage to ground above 150 volts but not more than 300 volts

Fluorescent lighting units are limited to use on 15-or 20-amp circuits

Electric discharge lamp ballast

Switch control shall not be integral part of fixture. Remote-control relay switching may be used.

Fluorescent or mercury vapor lamps

Fixtures shall be permanently installed

No restriction on mounting height for fixtures with other than screw-shell lampholders

---

c. An important addition to the code-accepted list of lighting applications at voltages over 150 volts to ground was made in Section 210-6 of the 1965 NE Code. Exception No. 5 now permits fluorescent and/or mercury vapor units to be installed on circuits rated up to 500 volts between conductors—but only where the lamps are mounted in permanently installed fixtures "on poles for the illumination of areas such as highways, bridges, athletic fields, parking lots, at a height not less than 22 ft, or on other structures such as tunnels at a height not less than 18 ft."

Prior to this addition to the code, lighting units had to be installed on circuits which have a pre-scribed voltage to ground. But this new permission

for use of fluorescent and mercury units under the conditions described is based on phase-to-phase voltage rather than phase-to-ground voltage. From a practical standpoint, this new rule has the effect of permitting the use of 480-volt *ungrounded* circuits for the lighting applications described.

Under the old limitations, electric discharge lighting could be used on: 120/240-volt, single-phase circuits; 120/208-volt, 3-phase circuits; 240-volt, 3-phase, 3-wire circuits, ungrounded; and 480/277-volt, 3-phase circuits. In all of those cases, the voltage to ground did not exceed 300 volts. In the case of 240-volt, 3-phase ungrounded circuits, the voltage to ground is taken as the maximum voltage between

FIG. 8—Fluorescent, mercury vapor or incandescent lighting on circuits not over 300 volts to ground

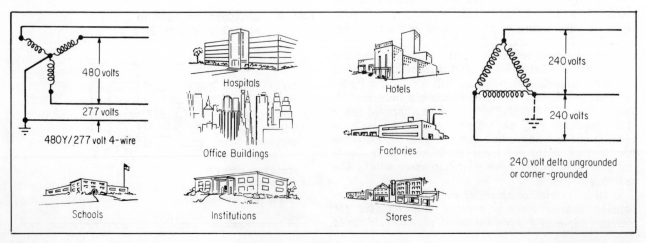

480 volts

277 volts

480Y/277 volt 4-wire

Hospitals

Office Buildings

Hotels

Factories

240 volts

240 volts

240 volt delta ungrounded or corner-grounded

Schools

Institutions

Stores

FIG. 9—Lighting at over 300 volts to ground

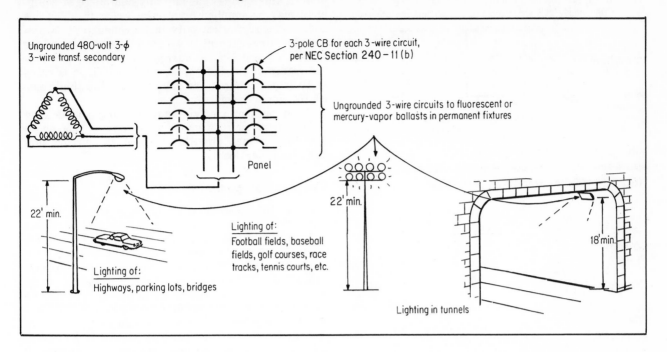

Ungrounded 480-volt 3-φ 3-wire transf. secondary

3-pole CB for each 3-wire circuit, per NEC Section 240–11(b)

Panel

Ungrounded 3-wire circuits to fluorescent or mercury-vapor ballasts in permanent fixtures

22' min.

Lighting of:
Highways, parking lots, bridges

22' min.

Lighting of:
Football fields, baseball fields, golf courses, race tracks, tennis courts, etc.

18' min.

Lighting in tunnels

phase conductors (which is the code definition of voltage to ground on ungrounded circuits). Of course, all of the foregoing applications are still permitted; but, now circuits rated up to 500 volts between conductors may also be used under the stated conditions. Thus, *ungrounded* circuits up to 500 volts between conductors may be used. Fig. 9.

d. Certain electric railway applications utilize higher circuit voltages.

e. Infrared lamp industrial heating appliances may be used on higher circuit voltages as allowed in Section 422-11 of the code. The requirements for circuits serving electric heating devices are given in a later section of this manual.

Circuit loading

Code limitations on the use of branch circuits with two or more outlets (using Type FEP, FEPB, R, RW, RU, RUW, RH-RW, SA, T, TW, RH, RUH, RHW, RHH, THHN, THW or THWN wires in raceway or cable) are as follows:

15- and 20-amp branch circuits may serve lighting units and/or appliances. The rating of any one

FIG. 10—General-purpose branch circuits

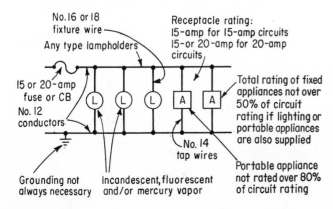

No. 16 or 18 fixture wire

Any type lampholders

15 or 20-amp fuse or CB
No. 12 conductors

Grounding not always necessary

Incandescent, fluorescent and/or mercury vapor

No. 14 tap wires

Receptacle rating:
15-amp for 15-amp circuits
15-or 20-amp for 20-amp circuits

Total rating of fixed appliances not over 50% of circuit rating if lighting or portable appliances are also supplied

Portable appliance not rated over 80% of circuit rating

portable appliance shall not exceed 80% of the branch-circuit rating. Fig. 10. Although fixed appliances may be connected to a circuit serving lighting units or portable appliances, provided the total rating of the fixed appliances does not exceed 50% of the circuit rating, good design provides separate circuits for individual fixed appliances. In commercial and industrial buildings, separate circuits should be provided for lighting and separate circuits for receptacles.

30-amp branch circuits may serve fixed lighting units (with heavy-duty type lampholders) in other than dwelling occupancies *or* appliances in any occupancy. Any individual portable appliance which draws more than 24 amps may not be connected to this type of circuit. Fig. 11.

40-amp branch circuits may serve fixed lighting units (with heavy-duty lampholders) or infrared heating units in other than dwelling occupancies; or fixed or stationary cooking appliances; or fixed water heaters; or clothes dryers. Recognition of the 40-amp multioutlet branch circuit was added to the 1965 NE Code. Fig. 12.

50-amp branch circuits may serve fixed lighting units (with heavy-duty type lampholders) in other than dwelling occupancies, fixed cooking appliances, or infrared lamp industrial heating appliances. See Fig. 13.

The term "fixed" as used in the above descriptions of permitted loads on multioutlet branch circuits recognizes cord connections where otherwise permitted.

It should be noted that the requirement of heavy-duty type lampholders for lighting units on 30-, 40- and 50-amp multioutlet branch circuits excludes the use of fluorescent lighting on these circuits because fluorescent lampholders are not rated "heavy-duty" in accordance with Section 210-8. Mercury vapor units with mogul lampholders may be used on these circuits provided tap conductor requirements are satisfied.

As indicated, branch circuits for lighting are limited to a maximum loading of 50 amps. Individual

FIG. 11—Multioutlet 30-amp circuits

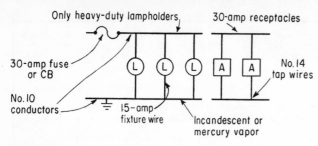

Note: Lighting **or** appliances, **not both**

FIG. 12—Multioutlet 40-amp circuits

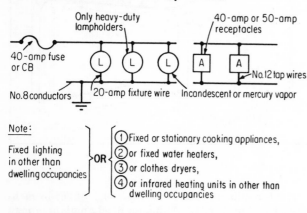

Note:
Fixed lighting in other than dwelling occupancies }OR{
① Fixed or stationary cooking appliances,
② or fixed water heaters,
③ or clothes dryers,
④ or infrared heating units in other than dwelling occupancies

FIG. 13—Multioutlet 50-amp circuits

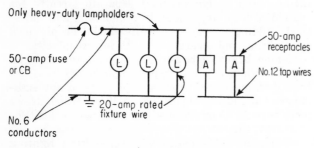

Note: Fixed lighting in other than dwelling occupancies · }OR{
① Fixed cooking appliances
② Or infrared lamp industrial heating appliances

BASIC RULES

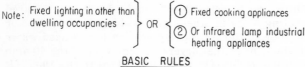

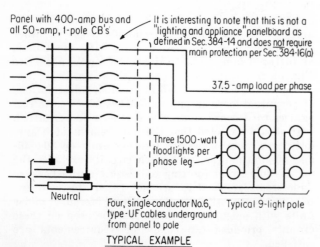

Panel with 400-amp bus and all 50-amp, 1-pole CB's

It is interesting to note that this is not a "lighting and appliance" panelboard as defined in Sec. 384-14 and does not require main protection per Sec. 384-16(a)

37.5 - amp load per phase

Three 1500-watt floodlights per phase leg

Typical 9-light pole

Neutral

Four, single-conductor No.6, type-UF cables underground from panel to pole

TYPICAL EXAMPLE

50-amp, 3-phase, 4-wire circuits to supply incandescent floodlights on pole for lighting of a baseball field.

---

branch circuits may supply any loads. Excepting motors, this means that an individual piece of equipment may be supplied by a branch circuit which has sufficient carrying capacity in its conductors, is protected against current in excess of the capacity of the conductors and against current in excess of 150% of the rating of the individual appliance (if it is rated at 10 amps or more) and supplies only the single outlet for the load device.

Fixed outdoor electric snow melting and deicing installations may be supplied by any of the above described branch circuits provided the circuit supplies no other load.

Residential circuits

Design of lighting and appliance branch circuits for dwelling-type occupancies (single-family houses and apartment houses) should be based on a minimum provision of one 20-amp, 2-wire, 120-volt circuit for each 800 sq ft of floor area. This is a code minimum and works out to be a capacity of 3 watts per sq ft. For hotel rooms, at least 2 watts per sq ft should be used. The number of circuits determined in this way will handle general illumination and convenience receptacles spaced (so no point is more than 6 ft from a receptacle) along the floor line in any wall space 2 ft wide or greater of the living room, bedrooms, parlor, library, den, sun room and recreation room. Fig. 14.

At least one 3-wire, 20-amp, 120/240- or 120/208-volt circuit shall be provided to serve the small appliance load in the kitchen, laundry, pantry, dining room and breakfast room of dwelling occupancies. The 3-wire circuit can be split-wired to convenient receptacle outlets in these areas and must have no other outlets. Of course, two 2-wire, 20-amp, 120-volt circuits are equivalent to the 3-wire circuit and could be used.

In dwelling-type occupancies, at least one outlet must be installed for the laundry. And outlets in sections of the dwelling for special appliances, such as laundry equipment, must be placed within 6 ft of the

FIG. 14—Spacing of residential receptacles
(NE Code Section 210-22b)

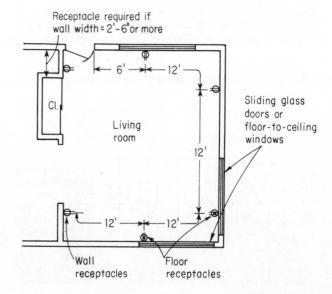

FIG. 15—Two appliance circuits must have outlets in kitchen area

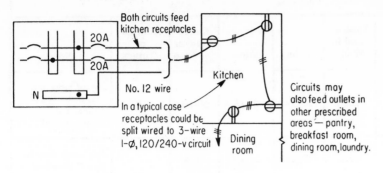

METHOD 1 – A 3-wire circuit to all outlets in prescribed areas.

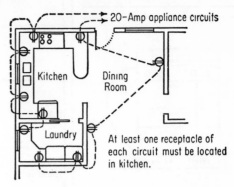

METHOD 2 – Two 2-wire circuits, each with at least one kitchen outlet.

intended location of the appliance. NE Code Section 210-22(b).

Code rules on the location and spacing of receptacle outlets in residential occupancies also apply to guest rooms in hotels, motels and similar occupancies.

The 1965 NE Code requires that two or more 20-amp branch circuits be provided to supply all of the receptacle outlets in the kitchen, laundry, pantry, family room, dining room and breakfast room of any dwelling occupancy — one-family houses, apartment houses and hotel suites with serving pantries. And these circuits must not have outlets in any other rooms. And the code says that at least two such circuits must supply receptacle outlets in the kitchen itself. Section 220-3(b).

The two circuits feeding outlets in the kitchen may also feed outlets in the other areas above—laundry, pantry, etc. What the code prohibits, is, say, one circuit feeding the kitchen outlets and the other circuit or circuits feeding the outlets in the other prescribed areas. At least two circuits must have outlets in the kitchen. Fig. 15 shows two ways of supplying kitchen outlets. In Method 2, one circuit could supply four of the five receptacles in the kitchen and the second circuit could supply the fifth receptacle.

Some difficulties in code application have arisen from the fact that Section 220-3(b) of the code includes "family room" in the list of rooms which must have their receptacle outlets connected on the 20-amp small-appliance circuits. But "family room" is not one of the rooms listed in Section 210-22(b) which must have receptacle outlets spaced around wall space so no point is more than 6 ft from a receptacle. From this it can be taken that only one receptacle outlet is required in the family room.

But it should be noted that "recreation room" is one of the rooms which must have receptacles spaced according to Section 210-22(b). Such receptacles, however, do not have to be connected to the 20-amp kitchen appliance circuits as set forth in Section 220-3(b). This matter of "family room" vs "recreation room" should be checked out with local inspection authorities to assure that the design layout of residential branch circuits conforms to local interpretation.

In single-family dwellings, apartment houses and hotel rooms, all receptacle outlets rated 15 amps or less (excepting air conditioning outlets and those outlets on the kitchen appliance circuits) are considered as outlets for general illumination and no additional branch-circuit capacity has to be provided for such outlets. They are connected on the circuits designed to handle the general lighting load.

In other occupancies, circuit capacity must be provided for all receptacle outlets and outlets serving loads separate from general illumination.

Outlet loads

For lighting other than general lighting, and for appliances other than motor-operated, circuit capacity for each outlet must be provided as follows:

For each outlet supplying a specific appliance or load device, circuit capacity equal to the amp rating of the appliance or device must be provided.

For each outlet supplying a heavy-duty lampholder, 5 amps of circuit capacity must be allowed.

For each other outlet, such as each general-purpose convenience receptacle outlet in other than dwelling occupancies, at least 1.5 amps must be allowed.

When a circuit supplies only motor-operated devices, the provisions of Article 430 of the code must be taken into consideration.

The above minimum load allowances for receptacle outlets and outlets for local lighting and appliances are modified as follows:

Table 220-5 of the code establishes the basis for computing the required branch-circuit capacity for electric cooking appliances.

For show-window lighting, 200 watts of load can be allowed for each linear foot of show window, measured along its base.

A capacity of 1.5 amps must be allowed for each 5 ft or fraction thereof of each separate and continuous length of fixed multioutlet assemblies. Each such length is considered as one outlet of 1.5-amp capacity. In those places where it is likely that a number of appliances will be used simultaneously, each 1 ft or fraction thereof is considered as an outlet and requires a load allowance of 1.5 amps. No branch-circuit capacity has to be included for multioutlet assemblies in dwellings or guest rooms in hotels. In such occupancies, the multioutlet assembly is considered part of the general lighting load—just as standard receptacle outlets are.

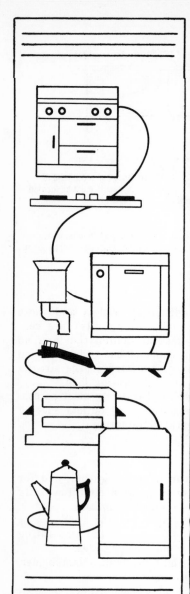

Use These Circuits in Kitchen and Dining Areas

	Typical Load in Watts	Volts	Wires	Circuit Breaker or Fuse	Number of Outlets	Notes
RANGE	12000	120/240	3- #6	50-60A	1	Use of more than one outlet is permitted, but not recommended.
OVEN (Built in)	4500	120/240	3- #10	30A	1	Appliance may be direct connected.
RANGE TOP	6000	120/240	3- #10	30A	1	Appliance may be direct connected.
RANGE TOP	3300	120/240	3- #12	20A	1 or more	
DISHWASHER	1200	120	2 #12	20A	1	These appliances may be direct connected on a single circuit. Grounded receptacles required otherwise.
WASTE DISPOSER	300	120	2 #12	20A	1	
BROILER	1500	120	2 #12			Heavy duty appliances regularly used at one location should have a separate circuit. Only one such unit should be attached to a single circuit at a time.
FRYER	1300	120	At Least Two Kitchen Appliance Circuits	20A	2 or more	
COFFEEMAKER	1000	120				
REFRIGERATOR	300	120	2 #12	20A	2	Separate circuit serving only refrigerator and freezer is recommended.
FREEZER	350	120	2 #12	20A	2	

Branch-circuit conductors

Although the code establishes No. 14 as the minimum size of wire to be used for branch-circuit wiring, good design practice dictates the use of No. 12 as the minimum size, protected at either 15 or 20 amps. For electric ranges of 8¾ kw or more, No. 8 is the code minimum size, but No. 6 is the recommended size to be used. In a 3-wire single-phase branch circuit to a household electric range, the neutral may be sized on the basis of 70% of the current-carrying capacity of the ungrounded conductors, although it may not be smaller than No. 10.

Calculation of the load current for a branch circuit can be readily made with the simple formulas given in Fig. 16.

Selection of insulated conductors for branch-circuit wiring should be based on all of the application conditions, including:

1. **Size of conductors** must provide sufficient current-carrying capacity for the load to be served.

2. **Branch-circuit protection** and conductors must be rated at least 25% greater than the load current when the load operates continuously over long periods (3 hours or more), such as general lighting in commercial buildings.

3. **Conductors** for individual motor circuits must generally be rated at least 25% greater than motor full-load current.

4. **Type of insulation** on conductors must be suited to operation at temperature of area in which it is used.

5. **Where ambient temperature** exceeds 86° F (room temperature maximum for which insulated conductors are rated in Tables 310–12 through 310–15 of the NE Code), the current-carrying capacities of conductors should be derated according to correction factors at bottom of each of the Tables.

6. **Where more than three conductors** are used in a raceway or cable, their current-carrying capacities must be reduced to compensate for proximity heating effect in an enclosed group of closely placed conductors. See Note 8 of Tables 310–12 through 310–15.

7. **Type of insulation** must be suited to application in the given moisture content. Advantages and limitations related to the dryness or wetness of the

Modern Circuits for Appliance Loads

Load Devices	Typical Load in Watts	Volts	Wires	Circuit Breaker or Fuse	Number of Outlets	Notes
for Laundry Areas						
IRONER	1650	120	2 #12	20A	1	Grounding type receptacle required.
WASHING MACHINE	1200	120	2 #12	20A	1	Grounding type receptacle required.
DRYER	5000	120/240	3 #10	30A	1	Appliance may be direct connected—must be grounded.
for Other Loads						
HAND IRON	1000	120	2 #12	20A	2 or more	
WATER HEATER	3000					Consult Utility Co. for load requirements
WORKSHOP	1500	120	2 #12	20A	2 or more	Separate circuit recommended.
PORTABLE HEATER	1300	120	2 #12	20A	1	Should not be connected to circuit serving other heavy duty loads.
TELEVISION	300	120	2 #12	20A	2 or more	Should not be connected to circuit serving appliances.

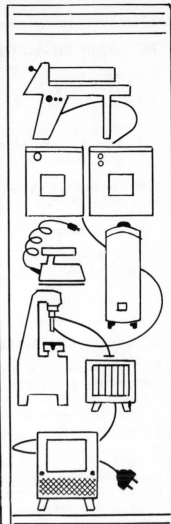

area in which conductors are to be used must be considered. Code regulations based on moisture content of the place of installation conform to the following definitions:

Damp Location: A location subject to a moderate degree of moisture, such as some basements, some barns, some cold storage warehouses, and the like.

Dry Location: A location not normally subject to dampness or wetness. A location classified as dry may be temporarily subject to dampness or wetness, as in the case of a building under construction.

Wet Location: A location subject to saturation with water or other liquids, such as locations exposed to weather, washrooms in garages, and like locations. Installations underground or in concrete slabs or masonry in direct contact with the earth shall be considered as wet locations.

And Section 310-5 of the code says:

Insulated conductors used underground, in concrete slabs or other masonry in direct contact with earth, in wet locations, or where condensation or accumula-

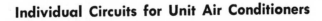

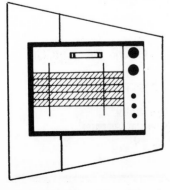

Individual Circuits for Unit Air Conditioners

Size of Air Conditioner	Average Wattage	Circuits Required	Size of Circ.	Number of Outlets	Remarks
¾ hp	1200	Separate Circuit	2 #12 120-v	1	Use of 3-wire, 120/240-volt circuits to unit conditioners offers circuit flexibility for 120 or 240 volts
1½ hp	2400	Separate Circuit	3 #12 120/240-v	1	

DC CIRCUIT CHARACTERISTICS

Ohm's Law:

$$E = IR \qquad I = \frac{E}{R} \qquad R = \frac{E}{I}$$

E = voltage impressed on circuit (volts)
I = current flowing in circuit (amperes)
R = circuit resistance (ohms)

In direct current circuits, electrical power is equal to the product of the voltage and current:

$$P = EI = I^2R = \frac{E^2}{R}$$

P = power (watts)
E = voltage (volts)
I = current (amperes)
R = resistance (ohms)

AC CIRCUIT CHARACTERISTICS

The instantaneous values of an alternating current or voltage vary from zero to a maximum value each half cycle. In the practical formulae which follow, the "effective value" of current and voltage is used, defined as follows:

Effective value = 0.707 × maximum instantaneous value

Impedance:

Impedance is the total opposition to the flow of alternating current. It is a function of resistance, capacitive reactance and inductive reactance. The following formulae relate these circuit properties:

$$X_L = 2\pi fL \qquad X_c = \frac{1}{2\pi fC} \qquad Z = \sqrt{R^2 + (X_L - X_c)^2}$$

X_L = inductive reactance (ohms)
X_c = capacitive reactance (ohms)
Z = impedance (ohms)
f = frequency (cyles per second)
C = capacitance (farads)
L = inductance (henrys)
R = resistance (ohms)
π = 3.14

Ohm's Law for AC Circuits:

$$E = I \times Z \qquad I = \frac{E}{Z} \qquad Z = \frac{E}{I}$$

POWER FACTOR

Power factor of a circuit or system is the ratio of actual power (watts) to apparent power (volt-amperes), and is equal to the cosine of the phase angle of the circuit:

$$PF = \frac{\text{actual power}}{\text{apparent power}} = \frac{\text{watts}}{\text{volts} \times \text{amperes}} = \frac{KW}{KVA} = \frac{R}{Z}$$

KW = kilowatts
KVA = kilovolt-amperes = volt-amperes × 1,000
PF = power factor (expressed as decimal)

SINGLE-PHASE CIRCUITS

$$KVA = \frac{EI}{1,000} = \frac{KW}{PF} \qquad KW = KVA \times PF$$

$$I = \frac{P}{E \times PF} \qquad E = \frac{P}{I \times PF} \qquad PF = \frac{P}{E \times I}$$

P = E × I × PF
P = power (watts)

THREE-PHASE CIRCUITS, BALANCED STAR OR WYE

$$I_N = 0 \qquad I = I_p \qquad E = \sqrt{3}\,E_p = 1.73\,E_p$$

$$E_p = \frac{E}{\sqrt{3}} = \frac{E}{1.73} = 0.577E$$

I_N = current in neutral (amperes)
I = line current per phase (amperes)
I_p = current in each phase winding (amperes)
E = voltage, phase to phase (volts)
E_p = voltage, phase to neutral (volts)

THREE-PHASE CIRCUITS, BALANCED DELTA

$$I = 1.732 \times I_p \qquad I_p = \frac{I}{\sqrt{3}} = 0.577 \times I$$

$$E = E_p$$

POWER: BALANCED 3-WIRE, 3-PHASE CIRCUIT, DELTA OR WYE

For unity power factor (PF = 1.0):

$$P = 1.732 \times E \times I$$

$$I = \frac{P}{\sqrt{3}\,E} = \frac{0.577P}{E} \qquad E = \frac{P}{\sqrt{3} \times I} = \frac{0.577P}{I}$$

P = total power (watts)

For any load:

$$P = 1.732 \times E \times I \times PF \qquad VA = 1.732 \times E \times I$$

$$E = \frac{P}{PF \times 1.73 \times I} = \frac{0.577 \times P}{PF \times I}$$

$$I = \frac{P}{PF \times 1.73 \times E} = \frac{0.577 \times P}{PF \times E}$$

$$PF = \frac{P}{1.73 \times I \times E} = \frac{0.577 \times P}{I \times E}$$

VA = apparent power (volt-amperes)
P = actual power (watts)
E = line voltage (volts) phase to phase
I = line current (amperes)

POWER LOSS: ANY AC OR DC CIRCUIT

$$P = I^2R \qquad I = \sqrt{\frac{P}{R}} \qquad R = \frac{P}{I^2}$$

P = power heat loss in circuit (watts)
I = effective current in conductor (amperes)
R = conductor resistance (ohms)

Type	Construction	Application
	IO R 600V	
R	Single rubber-insulated conductor with braided cotton covering, rated at 60 C maximum operating temperature.	For general use in dry locations.
RH	Similar to type R, but has heat-resistant rubber insulation, rated for 75 C operation.	For general use in dry locations. Has higher current-carrying capacity than type R.
RHH	Similar to type RH, but has heat-resistant rubber insulation rated for 90 C operation.	For general use in dry locations. Has same current-carrying capacity as type RH in sizes 14, 12 and 10. Has higher current rating for larger size conductors.
RW	Similar to type R, but has moisture-resistant rubber insulation, rated for 60 C operation.	For general use in dry or wet locations. Has same current capacity as Type R.
	--14-RW60C OR RH 75C-600V--	
RH-RW	Combines types RH and RW; has heat- and moisture-resistant rubber insulation rated 75 C in dry locations and 60 C in wet locations.	For general use in dry or wet locations. In dry locations, has current capacity of type RH; in wet locations, has current capacity of type RW.

Type	Construction	Application
	IO-RHW-600V	
RHW	Similar to RH-RW, rated for 75 C operation in all installations.	For general use in dry or wet locations. Has current capacity of type RH.
	12-TW-600V	
TW	Single plastic-insulated (polyvinylchloride) conductor; has moisture resistance, rated for 60 C operation.	For general use in dry or wet locations. Has smaller cross-sectional area than type R, but is held to the same conduit occupancy. Has same current capacity as type R.
THW	Single PVC conductor; moisture and heat resistant, rated for 75 C; similar to TW.	For general use in dry or wet locations. Same current rating as type RHW.
THWN	Single plastic-insulated conductor with an outer nylon jacket; moisture and heat resistant, rated for 75 C; jacket adds resistance to abrasion, gasoline, oils, chemicals.	For general use in dry or wet locations. Same current rating as type RHW. Has smallest cross sectional area of all building wires.

tion of moisture within the raceway is likely to occur, shall be moisture-resistant, rubber-covered (Type RW); moisture- and heat-resistant (Type RH-RW); moisture- and heat-resistant, rubber-covered (Type RHW); moisture resistant latex rubber (Type RUW); moisture-resistant, thermo-plastic-covered (Type TW); moisture- and heat-resistant, thermo-plastic-covered (Type THW); moisture-resistant thermoplastic (Type THWN); lead covered; aluminum sheathed cable (Type ALS); mineral insulated-metal sheathed (Type MI); or of a type approved for the purpose.

Such conductors are not suitable for direct burial in the earth unless of a type specifically approved for the purpose.

8. Where load additions are likely, spare capacity should be included in circuit conductors.

9. Size of conductors must keep voltage drop and power losses to a minimum. Modern design dictates a 1% voltage drop for branch circuits.

Wiring air-handling ceilings

A common application which raises questions about temperature and moisture effects on wire insulation is that of wiring above suspended ceilings when such spaces are used for distributing air. Section 300-22 of the NE Code says, "Where it is necessary to run a wiring system through air-handling ducts or *plenum chambers*, the wiring method shall be rigid conduit, electrical metallic tubing, flexible steel conduit with lead-covered conductors, Type ACL metalclad cable with fittings suitable for the location, Type MI mineral insulated-metal sheathed cable or Type ALS aluminum sheathed cable. . . ."

It is generally understood that all of the foregoing places specific limitations on the type of wiring methods which can be used in the space above suspended ceilings when that space is used for air handling. And

---

FIG. 16—How to figure circuit current

Branch circuits—lighting and appliance
Two-wire circuits at any power factor:

$$\text{Line current} = \frac{\text{volt-amperes of connected load (or watts at unity pf)}}{\text{line voltage}}$$

Three-wire circuits at any power factor:
Single-phase—Apply same formula as for 2-wire branch circuit, considering each line to neutral separately. Use line-to-neutral voltage; result gives current in line conductors.

Three-phase:

$$\text{Line current} = \frac{\text{volt-amperes of balanced 3-phase load}}{\text{line voltage} \times 1.732}$$

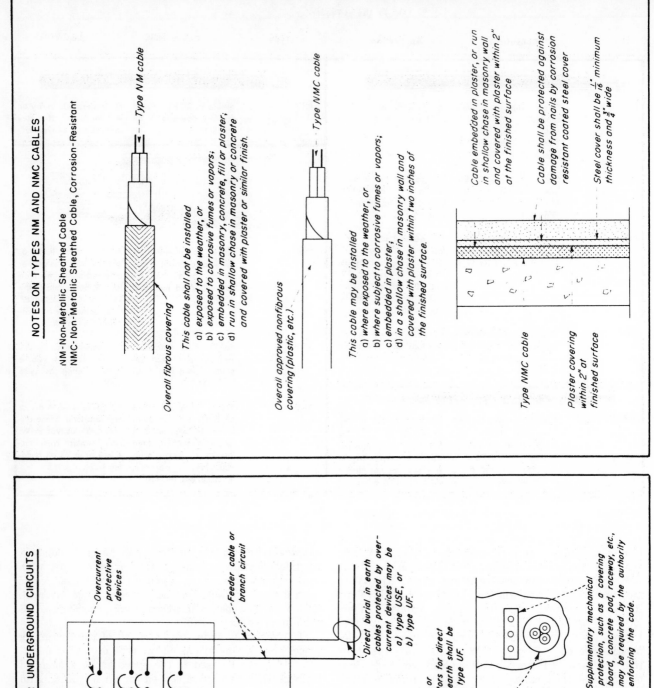

NOTES ON TYPES NM AND NMC CABLES

NM - Non-Metallic Sheathed Cable
NMC - Non-Metallic Sheathed Cable, Corrosion-Resistant

--- Type NM cable

Overall fibrous covering

This cable shall not be installed
   a) exposed to the weather, or
   b) exposed to corrosive fumes or vapors;
   c) embedded in masonry, concrete, fill or plaster;
   d) run in shallow chase in masonry or concrete
      and covered with plaster or similar finish.

--- Type NMC cable

Overall approved nonfibrous
covering (plastic, etc.)

This cable may be installed
   a) where exposed to the weather, or
   b) where subject to corrosive fumes or vapors;
   c) embedded in plaster;
   d) in a shallow chase in masonry wall and
      covered with plaster within two inches of
      the finished surface.

Cable embedded in plaster, or run
in shallow chase in masonry wall
and covered with plaster within 2"
at the finished surface

Cable shall be protected against
damage from nails by corrosion
resistant coated steel cover

Steel cover shall be $\frac{1}{16}$ minimum
thickness and $\frac{3}{4}$ wide

Type NMC cable

Plaster covering
within 2" at
finished surface

NOTES ON TYPE UF CABLE FOR UNDERGROUND CIRCUITS

Overcurrent
protective
devices

Feeder cable or
branch circuit

Direct burial in earth
cables protected by over-
current devices may be
   a) type USE, or
   b) type UF.

Service entrance cables

Direct burial in earth
cables without over-
current protective devices,
such as service drop and
service entrance, shall be
type USE.

Cables of one or
more conductors for direct
burial in the earth shall be
type USE or type UF.

Supplementary mechanical
protection, such as a covering
board, concrete pad, raceway, etc.,
may be required by the authority
enforcing the code.

All conductors for single
cables, including the neutral,
for each service, feeder, subfeeder
or branch circuit shall be run
continuously in the same
trench or raceway.

20

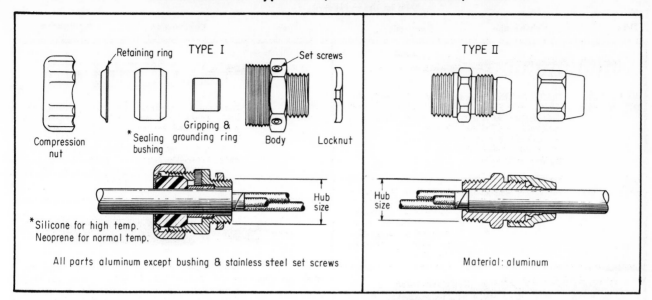

TYPE I

Retaining ring — Set screws

Compression nut · *Sealing bushing · Gripping & grounding ring · Body · Locknut

*Silicone for high temp.
Neoprene for normal temp.

Hub size

All parts aluminum except bushing & stainless steel set screws

TYPE II

Hub size

Material: aluminum

in various inspection jurisdictions, Section 300-22 has been taken to clearly require one of the designated methods for wiring in air-handling ceiling space. However, some inspection authorities do not enforce the above interpretation and do permit usual wiring methods in air-handling plenum chambers. Fig. 17 shows a typical installation which violates the clear wording of Section 300-22—even though thousands of installations have been made this way.

Great care should be taken in design to determine compliance with the local inspection rules because if the installation shown in Fig. 17 had been made to comply with the wiring requirements of Section 300-22, the installations would have been considerably more expensive in material and labor. Either armored cable with lead-covered conductors or flex with lead-covered conductors would have been required.

Overcurrent protection

According to the code, the rating or setting of overcurrent device in any branch circuit shall not exceed the current-carrying capacity of the circuit conductor. And, as stated previously, if a circuit serves only one outlet for a single appliance rated at 10 amps or more, the rating of the overcurrent device must not exceed 150% of the load current.

There are a number of general and specific code rules which apply to overcurrent protection for branch circuits (and the same rules apply to feeder circuits). These rules apply to both fuses and circuit breakers, as follows:

1. An overcurrent device (fuse or CB trip unit) must be placed in each ungrounded conductor of the circuit to be protected. Fig. 18.

2. Where the device protecting supply conductors is of rating or setting to provide protection for smaller conductors tapped from the larger conductors, there is no need to provide protection at the point

FIG. 17—This is a widely found violation of NE Code Section 300-22(a)

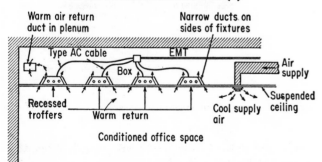

Warm air return duct in plenum · Narrow ducts on sides of fixtures

Type AC cable · EMT · Box · Air supply · Suspended ceiling · Recessed troffers · Warm return · Cool supply air

Conditioned office space

Ceiling plenum is used for return of air from the conditioned office space below the suspended ceiling. Supply of conditioned air to the space below the ceiling is made from ceiling mounted registers fed by insulated, supply-air ducts run through the ceiling plenum. Return of air from the conditioned space is made through special air ducts along both sides of each luminaire. Air flows up into the ceiling plenum. The plenum contains standard Type AC armored cable wiring for the luminaires. In this case, the ceiling space also contains plug-in busway above the ceiling panels. During very cold weather, the air returning to the plenum is heated air used for heating in the office space.

FIG. 18—An overcurrent device must be placed in each ungrounded conductor

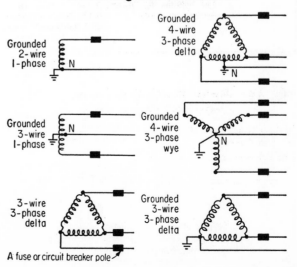

Grounded 2-wire 1-phase

Grounded 3-wire 1-phase

3-wire 3-phase delta

A fuse or circuit breaker pole

Grounded 4-wire 3-phase delta

Grounded 4-wire 3-phase wye

Grounded 3-wire 3-phase delta

Common Cable Assemblies for Branch Circuit Wiring

(Also for Use as Feeders)

Type	Construction	Application	Type	Construction	Application
AC and ACT (NEC Art. 334)	Flexible metallic armored cables. Rubber (AC) or thermoplastic (ACT) insulated conductors in wound and interlocked steel armor covering, with bonding strip under armor.	For general interior wiring, except in moist areas or in block walls below grade.	**NM** (NEC Art. 336)	Non-metallic sheathed cable. Rubber or thermoplastic insulated conductors, with or without separate grounding conductor, covered by heavy paper wrapping and braid or plastic.	For interior wiring, exposed or concealed in dry locations. Must not be used exposed to corrosive fumes or vapors or embedded in concrete, masonry, fill or plaster.
ACL (NEC Art. 334)	Flexible metallic armored cable with lead-covered conductors.	For use where exposed to weather or moisture, for underground runs, for embedding in masonry or concrete or where exposed to oil, gasoline or other deteriorating agents.	**NMC** (NEC Art. 336)	Same as type NM cable except that it has a corrosion-resistant outer covering of non-fibrous material, such as neoprene or thermoplastic.	For interior wiring, in same ways as type NM, except that it may be embedded in plaster or run in chase if a 1/16-in. steel plate is provided for protection against nails.
ALS (NEC Art. 331)	Aluminum sheathed (ALS) cable. Insulated conductors with color-coded coverings, cable fillers and over-all wrap of mylar tape—all in an impervious, continuous, closely fitting, seamless tube of aluminum.	For both exposed and concealed work in dry or wet locations, with approved fittings.	**MI** (NEC Art. 334)	Mineral-insulated, metal-sheathed cable. Conductors insulated by highly compressed refractory mineral material and enclosed in liquid-tight and gas-tight flexible metallic tube sheathing.	For exposed or concealed use in dry or wet locations, under plaster, embedded in plaster finish on brick or other masonry, exposed to weather or moisture, underground runs, embedded in masonry, concrete or fill, in buildings in course of construction, or exposed to oil, gasoline or other conditions not having a deteriorating effect on the metal sheath.
UF (NEC Art. 339)	Underground feeder and branch circuit cable. Conductors may be plastic or rubber insulated, with an outer covering which is flame-retardant, moisture-resistant fungus-resistant, corrosion-resistant and suitable for direct burial in the earth.	For use underground, directly buried in the earth, as branch circuit cable. Multi-conductor type UF cable may be used as NMC cable, and may be used in wet locations. Cable must be buried at least 18 in. below surface of ground when supplementary protection is not provided.			

FIG. 19—One set of protective devices protects two sizes of wires

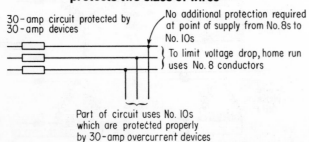

30-amp circuit protected by 30-amp devices

No additional protection required at point of supply from No. 8s to No. 10s

To limit voltage drop, home run uses No. 8 conductors

Part of circuit uses No. 10s which are protected properly by 30-amp overcurrent devices

where the smaller conductors are tapped from the larger conductors. Fig. 19.

3. An overcurrent device must not be placed in any permanently grounded conductor, except:

A. where the device simultaneously opens all conductors of the circuit; or B. where the device is used for motor-running overload protection and is required by note to Table 430-37 for the grounded conductor of a 3-phase, 3-wire circuit from a delta supply with a corner grounded. Fig. 20.

4. Branch-circuit taps—as covered in Section

FIG. 20—Two cases where overcurrent device is permitted in grounded conductor

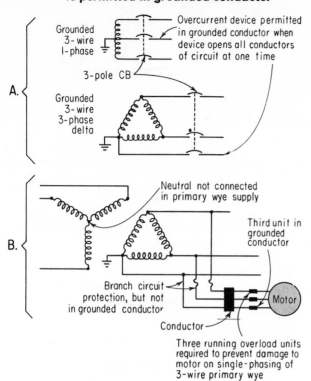

210-19 and 210-20—are considered protected by the branch-circuit overcurrent devices. Fig. 21.

5. **Overcurrent devices** must be located so they are readily accessible, excepting: service overcurrent devices, which may be at the outer end of the service; and overcurrent devices for circuits tapped from feeder busway, which may be in the device for tapping the busway, in the cord plug of a fixed or semi-fixed luminaire supplied from trolley busway, or mounted on a luminaire plugged into a busway. "Readily accessible" means "capable of being reached quickly, for operation, renewal or inspections, without requiring those to whom ready access is requisite to climb over or remove obstacles or to resort to portable ladders, chairs, etc." Fig. 22.

Plug fuses

1. **Plug fuses** must not be used in circuits of more than 125 volts between conductors, but they may be

FIG. 22—Exceptions to basic rule that overcurrent devices must be readily accessible

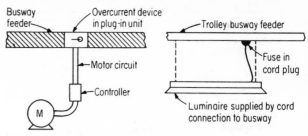

Note: Supplementary overcurrent protection, such as fuses used in luminaires to protect ballasts, are also exempted from the general rule that protective devices must be "readily accessible"

used in grounded neutral systems where the circuits have more than 125 volts between ungrounded conductors but not more than 150 volts between any ungrounded conductor and ground. Fig. 23. The screw-shell of plug fuseholders must be connected to the load side of the circuit. And the code does not require a disconnecting means on the supply side of a plug fuse.

2. **Fuseholders** for plug fuses must be Type S to accommodate Type S plug fuses. Fuseholders must be designed or equipped with adapters to take either 0- to 15-amp Type S fuse, a 16- to 20-amp Type S fuse, or 21- to 30-amp Type S fuse. The 0- to 15-amp fuseholders or adapters must not be able to take 20- or 30-amp fuses and the 20-amp fuseholder must not be able to take 30-amp fuses. Fig. 24. The purpose of this new rule is to prevent overfusing of 15- and 20-amp circuits. Edison-base plug fuses are recognized only for replacement use.

FIG. 23—"Yes" and "no" on plug fuses

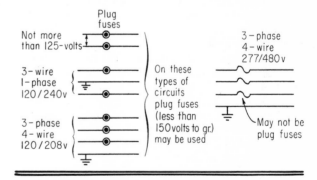

FIG. 21—Sizes of tap wires protected by branch-circuit devices

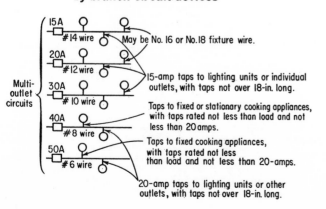

FIG. 24—Type S fuses provide safety through noninterchangeability

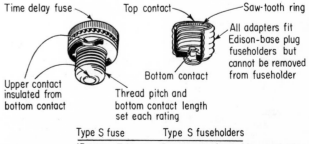

Type S fuse	Type S fuseholders
FOR CIRCUIT PROTECTION	15 amps -Takes a -15- amp rated fuseholder or adapter
	20 amps -Takes a -20- amp rated fuseholder or adapter
	30 amps -Takes a -30- amp rated fuseholder or adapter

FIG. 25—Current-limiting fuses and rejection clips

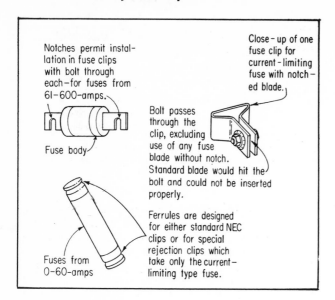

FIG. 26—Cartridge fuses must generally be used in switches

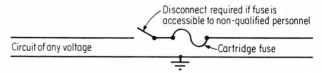

Cartridge fuses

1. Cartridge fuses and fuseholders must be such that a fuse of any given class cannot be used in a fuseholder of a lower current or higher voltage rating.

2. Fuseholders for current-limiting fuses must not permit insertion of fuses which are not current-limiting.

Low-voltage current-limiting cartridge fuses—up to 600 amps—are available with special ferrules or knife blades to provide installation in conformity with the requirements of Section 240-23 (b). Fig. 25. Such fuses can fit into current-limiting fuseholders and also fit standard NE Code fuseholders. But standard NE Code fuses (Class H) cannot be inserted into the current-limiting holders. This arrangement maintains safety in applications where, say, the bracing of busbars in a panel or switchboard is based only on the amount of short-circuit let-through current that a current-limiting fuse will pass but where the busbars could not take the higher current that would flow at that point in the event noncurrent-limiting fuses were used.

3. Fuses rated for 600 volts may be used at any lower voltage.

4. Disconnecting means must be provided on the supply side of all fuses in circuits of more than 150 volts to ground and cartridge fuses in circuits of any voltage, where the fuses would be accessible to other than qualified personnel. Fig. 26.

Circuit breakers

Circuit breakers shall open simultaneously all ungrounded conductors of circuits they protect; i.e., they must be multipole CB units, except that individual single-pole CBs may be used for protection of each ungrounded conductor of certain types of circuits, including ungrounded 2-wire circuits, 3-wire single-phase circuits or lighting or appliance branch circuits connected to 4-wire, 3-phase systems provided such lighting or appliance circuits are supplied from a grounded neutral system. Fig. 27.

Outlet devices

Specific limitations are placed on outlet devices for branch circuits: lampholders must not have a rating lower than the load to be served; and lampholders connected to circuits rated over 20 amps must be heavy-duty type. Again, this has been interpreted to exclude the use of fluorescent luminaires on 30-, 40- and 50-amp circuits (unless the luminaires are individually protected, such as by a fuse in the cord plug of a luminaire cord connected to, say, a 50-amp trolley or plug-in busway).

Receptacles must have ratings at least equal to the load. On circuits having two or more outlets, receptacles shall be rated as follows:

On 15-amp circuits—not over 15-amp rating.
On 20-amp circuits—15- or 20-amp rating.
On 30-amp circuits—30-amp rating.
On 40-amp circuits—40- or 50-amp rating.
On 50-amp circuits—50-amp rating.

The code requires that only grounding-type receptacles be installed on 15- and 20-amp branch circuits. Section 210-21 (b). This means that all general-purpose 120-volt plug outlets must be of the three-pole type. Fig. 28. The rule applies to all types of buildings and areas and to receptacles at any voltage level. The grounding terminal on such receptacle outlets must be connected to ground either by a specific grounding conductor run with the circuit conductors or by means of metallic jacketing on cable or a metallic raceway system.

With a properly grounded metallic system (conduit or armored cable) run to a surface-mounted outlet box, receptacles are grounded through the mounting bracket which is metallically connected to the metal box which, in turn, is grounded through the metal raceway or cable armor supplying it. Fig. 29. At recessed boxes set back in the wall, a separate jumper must be used from the green hex head screw on the

FIG. 27—Multipole CB vs multiple 1-pole CBs

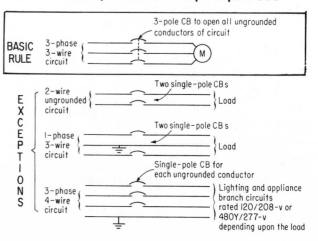

receptacle to a solid connection on the grounded box. The grounding wire is mandatory in nonmetallic wiring systems.

The code notes the possibility of using both ac and dc energy in a single building and requires the use of attachment plug caps which are not interchangeable between ac and dc receptacles.

All of the foregoing constitutes minimum standards for branch circuits. Actual design of circuiting begins with these requirements.

General circuit standards

Summarizing the recommendations made in foregoing discussion of code sections, the following are important standards for modern branch-circuit design. Of course, in many cases, practical considerations such as size of area or type of load devices will require deviation from the letter of these standards. General standards for the majority of applications, however, are as follows:

● Separate branch circuits should be provided for general lighting, for automatic appliances, for fixed appliances and for plug receptacles. Generally, each automatic or fixed appliance should be served by an individual circuit.

● Branch circuits with more than one outlet should not be loaded in excess of 50% of their carrying capacity.

● Individual branch circuits should have spare capacity to permit a 20% increase in load before reaching the level of maximum continuous load current permitted by the code for that circuit.

● At least one spare circuit should be allowed for each five circuits in use.

● The smallest wire size used in branch circuiting should be No. 12.

● Size of wire to be used in a branch-circuit home-run should be at least one size larger than that computed from the loading when the distance from the overcurrent protective device to the first outlet is over 50 ft.

● When the distance from the overcurrent protective device to the first plug outlet on a receptacle circuit is over 100 ft, the size of the circuit home-run should not be less than No. 10 for a 20-amp branch circuit and may be larger depending upon the rating of the particular circuit, the actual distance, voltage drop and the load conditions.

● Home-runs on lighting circuits should be limited to a maximum of 100 ft, unless the load on the circuit is so small that voltage drop between the overcurrent protective device and any outlet is under 1%. Careful layout of panelboard locations and use of sufficient number of panelboards will avoid this problem of long home-runs.

Design standards for lighting and appliance circuits are aimed at providing convenience, flexibility, operating efficiency and reliability in using the available energy. To assure all the advantages of sufficient circuit capacity plus spare capacity for load growth, modern design practice dictates separation of loads into known, approximated and unknown loads.

General illumination is a known load—whether derived from a detailed lighting layout, or developed from a watts-per-sq-ft calculation. Number, rating and layout of outlets for general illumination can easily and accurately be apportioned among a number of branch circuits. Such circuits can be carefully

FIG. 28—Only grounding receptacles on all 15- and 20-amp circuits

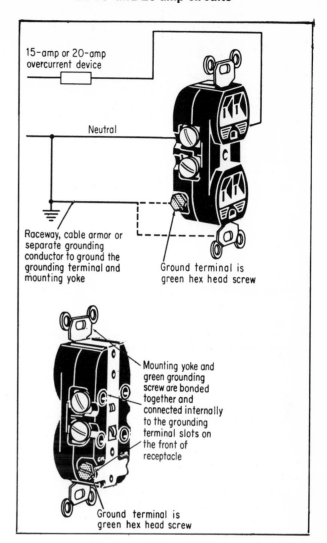

15-amp or 20-amp overcurrent device

Neutral

Raceway, cable armor or separate grounding conductor to ground the grounding terminal and mounting yoke

Ground terminal is green hex head screw

Mounting yoke and green grounding screw are bonded together and connected internally to the grounding terminal slots on the front of receptacle

Ground terminal is green hex head screw

FIG. 29—Grounding jumper not required for receptacle in surface box

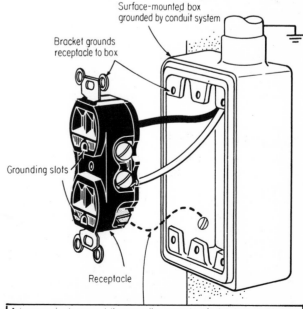

Surface-mounted box grounded by conduit system

Bracket grounds receptacle to box

Grounding slots

Receptacle

A jumper wire to connect the grounding-screw terminal to the grounded box is not required with a surface-mounted box, but is required when receptacle is used in a recessed box (Section 250-74)

FIG. 30—Examples of circuit loadings in lighting panelboards

G Lighting Panelboard				K Lighting Panelboard			
Circ. No.	No. of Outlets	Wattage Bus A	Bus B	Circ. No.	No. of Outlets	Wattage Bus A	Bus B
1	4	1000		1	4	480	
2	4		1000	2	3		1500
3	4	1000		3	3	1500	
4	4		1000	4	5		750
5	4	1000		5	5	750	
6	4		1000	6	2		800

A

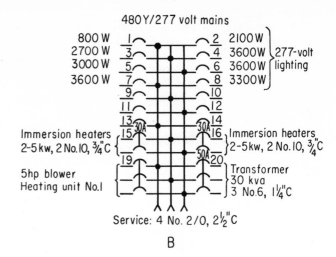

B

loaded with due regard to voltage drop, operating cycle, possible increase in lighting level in the future and required control.

Fig. 30. shows branch-circuit loading schedules for two different installations. In "A," the number of outlets and total load for each branch circuit in each panelboard are indicated. And the relative balancing of loads on the two busbars is shown. The top part of the panel in "B" shows the loading of 277-volt fluorescent lighting on 20-amp circuits each of which has a load capacity of 5500 watts. The schedule at "B" is actually a loadcenter in 480/277-volt distribution serving a modern school. Classroom and corridor lighting is supplied by 277-volt fluorescent lighting circuits from the 480/277-volt panel (circuits 1 to 8 in schedule). The 30-kva transformer fed by circuit 20 in this panel supplies 120/208-volt power to a general-purpose lighting and appliance panelboard. Note spare circuits.

Depending upon the type of occupancy and how the interior is to be laid out from a work standpoint, outlets for local and/or special lighting units represent approximated loads. Such outlets are included in the overall lighting design, either as fixed unit loads or estimated plug-in loads. Outlets—either lampholders or plug receptacles—for such lighting units may be connected to general lighting circuits, provided with separate circuiting or included in circuits allowed for plug receptacles.

Receptacle circuits

Design of branch circuits for plug receptacles requires careful determination of particular requirements. The type and size of occupancy and nature of the work performed there will indicate the best manner of handling plug-connected loads. For known appliances, individual or multioutlet branch circuits should be used, depending on the size of the load.

Automatic appliances should always be provided with separate circuits to isolate such appliances from the effects of faults or other disturbances in other load devices. Fans or heaters might be individually fed by branch circuits, grouped on their own branch circuits or connected to receptacles on general lighting circuits.

Of course, the number of plug-in appliances in a particular area will greatly affect the circuiting. In general, plug-in devices should be supplied from receptacles on circuits other than general lighting circuits. In this way, the loading of circuits can be kept under control, and spare capacity can be much more realistic.

Code limitations on the number of plug outlets on any one branch circuit should be carefully observed in selecting the number of receptacle circuits. In dwelling occupancies—single-family houses, apartment units and hotel guest rooms—receptacle outlets are considered as part of the general lighting load and no additional load has to be added for such outlets. As a result, any number of plug outlets can be put on one circuit in dwelling occupancies. In other than dwelling occupancies, however, each general-purpose plug outlet must be considered to be a load of $1\frac{1}{2}$ amps. Thus a 15-amp branch circuit has capacity to supply $15 \div 1\frac{1}{2}$ or 10 plug outlets, maximum. A 20-amp circuit can supply no more than $20 \div 1\frac{1}{2}$ or 13 plug outlets. These are maximum numbers of receptacles. In many cases, good practice will dictate use of less than the maximum number of plug outlets on any one circuit.

FIG. 31—Loading receptacle circuits

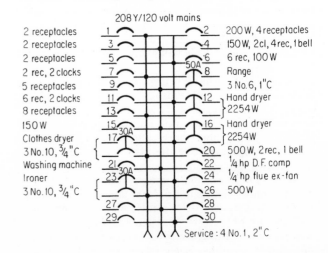

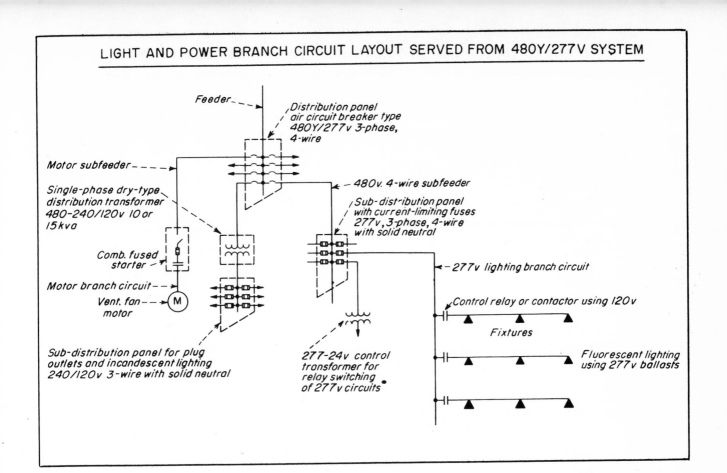

LIGHT AND POWER BRANCH CIRCUIT LAYOUT SERVED FROM 480Y/277V SYSTEM

Feeder

Distribution panel air circuit breaker type 480Y/277v 3-phase, 4-wire

Motor subfeeder

480v. 4-wire subfeeder

Single-phase dry-type distribution transformer 480-240/120v 10 or 15kva

Sub-distribution panel with current-limiting fuses 277v, 3-phase, 4-wire with solid neutral

Comb. fused starter

277v lighting branch circuit

Motor branch circuit

Vent. fan motor

Control relay or contactor using 120v

Fixtures

Sub-distribution panel for plug outlets and incandescent lighting 240/120v 3-wire with solid neutral

277-24v control transformer for relay switching of 277v circuits

Fluorescent lighting using 277v ballasts

TYPICAL DETAILED SCHEDULE OF LIGHTING PANELBOARDS GIVES SELECTION AND INSTALLATION DATA FOR ALL PANELS

LIGHTING PANELBOARD SCHEDULE

Panel Designation	Location	Equip.	Branch Circuits					Mains		Service			Remarks
			No. Active	No. Spares	Total No.	Poles	Trip Calibr.	Type	Cap	Phase	Feed	Voltg.	
LP1A	1st Floor Stair No. 5	Cct. Bkr.	25	7	32	SP	20A	Cct. Bkr.	225/125	3	4-300 MCM	120/208	
LP1C	1st Floor / Main Stair		27	7	34	SP	20A	"	225/150	3	4-4/0	"	
LP2A	2nd Floor Stair No. 6		29	7	36	SP	20A	"	225/150	3	4-300 MCM	"	
LP2B	2nd Floor Stair No.1		1 22	1 8	2 30	2P SP	20A 20A	"	225/125	3	4-4/0	"	
LP2C	2nd Floor Main Stair		14	6	20	SP	20A	"	100/70	3	4-4/0	"	
LP3A	3rd Floor Stair No. 6		39	3	42	SP	20A	"	225/175	3	4-350 MCM	"	
LP3B	3rd Floor Stair No.1		1 20	1 6	2 26	2P SP	20A 20A	"	100/100	3	4-4/0	"	
LP3C	3rd Floor Main Stair		12	4	16	SP	20A	"	100/100	1	–	"	Connect to Existing 3 Wire Feed
LP4A	4th Floor Stair No. 6		18	4	22	SP	20A	"	100/100	3	4-350 MCM	"	
LP4B	4th Floor Stair No.1		1 13	0 5	1 18	2P SP	20A 20A	"	100/70	3	4-300 MCM	"	
LP5A	5th Floor Stair No. 6		11	9	20	SP	20A	"	100/100	3	4-400 MCM	"	
LP5B	5th Floor Stair No.1		1 11	1 5	2 16	2P SP	20A 20A	"	100/70	3	4-300 MCM	"	
LP6A	6th Floor Stair No. 6		14	8	22	SP	20A	"	100/100	3	4-400 MCM	"	
LP6B	6th Floor Stair No.1		1 15	1 5	2 20	2P SP	20A 20A	"	100/70	3	4-300 MCM	"	
LPPH-1A	Penthouse		3	3	6	SP	20A	Lugs Only	NEMA STD	1	3 No.12	"	
LPBA	Basement Near Stair No.1		9	3	12	SP	20A	Lugs Only	NEMA STD	3	4 No. 2	"	
LPBB	Basement Near Stair No.1		11	3	14	SP	20A	Lugs Only	NEMA STD	3	4 No. 2	"	
LPBC	Basement Near Col. 32		5 0	5 1	10 1	SP 2P	20A 20A	Lugs Only	NEMA STD.	3	4 No. 6	"	
LPBD	Basement Near Col. 8		6 0	4 1	10 1	SP 2P	20A 20A	Lugs Only	NEMA STD	3	4 No. 8	"	

GRAPHICAL ELECTRICAL SYMBOLS FOR ARCHITECTURAL PLANS

Ceiling Wall

GENERAL OUTLETS

Outlet
Blanked Outlet
Drop Cord
Electric Outlet; for use only when circle used alone might be confused with columns, plumbing symbols, etc
Fan Outlet
Junction Box
Lamp Holder
Lamp Holder with Pull Switch
Pull Switch
Outlet for Vapor Discharge Lamp
Exit Light Outlet
Clock Outlet (Specify Voltage),

CONVENIENCE OUTLETS

Duplex Convenience Outlet
Convenience Outlet other than Duplex 1=Single, 3=Triplex, etc
Weatherproof Convenience Outlet
Range Outlet
Switch and Convenience Outlet
Radio and Convenience Outlet
Special Purpose Outlet (Des. in Spec.)
Floor Outlet

SWITCH OUTLETS

S Single Pole Switch
S_2 Double Pole Switch
S_3 Three Way Switch
S_4 Four Way Switch
S_D Automatic Door Switch
S_E Electrolier Switch
S_K Key Operated Switch
S_P Switch and Pilot Lamp
S_{CB} Circuit Breaker
S_{WCB} Weatherproof Circuit Breaker
S_{MC} Momentary Contact Switch
S_{RC} Remote Control Switch
S_{WP} Weatherproof Switch
S_F Fused Switch
S_{WF} Weatherproof Fused Switch

SPECIAL OUTLETS

$O_{a,b,c,etc}$
$\ominus_{a,b,c,etc}$
$S_{a,b,c,etc}$

Any standard symbol as given above with the addition of a lower case subscript letter may be used to designate some special variation of standard equipment of particular interest in a specific set of architectural plans.

When used they must be listed in the Key of Symbols on each drawing and if necessary further described in the specifications.

PANELS, CIRCUITS, AND MISCELLANEOUS

Lighting Panel
Power Panel
Branch Circuit; Concealed in Ceiling or Wall
Branch Circuit; Concealed in Floor
Branch Circuit; Exposed
Home Run to Panel Board. Indicate number of circuits by number of arrows.
Note: Any circuit without further designation indicates a two-wire circuit. For a greater number of wires indicate as follows: —⧸⧸— (3 wires) ⧸⧸⧸⧸ (4 wires), etc
Feeders. Note: Use heavy lines and designate by number corresponding to listing in Feeder Schedule.
Underfloor Duct and Junction Box. Triple System. Note: For double or single systems eliminate one or two lines. This symbol is equally adaptable to auxiliary system layouts.
Generator
Motor
Instrument
Power Transformer (Or draw to scale.)
Controller
Isolating Switch

AUXILIARY SYSTEMS

Pushbutton
Buzzer
Bell
Annunciator
Outside Telephone
Interconnecting Telephone
Telephone Switchboard
Bell-Ringing Transformer
Electric Door Opener
Fire Alarm Bell
Fire Alarm Station
City Fire Alarm Station
Fire Alarm Central Station
Automatic Fire Alarm Device
Watchman's Station
Watchman's Central Station
Horn
Nurse's Signal Plug
Maid's Signal Plug
Radio Outlet
Signal Central Station
Interconnection Box
Battery
Auxiliary System Circuits
Note: Any line without further designation indicates a 2-wire system. For a greater number of wires designate with numerals in manner similar to —··— 12-No. 18W-3/4"C., or designate by number corresponding to listing in Schedule.
Special Auxiliary Outlets. Subscript letters refer to notes on plans or detailed description in specifications.

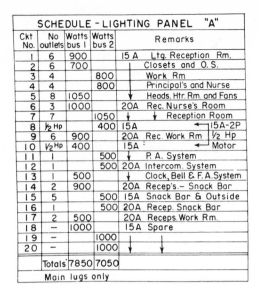

SCHEDULE – LIGHTING PANEL "A"

Ckt No.	No outlets	Watts bus 1	Watts bus 2	Remarks
1	6	900		15 A Ltg. Reception Rm.
2	6	700		Closets and O.S.
3	4		800	Work Rm
4	4		800	Principal's and Nurse
5	8	1050		Heads. Htr. Rm. and Fans
6	3	1000		20A Rec. Nurse's Room
7	7		1050	Reception Room
8	½ Hp		400	15A 15A-2P
9	6	900		20A Rec. Work Rm ½ Hp
10	½ Hp	400		15A Motor
11	1		500	P. A. System
12	1		500	20A Intercom. System
13	1	500		Clock, Bell & F.A.System
14	2	900		20A Recep's.– Snack Bar
15	5		500	15A Snack Bar & Outside
16	1		500	20A Recep. Snack Bar
17	2	500		20A Receps. Work Rm.
18	–	1000		15A Spare
19	–		1000	↓
20	–		1000	↓ ↓
	Totals	7850	7050	
	Main lugs only			

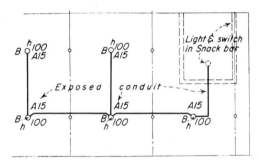

Plan – Covered Eating Area

LEGEND

 Fluorescent fixtures-
capital letter and number indicate panel and circuit number per schedule. Lower case
letter corresponds to letter
on switch controlling unit

 Duplex convenience receptacle-
letter and number show panel
and circuit

 Incandescent lighting fixture –
letter in circle gives fixture type
from fixture schedule, "A2" gives
panel and circuit, "e" indicates
switch controlling unit and "100"
is unit wattage

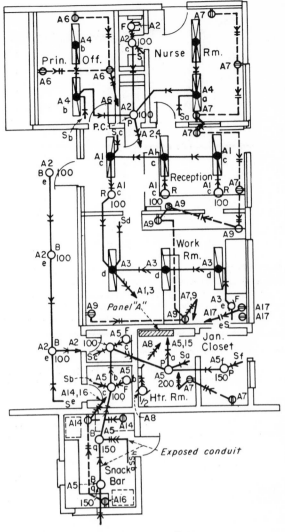

Floor Plan – Light and Power

Se ⎰ Switch – lower case letter indi-
   ⎱ cates lighting units controlled
     by switch

Ⓕ Fan motor

——➤ Concealed branch circuit home run

—— Concealed branch circuit conduit

- - -➤ Underfloor branch circuit home run

- - - Underfloor branch circuit conduit

CIRCUITING DESIGNATIONS

→|← One circuit, two wires, ½" conduit

→||← Two circuits, three wires, ½" conduit

→||← Two circuits, four wires, ¾" conduit

⎰ → Two wires   —|— ½" conduit
⎱ → Three wires   —||— ¾" conduit
  → Four wires

GRAPHICAL INTERPRETATION of electrical design involves the indication of types of electrical equipment on scaled representations of the building areas served by the equipment. The indications include the wire and raceway interconnections among the various elements and must convey all of the design concepts to the mind of the installer who will work from the plans. The above illustration shows the branch circuiting for a small school building with an outside covered eating area. A legend clarifies the use of symbols and a schedule of the panelboard serving the circuits shows the various loads. For the lighting circuits these loads are known from the lighting design which established the number and ratings of the various lighting units. For the ½-hp motor on circuits 8 and 10, the load is known. For receptacle circuits, loads are determined either by allowing 1½ amps for each outlet or by using load figures for known or estimated ratings of appliances. Rating of overcurrent protection for the branch circuits is given under "REMARKS" in the schedule.

Distribution for Plug Outlets

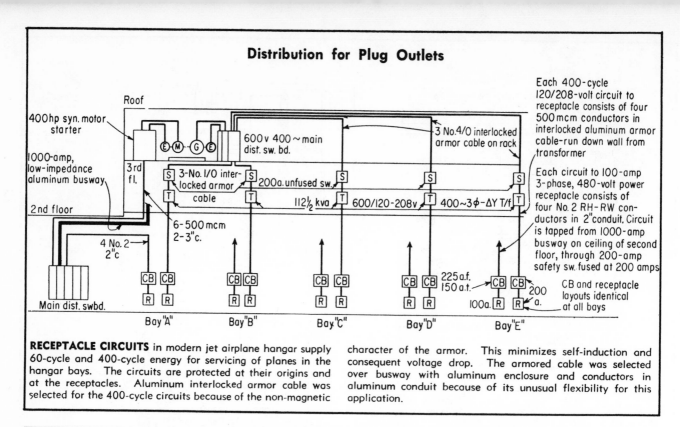

Each 400-cycle 120/208-volt circuit to receptacle consists of four 500 mcm conductors in interlocked aluminum armor cable-run down wall from transformer

Each circuit to 100-amp 3-phase, 480-volt power receptacle consists of four No. 2 RH-RW conductors in 2" conduit. Circuit is tapped from 1000-amp busway on ceiling of second floor, through 200-amp safety sw. fused at 200 amps

CB and receptacle layouts identical at all bays

RECEPTACLE CIRCUITS in modern jet airplane hangar supply 60-cycle and 400-cycle energy for servicing of planes in the hangar bays. The circuits are protected at their origins and at the receptacles. Aluminum interlocked armor cable was selected for the 400-cycle circuits because of the non-magnetic character of the armor. This minimizes self-induction and consequent voltage drop. The armored cable was selected over busway with aluminum enclosure and conductors in aluminum conduit because of its unusual flexibility for this application.

Three Types of Underfloor Raceway Systems for Branch Circuits

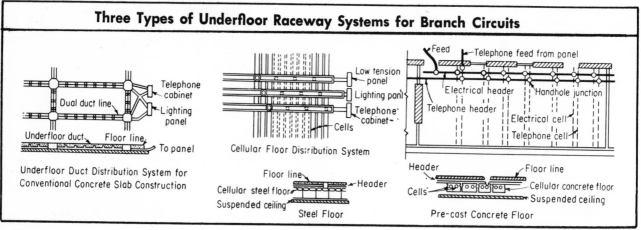

The number of plug outlets connected on a single circuit should be related to the amount of load likely to be connected to any one receptacle in a particular occupancy. When plug-connected loads are known, determination of the proper number of plug outlets is relatively easy. And the number of circuits required in such cases follows directly from the loads and circuit capacities.

When plug-connected loads are not known, the type of occupancy will indicate the possible appliances to be provided for. If the possible appliances are relatively heavy-current devices, two or three outlets per circuit might be the maximum number to allow efficient and convenient use of the circuits. If the possible appliances are low-current devices, up to ten or even more plug outlets may be connected on the circuit without the likelihood of overload.

Fig. 31 shows a school panelboard with wide variation in number of receptacle outlets connected to 120-volt circuits. Layout and circuiting of receptacles were based on study of likely loads, possible simultaneous use of appliances and habits of use of electrical appliances. In a home economics classroom, for example, heavy appliance loads and sewing machine desks dictated use of only two receptacles per No. 12 two-wire circuit.

Of course, the possible number of appliances to be used in any area will also affect the design of receptacle circuits. When special requirements for receptacle circuits arise after tenants move into an area, the spare circuits in the panelboard and extra capacity in the existing system of raceways or underfloor system will offer solution to the need.

Number of plug outlets required for different occupancies is not a matter of easy or standard calculation. The following are suggestions for receptacle layouts in various areas:

1. In office buildings, growing use of business machines dictates heavier load allowances for plug outlets. In separate offices of less than 400 sq ft area, at least one plug outlet should be allowed for each 10 linear feet of wall space. In each office area of over 400 sq ft, eight plug outlets should be allowed for the first 400 sq ft of floor area and three plug outlets for each additional 400 sq ft of floor area or fraction thereof. The number of outlets obtained in this way should be evenly distributed throughout the area.

2. **In schoolrooms,** common practice has been to provide at least one plug outlet on each wall of the room.

3. **In stores,** at least one plug outlet should be provided for each 400 sq ft of floor area or major fraction thereof.

4. **In industrial areas,** plug outlets should be provided on the basis of particular conditions.

In addition to conventional receptacle circuits, there is a growing requirement in all types of modern buildings for new and often complex types of receptacle circuits. In particular, data processing equipment and other special machines used in today's commercial and industrial buildings call for multi-wire receptacle circuits of varying voltage, phase and frequency characteristics.

Control of branch circuit

Branch-circuit design must include provision for control of the circuits. This may take the form of control over individual outlets or groups of outlets or may consist of control of the entire circuit.

Local control of one or more lighting outlets (less than the entire circuit) is commonly accomplished with manual, direct-acting wiring-device switches. Local control is not generally required for receptacle outlets, although such control is sometimes desirable and recommended. A commonly used technique for plug outlet control is to split-wire a duplex receptacle so the top outlet is controlled by a wall switch and the bottom outlet is always hot, as shown in Fig. 32.

An important new rule on use of wiring device switches is contained in the second paragraph of Section 380-8 of the 1965 NE Code, as follows:

"Snap switches shall not be grouped or ganged in outlet boxes unless they can be so arranged that the voltage between exposed live metal parts of adjacent switches does not exceed 300 volts."

This new rule applies where 277-volt switches, mounted in a common box (such as 2- or 3-ganged), control 277-volt loads, with the voltage between exposed line terminals of *adjacent* switches in the common box being 480 volts. If the adjacent switches have exposed live terminals, anyone changing one of the switches without disconnecting the circuit at the panel could contact 480 volts. Fig. 33.

If screwless-terminal switches (with no exposed live parts) are used, it would *not* be a violation of the new second paragraph of Section 380-8 if any number of such switches are ganged in a common box. Fig. 34 shows an arrangement where screwless and screw-type switches are mounted side-by-side in a 2-gang box. This satisfies the intent (and literal text) of Section 380-8 because only one switch has exposed live terminals.

When local switching is not necessary, the entire circuit can be controlled by the branch-circuit circuit breaker or switch in the panelboard. Although panelboard control is a common and satisfactory practice in many occupancies—particularly industrial and large commercial areas—most areas should be provided with the convenience and economy of operation

FIG. 32—Split-wiring control of receptacles

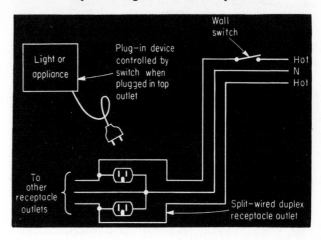

FIG. 33—This hookup violates the code

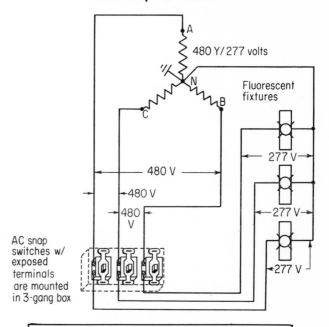

Snap switches shall not be grouped or ganged in outlet boxes where voltage between exposed live metal parts of adjacent switches exceeds 300 volts.

Installation shown would be acceptable if a separate single-gang box and plate are used for each switch, or a common wire from only one phase (A, B or C) supplies switches in 3-gang box or if switches were screwless type.

afforded by local switching. Switching at the panelboard requires a separate circuit for each group of outlets to be controlled together.

Such factors as distance from panelboard to lighting fixtures, partitioning of the area of lighting coverage fed from the panelboard, need for 3- or 4-way switch control will determine the amount of local switching, the amount of panelboard switching and the number of circuits needed.

Automatic direct switching of lighting circuits is commonly accomplished by means of time switches, as shown for the double-pole time switch in Fig. 35. But, there is a growing trend toward the convenience and flexibility of different types of remote-control magnetic switching using relays and contactors.

FIG. 34—Complying with 1965 NE Code Section 380-8.

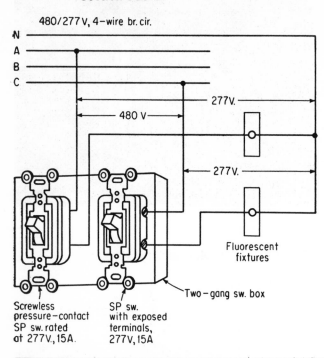

480/277V, 4-wire br. cir.

277V.

480 v

277V.

Fluorescent fixtures

Two—gang sw. box

Screwless pressure—contact SP sw. rated at 277V., 15A.

SP sw. with exposed terminals, 277V, 15A.

FIG. 36—Low-voltage relay control

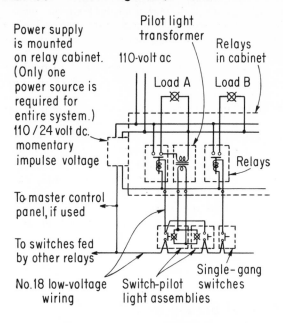

Power supply is mounted on relay cabinet. (Only one power source is required for entire system.) 110 / 24 volt dc. momentary impulse voltage

Pilot light transformer

110-volt ac

Load A   Load B

Relays in cabinet

Relays

To master control panel, if used

To switches fed by other relays

No. 18 low-voltage wiring

Switch-pilot light assemblies

Single—gang switches

FIG. 35—Time switch control of lighting

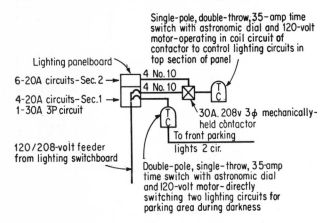

Single-pole, double-throw, 35-amp time switch with astronomic dial and 120-volt motor-operating in coil circuit of contactor to control lighting circuits in top section of panel

Lighting panelboard

6-20A circuits-Sec. 2

4-20A circuits-Sec. 1
1-30A 3P circuit

4 No. 10

4 No. 10

TC

30A. 208v 3φ mechanically-held contactor

To front parking lights 2 cir.

120/208-volt feeder from lighting switchboard

TC

Double-pole, single-throw, 35-amp time switch with astronomic dial and 120-volt motor- directly switching two lighting circuits for parking area during darkness

FIG. 37—Relay switching control of lighting

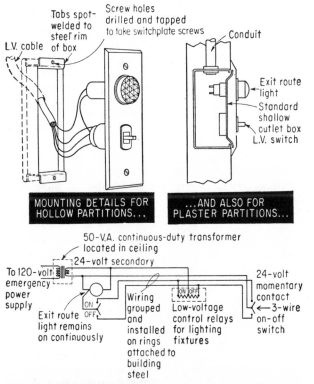

Tabs spot-welded to steel rim of box

Screw holes drilled and tapped to take switchplate screws

L.V. cable

Conduit

Exit route light

Standard shallow outlet box

L.V. switch

MOUNTING DETAILS FOR HOLLOW PARTITIONS...

...AND ALSO FOR PLASTER PARTITIONS...

50-V.A. continuous-duty transformer located in ceiling

24-volt secondary

To 120-volt emergency power supply

Exit route light remains on continuously

Wiring grouped and installed on rings attached to building steel

Low-voltage control relays for lighting fixtures

24-volt momentary contact

3-wire on-off switch

WIRING DIAGRAM FOR EXIT ROUTE LIGHT AND L.V. SWITCHES

Low-voltage relay switching

Low-voltage relay switching is used where remote control or control from a number of spread-out points is required for each of a number of small 120-volt or 277-volt lighting or heating loads. In this type of control, contacts operated by low-voltage relay coils are used to open and close the hot conductor supplying the one or more luminaires or load devices controlled by the relay. The relay is generally a 3-wire, mechanically held, ON-OFF type, energized from a step-down control transformer.

In some cases, all of the relays may be mounted in an enclosure near the panelboard supplying the branch circuits which the relays switch, with a single transformer mounted there to supply the low voltage. Where a single panelboard serves a large number of lighting branch circuits over a very large area—such as large office areas in commercial buildings, a number of relays associated with each section of the overall area may be group-mounted in an enclosure in that area.

Fig. 37 shows 24-volt control of 277-volt fixtures, with constantly illuminated switchplates alongside doorways to define interior exit routes and practical hollow-partition clip-in switch boxes in interior labs of a medical research center. Control relays are in compact boxes atop luminaires. Relays are connected to switches and to 50-va continuous-duty 120/24-volt transformers by multiwire Class 2 remote-control circuits routed through overhead plenums and supported by insulator rings attached to fixture hangers by spring clips. No switching circuit controls more than four relays. Switching circuits and exit lights are served from an emergency power source, with general lighting fixtures served through normal 480/277-volt feeders. Interior-area route-indicating lights and general-lighting switches are mounted together in thin boxes set in partitions.

Contactor control

One of the most popular types of modern branch-circuit control is contactor switching. Magnetic contactors—electrically held or mechanically held types, depending upon the stability of control voltage and such factors as coil hum and coil power drain—may be used in individual enclosures for control of circuit or load devices. The basic difference between magnetically held contactors and mechanically held contactors is shown in Fig. 38. They also may be mounted in split-bus type panelboards for block control of a section of the panel bus supplying a number of circuits. The operating coil of a contactor (or remote control switch, as it also is known) may be either manually or automatically switched. Fig. 39 presents basic design considerations for contactor coil circuits.

A typical contactor application for full panel control might involve locating the contactors at widely spaced lighting panelboards supplying outdoor lighting with all of the control circuits brought to pilot switches at a common point of control. Such an installation is shown in Fig. 40. For control of individual circuits supplying lighting loads, contactors may be located near the panelboard or near the load with the control circuit arranged for maximum convenience of operation at any number of points, depending upon the job requirements.

Typical coil-circuit control devices for contactors include: maintained-contact and momentary-contact pushbuttons, selector switches, control and master type switches, pressure switches, float switches, limit switches, time switches, thermostats, plugging switch and contacts of control relays. Use of one or more of these devices will depend upon the nature and layout of the load. Contactors may be used for control of branch circuits or feeders, supplying lighting loads and/or motor loads.

Panelboard selection and layout

Lighting and appliance branch circuits originate in panelboards in which the overcurrent protective devices for the circuits are mounted.

Selection of a panelboard is based first on the number of circuits which it must serve. Then it must be assured that the busbars in a panelboard for any application have sufficient current rating for the demand load of all of the branch circuits, according to Fig. 41.

The code defines a lighting and appliance branch circuit panelboard as "one having more than 10% of its overcurrent devices rated 30 amps or less, for which neutral connections are provided." Fig. 42 shows a panelboard which just meets code rules for classification as a lighting and appliance panel, as follows:

1. There is a total of 24 overcurrent devices in the panel.

2. There are three overcurrent devices which are

FIG. 38—Types of magnetic contactors

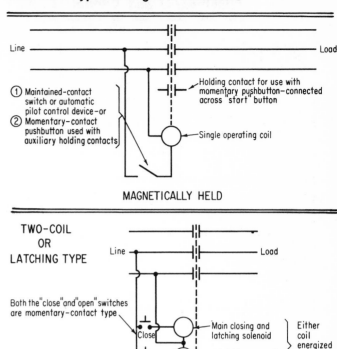

MAGNETICALLY HELD

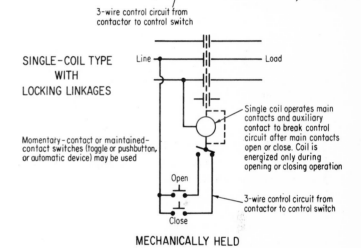

MECHANICALLY HELD

rated 30 amps or less, with neutral connection provided for them.

3. 10% of the number of overcurrent devices (24) is 2.4.

4. Panelboard, therefore, has more than 10% of its overcurrent devices rated 30 amps or less, with neutral connections.

5. Such a panelboard is designated by the NE Code as a "lighting and appliance" panelboard and must be protected in accordance with NE Code Section 384-16.

The overcurrent devices referred to in the foregoing determination may be fuses or CB poles. A 2-pole CB is considered to be two overcurrent devices; a 3-pole CB is three overcurrent devices. And the code says that not more than 42 overcurrent devices, "other than those provided for in the mains," may be installed in any one cabinet or cutout box for a lighting and appliance panelboard. Thus, a panel may have 42 overcurrent poles in it plus mains protection—such as a 3-pole main CB ahead of the 42 devices.

In addition to the protective feature, the panel-

Panelboards and Control Layout For High Frequency Lighting Circuits

120-v motored dual coded relays operated by carrier pulses

Contactor coil-circuit switching relays operated at 120 volts

Panelboard supplied from dry type transf provides circuits for receptacles, for relays above and for contactor coils

120/208-v 3φ, 4W 60-cycle panelboard

Unit reactor coils connected across 840-cycle circuit for power factor correction

1	2
3	4
5	6

Emergency panel

1	2
3	4
5	6

Normal panel

30-amp 2-pole "F" frame CBs protect 840-cycle 600-v circuits

Cir. 1   Cir. 2

Cir. 1   Cir. 2   Cir. 3

Cir. 4   Cir. 5

5-sec. time-delay relays connect PF coils to load sides of contactors after lamps are lighted

Spares

2-pole, 30-amp 600-volt contactors (120-v, 60-cycle coils) switch 840-cycle circuits as indicated

HIGH FREQUENCY LIGHTING branch circuits are supplied from this panelboard layout on one floor of a bank building. Feeders operating at 600 volts between conductors (300 volts to ground) and 840 cycles per second are supplied to the two CB panels at upper right, from main switchboard in frequency conversion room. Each circuit is rated 2-pole, 600 volts and protected by one 2-pole breaker. Control of circuits is made by 2-pole contactors connected on load side of branch CB's. At left, a 120/208-volt, 60-cycle panelboard provides circuits which operate the contactor coils through carrier frequency actuated relays at upper left. The carrier frequency pulses are transmitted over the 120/208-volt wiring from a central time control panel which schedules the pulse transmissions to operate the contactors at given times of the day for turning lights on or off. Relays sense the carrier pulses and close the contactor coil circuits.

Major Considerations in Circuit Design for Contactor Control

1. Size of feeder from bus plug switch to main contactor is based on total volt-amperes of fluorescent lighting load at 100% demand.

2. Additional feeder capacity is included for load growth.

3. Further upsizing of feeder conductors keeps voltage drop under 1% from service to branch circuit panelboard and reduces the heating effect of continuous load operation.

4. Main contactor is sized to match feeder capacity.

5. Lighting panelboard is rated for the total feeder capacity.

6. Branch circuit protection consists of 20-amp, 3-pole CB's for multi-wire branch circuits to 277-volt fluorescent ballast.

7. Individual branch circuit contactors are 3-pole, 30-amp remote-control switches connected in the lighting panelboard on the load side of the branch CB's.

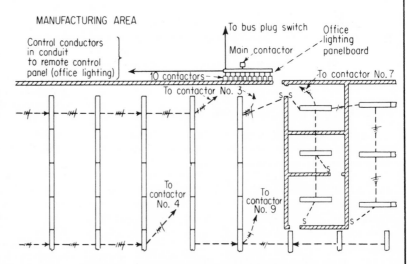

MANUFACTURING AREA

Control conductors in conduit to remote control panel (office lighting)

To bus plug switch

Main contactor

Office lighting panelboard

10 contactors

To contactor No. 3

To contactor No. 7

To contactor No. 4

To contactor No. 9

8. Each branch circuit is loaded to 50% of its capacity. (80% loading is the NEC maximum for continuously operating circuits).

OFFICE LIGHTING of continuous row fluorescent luminaires is circuited from a remote control contactor panelboard which is outside the office area, on the wall of the adjoining manufacturing area. The special panelboard is fed by conductors tapped from a busway plug switch, as indicated. The panel is equipped with a main contactor which switches the supply to the panel mains. Each branch circuit consists of a branch CB and a remote control contactor. All control circuits are carried in conduits to a control panel on the wall at one end of the office area.

FIG. 39—Designing coil circuits for magnetic contactors

1. Voltage supply to operating coil

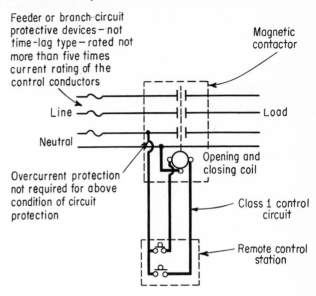

Line — Load

Coil supplied from line at line voltage

Holding contacts for use with momentary pushbutton station

Mechanical operating connection

Coil supplied from separate control voltage source

Operating coil

Coil supplied from built-in control transformer

Remote control by toggle switch, pushbuttons or relay contacts

2. Requirements for Class 1 control conductors

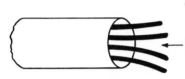

Conductors generally limited to minimum of No. 14 size, but No. 18 or No. 16 may be used if installed in raceway or approved cable or flexible cord and protected at not more than 20 amps

1. Number of conductors in raceway in accordance with Section 300-17.
2. Control conductors do not have to be derated according to number in raceway.
3. When control conductors are run in raceway with power and light conductors, all conductors must be derated in accordance with Note 8 of Tables 310-12 through 310-15—determining the derating factor on the basis of the number of power and light conductors only.
4. Conductors for two or more remote control circuits may be run in the same raceway—ac and/or dc circuits—if all conductors are insulated for the maximum voltage of any conductor in the raceway.

3. Overcurrent protection of control circuit

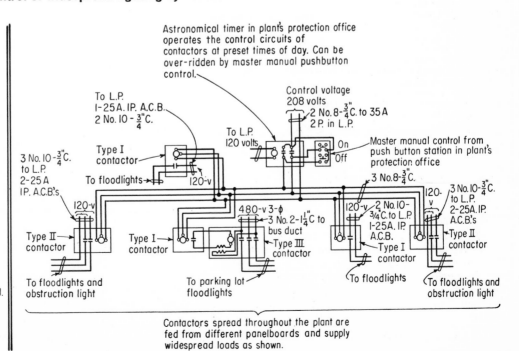

Feeder or branch-circuit protective devices—not time-lag type—rated not more than five times current rating of the control conductors

Magnetic contactor

Line — Load

Neutral

Overcurrent protection not required for above condition of circuit protection

Opening and closing coil

Class 1 control circuit

Remote control station

Protection of contactor remote-control conductors must follow Section 240-5, Exception No. 5. As shown above, separate protection of the control conductors is not required under the given conditions. If the stated requirements were not satisfied, a fuse or circuit breaker would have to be inserted in the control circuit tap from the operating coil to the hot line conductor. And if the control circuit were energized from two hot conductors, both taps would have to be protected. Control circuit could have been derived from a separate source instead of the line side of the remote control switch.

FIG. 40—Central control of widespread lighting by contactors

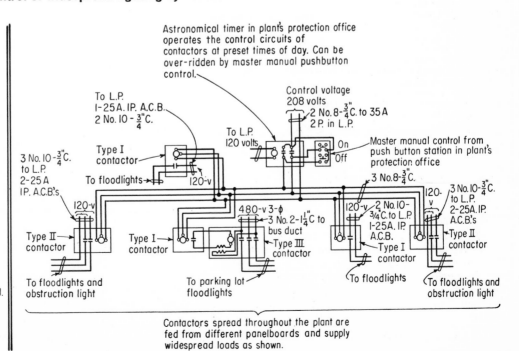

TYPES OF CONTACTORS USED IN THIS SYSTEM

Type I—
Electrically-operated, mechanically-held, 60-amp 250-volt ac contactor, with 1 NO contact and with 208-volt operating coil

Type II—
The same as Type I but with 2 NO contacts

Type III—
Electrically-operated, electrically-held, NEMA Size 4,600-volt contactor, with 480/120-volt control transformer and 120-volt operating coil.

Astronomical timer in plant's protection office operates the control circuits of contactors at preset times of day. Can be over-ridden by master manual pushbutton control.

Control voltage 208 volts

Master manual control from push button station in plant's protection office

Contactors spread throughout the plant are fed from different panelboards and supply widespread loads as shown.

35

Remote Control Switching for Large-Block Control of Lighting

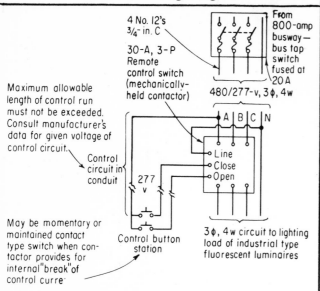

4 No. 12's 3/4-in. C

30-A, 3-P Remote control switch (mechanically-held contactor)

From 800-amp busway—bus tap switch fused at 20 A

480/277-v, 3 φ, 4w

Maximum allowable length of control run must not be exceeded. Consult manufacturer's data for given voltage of control circuit.

Control circuit in conduit

277 v

May be momentary or maintained contact type switch when contactor provides for internal "break" of control curre·

Control button station

Line
Close
Open

3 φ, 4w circuit to lighting load of industrial type fluorescent luminaires

INDUSTRIAL APPLICATION of remote control switching can follow this basic hookup, with the individual mechanically-held contactors mounted in enclosures high up on columns in plant areas. Each contactor can be located at the approximate center of its lighting load to keep circuit wiring as short as possible for minimum voltage drop and can be tapped from the nearest point on the busway. Control circuits are then carried to one or more control panels.

FIG. 41—Calculating size of branch-circuit panelboards for lighting and appliance circuits

Two-wire dc or single-phase:
Total connected load (amperes) = sum of branch loads. At least 10 amps should be allowed for each spare or appliance circuit.

Three-wire dc or single-phase:
Same calculations apply as for two-wire panel, applied separately to each side of panel.

Four-wire, three-phase:
The load on any bus, except the neutral, is computed the same as for a two-wire panel. The load on each of the phase buses is taken as that of the most heavily loaded bus.

NOTE: Section 384-13 requires that a panelboard must have a rating (amperes capacity of its busbars) not less than the minimum feeder capacity required for the total load. A panelboard may have a higher rating than the current rating of a feeder required for the load, but not a lower rating.

board usually contains a means for switching each circuit. Typical panelboard configurations are shown in Fig. 43. Some panelboards have a switch and fuse for each circuit; other panelboards use circuit breakers which provide both protection and switching for the circuits. Overcurrent protection is a code requirement for branch circuits, but disconnect provisions are not required for branch circuits (although means are required to be able to disconnect cartridge fuses in circuits at any voltage if they are accessible to other than qualified persons). A panelboard, therefore, may contain only fuses. In the great majority of cases, however, the advantages of switch or CB control of each circuit at the panelboard dictate

FIG. 42—A panel with more than 10% of its overcurrent devices rated 30 amps or less, for which neutral connections are provided, is a lighting and appliance panelboard.

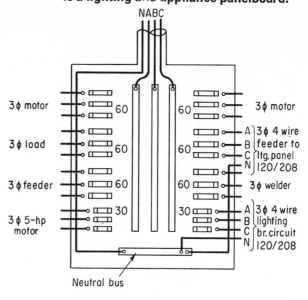

N A B C

3 φ motor — 60
3 φ load — 60
3 φ feeder — 60
3 φ 5-hp motor — 30

60 — 3 φ motor
60 — A B C N 3 φ 4 wire feeder to ltg. panel 120/208
60 — 3 φ welder
30 — A B C N 3 φ 4 wire lighting br. circuit 120/208

Neutral bus

FIG. 43—Typical circuit makeups in panelboards

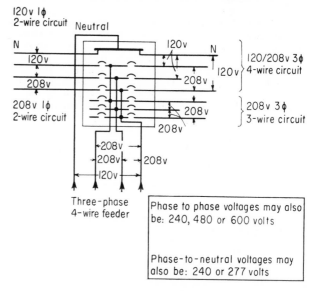

120v 1φ 2-wire circuit

Neutral

N
120v
208v

120v
208v
208v

208v 1φ 2-wire circuit

208v
208v
120v

120v
120v
208v N

120v
208v

120/208v 3φ 4-wire circuit

208v 3φ 3-wire circuit

Three-phase 4-wire feeder

Phase to phase voltages may also be: 240, 480 or 600 volts

Phase-to-neutral voltages may also be: 240 or 277 volts

CIRCUIT BREAKER PANEL

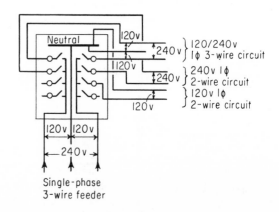

Neutral

120v
120v
120v

240v
240v
120v

120/240v 1φ 3-wire circuit
240v 1φ 2-wire circuit
120v 1φ 2-wire circuit

120v 120v
240v

Single-phase 3-wire feeder

SWITCH-AND-FUSE PANEL

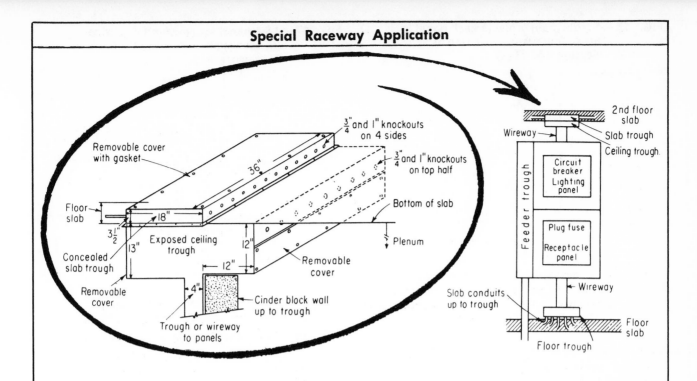

AUXILIARY GUTTERS and various configurations of metal troughs can often simplify design of panelboard distribution centers for branch circuits. Typical example at left shows concealed trough set in floor slab to provide termination for branch circuit conduits run in slab. This open-bottom trough was mounted on deck forms during slab construction. The bottom section of trough was added after forms were removed. Connections between troughs and panel enclosure are made by steel raceway with interior partitions to group circuit conductors for each panel. Wireways are designed to conform to NEC 362, including cross-sectional fill and number of conductors in each section. This method was dictated by confined space at electrical centers under stairways. It eliminated stubbing down conduit home runs with the inherent nippling-out to panels. Crossovers of home run conduits in the slab were also eliminated. At right, method is adapted to special branch circuit center which separates lighting and receptacle circuits. Feeder trough keeps these conductors out of the panel gutters. Floor trough for slab conduits to receptacles is raised to keep moisture out of conduits.

against just fuses in the panelboard. In fact, commercial and industrial practice frequently finds the panelboard switches or CBs used as the only control of the circuits.

Panelboard protection

It is important to consider carefully the busbar ratings of lighting and appliance branch-circuit panelboards. Standards of UL and NEMA base the ratings of main switches, overcurrent devices and busbars feeding lighting and/or appliance branch devices within the panel on an assumed average load current of not more than 10 amps per branch circuit. Where the continuous loading will be in excess of an average of 10 amps per branch circuit, busbars and integral main switches and overcurrent devices of greater capacity will be required.

Important new rules in Section 384-16 of the 1965 NE Code concern the selection of lighting and appliance branch-circuit panelboards. In general, such panels must be individually protected on the supply side by not more than two main circuit breakers or two sets of fuses having a combined rating not greater than that of the panelboard. Fig. 44. Where a number of panels are tapped from a single feeder protected at a current rating higher than that of the busbars in any of the panels, the main protection may be installed as a separate device just ahead of

FIG. 44—Each L&A panelboard must be protected by one or two main devices
(i.e., one or two CBs or sets of fuses)

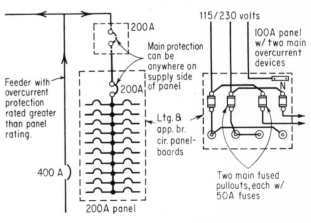

ONE main protective device, either in panel or just ahead of it, rated not greater than panel busbar rating.

TWO main protective devices, dividing supply into two circuits, have combined rating not greater than panel busbar rating.

the panel or as a device within the panel feeding the busbars. Fig. 45. The main protection would normally be a circuit breaker or fused switch, of the number of poles corresponding to the number of busbars in the panel.

FIG. 45—Single main protects each panel in accordance with basic rule of Section 384-16(a)

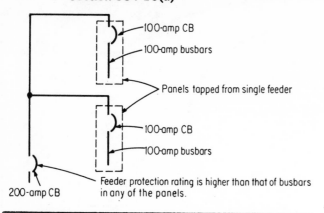

- 100-amp CB
- 100-amp busbars
- Panels tapped from single feeder
- 100-amp CB
- 100-amp busbars
- 200-amp CB
- Feeder protection rating is higher than that of busbars in any of the panels.

FIG. 46—Panels do not require main protection because feeder protection protects panels
(Exception No. 1, Section 384-16a)

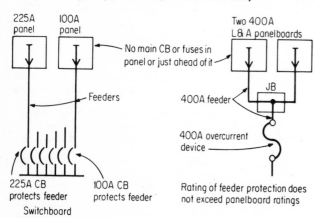

- 225A panel
- 100A panel
- Two 400A L&A panelboards
- No main CB or fuses in panel or just ahead of it
- Feeders
- JB
- 400A feeder
- 400A overcurrent device
- 225A CB protects feeder
- 100A CB protects feeder
- Switchboard
- Rating of feeder protection does not exceed panelboard ratings

FIG. 47—L&A panel for residential service
(Exception No. 2, Section 384-16a)

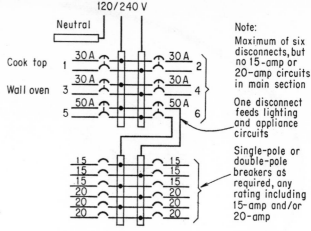

120/240 V

Neutral

- Cook top 1 30 A 30 A 2
- Wall oven 3 30 A 30 A 4
- 5 50 A 50 A 6
- 15 15
- 15 15
- 15 15
- 20 20
- 20 20
- 20 20

Note:
Maximum of six disconnects, but no 15-amp or 20-amp circuits in main section

One disconnect feeds lighting and appliance circuits

Single-pole or double-pole breakers as required, any rating including 15-amp and/or 20-amp

SPLIT-BUS PANEL: RESIDENTIAL ONLY

FIG. 48—L&A panel for nonresidential service

FOR INDIVIDUAL OCCUPANCY:
Panel used for service equipment must have protection on supply side with rating not greater than that of panel bus.

TWO-STORY OFFICE BUILDING OF MULTIPLE-OCCUPANCY

There are two cases in which the prescribed mains protection is not required: Individual protection is not required when a lighting and appliance branch-circuit panelboard is connected to a feeder which has overcurrent protection not greater than that of the panelboard. Fig. 46.

Individual protection for lighting and appliance branch-circuit panelboard is also not required where such panelboards are used as service equipment in supplying an individual residential occupancy and where any bus supplying 15- or 20-amp circuits is protected on the supply side by an overcurrent device. In such instances, a panel can have up to six mains, provided that none of the mains is rated at 20 amps or less where more than two main overcurrent devices are used. Fig. 47. All 15- and/or 20-amp circuits must be fed from the bottom (main-protected) section of busbars.

As noted, therefore, split-bus panels with more than two mains may be used for service equipment only in single-family houses and in apartments. But in the case of, say, a two-story multi-occupancy office building where a sub-set of service entrance conductors is run to each office suite (as permitted by the code), the usual split-bus panel with up to six mains must not be used. A panelboard used for service equipment in other than "an individual residential occupancy" must have individual protection on its supply side of rating not greater than that of the panelboard, if it is a lighting and appliance panel-

board. That means, only one or two main overcurrent protective devices may be used. Fig. 48.

The actual wording of Section 384-16(a) states: "Each lighting and appliance branch-circuit panelboard shall be individually protected on the supply side by not more than two main circuit breakers or two sets of fuses having a combined rating not greater than that of the panelboard." At this point it is significant to note that this *basic rule* applies to *all* lighting and appliance branch-circuit panelboards—even those used as service equipment. Continuing the section, "Exception No. 1. Individual protection for a lighting and appliance panelboard is not required when the panelboard feeder has overcurrent protection not greater than that of the panelboard.

"Exception No. 2. Individual protection for lighting and appliance branch-circuit panelboards is not required where such panelboards are used as service equipment in supplying an individual residential occupancy and where any bus supplying 15- or 20-amp circuits is protected on the supply side by an overcurrent device."

The phrase, "individual residential occupancy," is not limited to a single-family house but includes an individual flat or apartment in a multiple-family building.

Section 384-16(b) says that, "Panelboards equipped with snap switches rated at 30 amps or less shall have overcurrent protection not in excess of 200

38

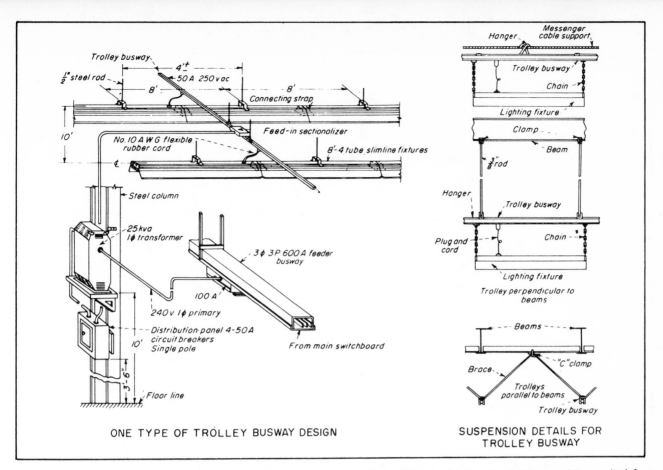

ONE TYPE OF TROLLEY BUSWAY DESIGN

SUSPENSION DETAILS FOR TROLLEY BUSWAY

TROLLEY BUSWAY serves as lighting branch circuit, fed from four 50-amp CB's in lighting panel. The panel is supplied from transformer secondary, powered from a tap to a busway feeder or subfeeder. The lighting fixtures are suspended from the trolley busway, from beams or from the ceiling. The trolley busway is supported from ceiling, beams, messenger cable, or braces supported from the beams.

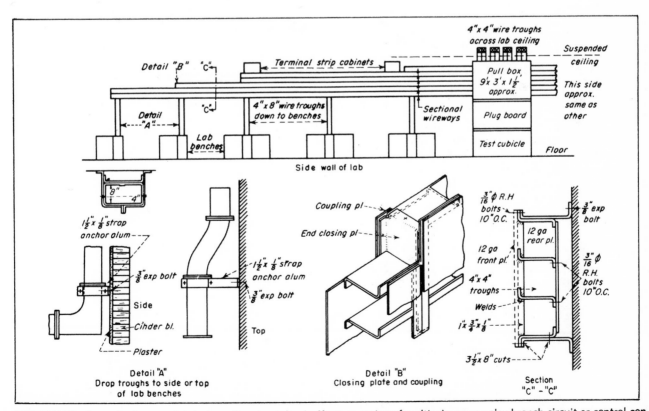

Detail "A"
Drop troughs to side or top of lab benches

Detail "B"
Closing plate and coupling

Section "C" – "C"

WIREWAYS of standard or special design offer simple and effective routing of multi-wire or complex branch circuit or control conductors. In many cases where access to wiring is required or desirable for changing of circuiting, specially fabricated sheet steel wire enclosures with removable panels offer distinct advantages over any other type of raceway. This is particularly true for motor and control circuits.

39

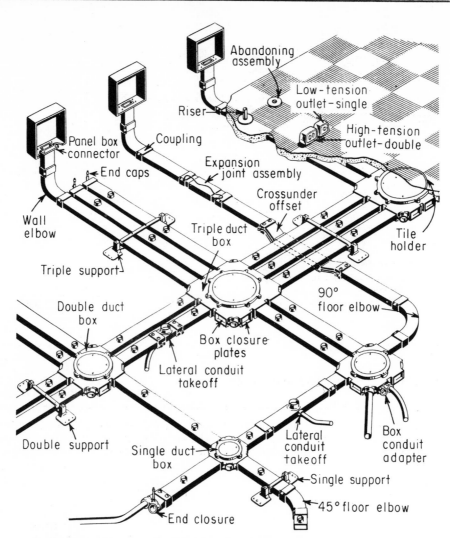

Underfloor Raceway for Use in Conventional Concrete Slab Floors

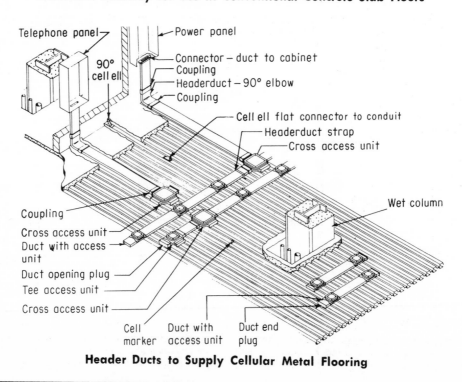

Header Ducts to Supply Cellular Metal Flooring

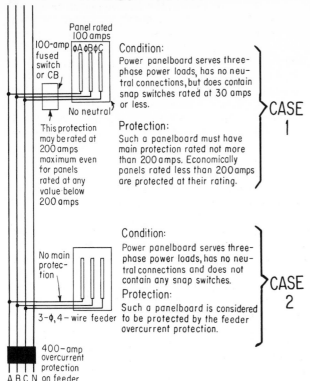

Panel rated 100 amps

100-amp fused switch or CB

No neutral

This protection may be rated at 200 amps maximum even for panels rated at any value below 200 amps

Condition:
Power panelboard serves three-phase power loads, has no neutral connections, but does contain snap switches rated at 30 amps or less.

Protection:
Such a panelboard must have main protection rated not more than 200 amps. Economically panels rated less than 200 amps are protected at their rating.

CASE 1

No main protection

3-φ, 4-wire feeder

Condition:
Power panelboard serves three-phase power loads, has no neutral connections and does not contain any snap switches.

Protection:
Such a panelboard is considered to be protected by the feeder overcurrent protection.

CASE 2

400-amp overcurrent protection on feeder

A B C N

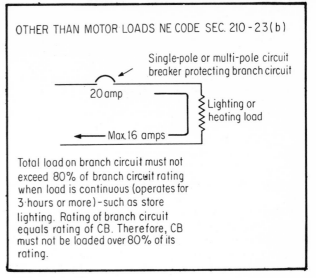

OTHER THAN MOTOR LOADS NE CODE SEC. 210-23(b)

Single-pole or multi-pole circuit breaker protecting branch circuit

20 amp

Max. 16 amps

Lighting or heating load

Total load on branch circuit must not exceed 80% of branch circuit rating when load is continuous (operates for 3 hours or more)—such as store lighting. Rating of branch circuit equals rating of CB. Therefore, CB must not be loaded over 80% of its rating.

1965 NE Code
NOTE: "Section 384-16(c). The total load on any overcurrent device located in a panelboard shall not exceed 80% of its rating where in normal operation the load will continue for three hours or more." This appears to apply to CBs used for motor loads as well as lighting or heating loads.

amps." Any panel, a lighting panel or a power panel, which contains snap switches rated 30 amps or less must have overcurrent protection not in excess of 200 amps. Panels which are not lighting and appliance panels and do not contain snap switches rated 30 amps or less do not have to be equipped with main protection and may be tapped from any size of feeder. Fig. 49 shows these two examples of overcurrent protection requirements for panelboards.

Another new code rule, Section 384-16(c), states that "the total load on any overcurrent device located in any panelboard shall not exceed 80% of its rating where in normal operation the load will continue for three hours or more." An exception to this would be an assembly, together with the overcurrent device, which has been found suitable for *continuous duty* at 100% of its rating. Fig. 50 relates the rule of Section 384-16(c) with that of Section 210-23(b), which has

FIG. 51—Remote-control contactors switch sections of split-bus panelboard

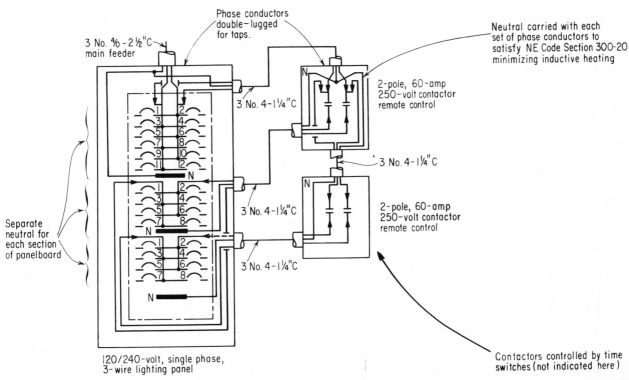

Phase conductors double-lugged for taps.

3 No. ⅚-2½"C main feeder

Neutral carried with each set of phase conductors to satisfy NE Code Section 300-20 minimizing inductive heating

3 No. 4-1¼"C

2-pole, 60-amp 250-volt contactor remote control

3 No. 4-1¼"C

3 No. 4-1¼"C

2-pole, 60-amp 250-volt contactor remote control

3 No. 4-1¼"C

Separate neutral for each section of panelboard

120/240-volt, single phase, 3-wire lighting panel

Contactors controlled by time switches (not indicated here)

FIG. 52—Switched neutral for gas pumps

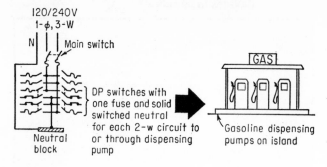

120/240V
1-φ, 3-W

N — Main switch

DP switches with one fuse and solid switched neutral for each 2-w circuit to or through dispensing pump

Neutral block

GAS

Gasoline dispensing pumps on island

the same effect of limiting load on the protective device.

Panels containing plug fuses are required to have fuseholders of the Edison-base or Type S designs. As a practical matter, panelboards with nonremovable plug-fuseholder assemblies are furnished with Edison-base types. Then, to conform to the latest NE Code rules, Type S fuses and proper adapters, classified 0-15 amps, 16-20 amps and 21-30 amps, must be installed as designated by circuit ratings. With the detachable-type plug-fuseholder assemblies, fuse blocks containing either Edison-base or Type S fuseholders are available.

Although the noninterchangeable (NI) circuit breaker rule has been deleted from the NE Code, a new provision in Section 384-15 states: "A lighting and appliance branch-circuit panelboard shall be provided with physical means to prevent the installation of more overcurrent devices than that number for which the panelboard was designed, rated and approved." UL will regulate the way of providing "physical means" to accomplish the objectives indicated in Section 384-15.

With the new code changes, it is now clear that lighting and appliance branch circuits may be rated and protected in excess of 200 amps except where a panelboard contains snap switches rated 30 amps or less.

Panelboards may be equipped with a main switch or circuit breaker feeding the entire bus or a section of bus in the board. In cases where a lighting panel is supplied by a tap from a feeder with overcurrent protection greater than the main busbar rating of the panel, a main CB or fused switch required for the panel provides simultaneous disconnect of circuits from the feeder. In many cases, a remote control switch, operated by a manual pilot switch or by some automatic pilot device like a time clock, is used to control the circuits connected to the bus in the panel by switching the feed to the bus, as shown in Fig. 51.

In addition to standard panelboard hookups, there are cases which call for careful design of special panel arrangements. A typical special panel application is commonly used in gas stations. Section 514-5 (in Article 514 on Gasoline Dispensing and Service Stations) of the NE Code makes a specific requirement on "Circuit Disconnects." It states: "Each circuit leading to or through a dispensing pump shall be provided with a switch or other acceptable means to disconnect simultaneously from the source of supply all conductors of the circuit, including the grounded neutral, if any." Fig. 52 shows how this can be accomplished using a gas-station type panelboard, which has its bussing arranged to permit hookup of standard solid-neutral circuits in addition to the switched-neutral circuits required. Another way of supplying such switched-neutral circuits is with circuit-breaker type panelboards for which there are standard accessory breaker units, which have a trip element in the ungrounded conductor and only a switching mechanism in the other pole of the common-trip breaker, as shown in Fig. 53. Either 2- or 3-pole units may be used for 2-wire or 3-wire circuits, rated 15, 20 or 30 amps. No electrical connection is made to panel busbar by the plug-in grip on the neutral breaker unit. A wire lead connects line side of neutral breaker to neutral block in panel, or two clamp terminals are used for neutral.

To supplement the allowance of spare capacity in the branch-circuit design work, spare circuit capacity should be allowed in panelboards. As recommended previously, one spare circuit should be allowed in the panel for each five active circuits. Inasmuch as panelboards are made in multiples of four switch-and-fuse units or circuit breakers, provision of the spare circuits can often be made without using a panelboard larger than required for the active circuits.

When spare circuits are provided in flush type panelboards, the required conduit capacity to wire these circuits also should be provided to avoid future tearing out of the wall. This may consist of empty conduit runs to the ceiling and floor, terminated in covered outlet boxes, design of spare capacity in other raceways for branch circuits from panelboard, etc.

GENERAL DESIGN STANDARDS for selection and layout of panelboards are as follows:

● No more than 42 branch-circuit phase conductors (i.e., 42 single-pole protective devices) may originate from a single lighting and appliance panelboard. And, again, when determining number of poles in a panel, a 2-pole CB is considered to be two single poles, and a 3-pole CB is three single poles.

● No branch circuit in a panelboard should run more than 100 ft to the first outlet of the circuit.

● All panelboards should be readily accessible.

● Panelboards should be placed as near as possible to the center of the load they handle.

● If circuit switching from the panelboard is desired, a switch-and-fuse or CB panelboard must be used.

● Panelboard locations should be selected to conform as much as possible to the routing of feeders, assuring shortest possible feeder runs and minimum of bends.

● Every panelboard must have a rating not less than the minimum feeder capacity required to serve

FIG. 53—Panel CB for switched neutral

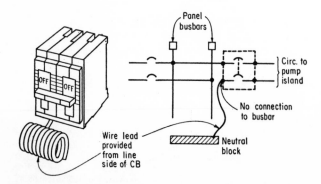

Panel busbars

OFF   OFF

Circ. to pump island

No connection to busbar

Wire lead provided from line side of CB

Neutral block

FIG. 54—Hazardous area around gas pump

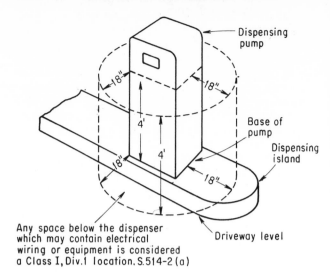

Dispensing pump

Base of pump

Dispensing island

Driveway level

Any space below the dispenser which may contain electrical wiring or equipment is considered a Class I, Div.1 location. S.514-2 (a)

FIG. 55—Sealing of gas pump conduits

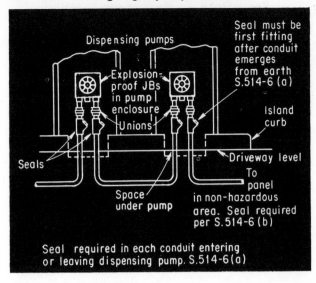

Dispensing pumps

Seal must be first fitting after conduit emerges from earth S.514-6 (a)

Explosion-proof JBs in pump enclosure

Unions

Island curb

Seals

Driveway level

Space under pump

To panel in non-hazardous area. Seal required per S.514-6 (b)

Seal required in each conduit entering or leaving dispensing pump. S.514-6(a)

the load as determined from Article 220 of the code.

● At least one lighting and appliance branch-circuit panelboard should be provided on each active floor of the building.

When lighting and appliance branch circuits, with their controls and panelboards, have been laid out, a panelboard schedule should be made up and included in the plans and specifications. This schedule should give some code letter designation to each panelboard —such as L1a for lighting panel "a" on the first floor, L2b for lighting panel "b" on the second floor, etc.— and should tabulate panel locations, number and size of circuits in each panel, type and rating of circuit protective devices, capacity of mains, size and type of main protection and disconnect and any pertinent remarks about each panelboard which might clarify design intent for the installer.

Special applications

Although the majority of electrical design covers conventional installations, there are many and varied areas which call for special treatment. Articles 500 to 680 of the code cover such places as: aircraft hangars, anesthetizing locations, theatres, X-ray areas, swimming pools, and elevator locations. Special branch-circuit problems in such areas have to be carefully studied in relation to codes and other known standards of electrical design for the areas.

A typical example of special application is that of electrical wiring for gasoline service stations. Article 514 of the NE Code covers the special requirements of electrical design made necessary by the hazardous nature of such locations. Careful reference should always be made to these rules when designing such systems. Fig. 54 shows the space around a gasoline pump which is classified as a Class I, Div. 1 hazardous location. Wiring in this area must follow the special techniques set forth in the code. Fig. 55 shows the method of complying with rules on sealing, "An approved seal shall be provided in each conduit run entering or leaving a dispenser or any cavities or enclosures in direct communication therewith. The sealing fitting shall be the first fitting after the conduit emerges from the earth or concrete."

Another special area is the operating room in hos-

pitals. The following resume of the details required in operating rooms indicates how involved special areas can be and points up the need for a thorough and painstaking approach to electrical design for special areas.

In an anesthetizing location, "the entire area shall be considered to be a Class I, Div. 1 location which shall extend upward to a level 5 ft above the floor," per Section 517-2(b). Storage rooms for flammable anesthetics are Class I, Div. 1 locations throughout. Class I, Div. 1 equipment in each operating room, delivery room and anesthesia room usually includes explosion-proof, foot-operated nurse-call switch and explosion-proof, 120-volt receptacle outlet.

Circuits within anesthetizing locations—

1. Shall be ungrounded and supplied from an ungrounded distribution system which is isolated from other distribution systems by means of one or more transformers having no electrical connection between primary and secondary windings.

2. Shall be controlled by a switch having a disconnecting pole in each conductor.

3. Shall operate at not more than 300 volts between conductors.

4. Shall have an approved overcurrent device of proper rating in each conductor.

5. Shall be provided with an approved ground contact indicator.

Circuits supplying isolating transformers—

1. Shall operate at not more than 300 volts between conductors.

2. Shall be provided with proper overcurrent protection.

Isolating transformers and overcurrent devices—

1. Shall be installed in nonhazardous locations.

Ground contact indicator (a typical installation is shown in Fig. 56) is required, and—

1. Shall respond if any conductor of the system becomes grounded, that is if the impedance to ground drops below 60,000 ohms.

2. Shall limit the leakage current to 2 ma and warn if leakage current to ground exceeds 2 milliamperes.

3. Shall include a green signal lamp conspicuously visible to personnel in the anesthetizing location which shall remain lighted as long as no ground exists.

Basic Data on Hazardous Locations

Here's how the code designates different types of hazardous locations—

Class I—Locations in which flammable gases or vapors are or may be present in the air in quantities sufficient to produce explosive or ignitible mixtures.

Class II—Locations which are hazardous because of the presence of combustible dust.

Class III—Locations which are hazardous because of the presence of easily ignitible fibers or flyings, but in which such fibers or flyings are not likely to be in suspension in air in quantities sufficient to produce ignitible mixtures.

Each Class of hazardous location is further subdivided into two divisions:

Division 1—Locations where the hazardous condition is continuously present.

Division 2—Locations in which the hazardous condition is not always present but in which the possibility of explosion or flash fire exists.

Various atmospheric mixtures have been grouped on the basis of their hazardous characteristics and serve to further classify hazardous locations:

Group A—Atmosphere containing acetylene.

Group B—Atmospheres containing hydrogen, or gases or vapors of equivalent hazard such as manufactured gases.

Group C—Atmospheres containing ethyl-ether vapors, ethylene or cyclo-propane.

Group D—Atmospheres containing gasoline, hexane, naphtha, benzine, butane, propane, alcohol, acetone, benzol, lacquer solvent vapors or natural gas.

Group E—Atmospheres containing metal dust including aluminum, magnesium and their commercial alloys.

Group F—Atmospheres containing carbon black, coal or coke dust.

Group G—Atmospheres containing flour, starch or grain dust.

And here are the design fundamentals for wiring in hazardous locations—

Class I Locations

Division 1—Wiring must be in rigid metal conduit with threaded explosion-proof joints and explosion-proof boxes and fittings. All outlet and junction boxes, switches, controllers and motors must be of explosion-proof design. To prevent passage of gases, vapors or flames from one portion of the electrical system to another, conduit runs must have sealing fittings not more than 18 inches from the point where the conduit enters enclosures housing equipment which may produce sparks, arcs or high temperatures. Such seals must also be installed in each conduit run of 2-inch or larger size entering the enclosure or fitting housing terminals, splices or taps, and must be within 18 inches from the enclosure. Seals must also be used in conduit runs where they leave a hazardous area to enter a non-hazardous area. All conduit and box connections must be of the threaded type.

Division 2—Requirements for explosion-proof equipment are essentially the same as for Division 1. However, conduit may be either rigid metal or electrical metallic tubing. Seals are required as set forth in Section 501-5.

Class II Locations

Division 1—Wiring must be in rigid conduit with threaded dust-tight fittings and boxes. Other equipment must also be of dust-tight design.

Division 2—Wiring requirements are generally the same as for Division 1, but again either rigid or thinwall conduit may be used.

Class III Locations

Divisions 1 and 2 require rigid conduit with threaded fittings and boxes designed to prevent escape of sparks or flames. Fixtures, switches and controller enclosures as well as motors must be of dust-tight construction.

FIG. 56—Ground indicator for hospital operating room

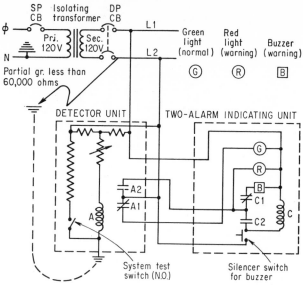

Schematic shows major circuit components of a typical ground detector/alarm system. Partial ground energizes current-relay A, opening contact A1 (disconnecting green light), and closing contact A2 (energizing red light and warning buzzer). Pressing MC switch energizes coil C, opening contact C1 (disconnecting buzzer), and closing holding contact C2. When ground is cleared contacts resume position shown in drawing.

The purpose of a ground indicator is to provide warning of the danger of shock hazard and the possibility of a fault in the system due to accidental grounding of more than one conductor. If one conductor of an isolated system becomes grounded at one point, normal protective devices (fuses or circuit breakers) will not operate because there is no return path and, therefore, no flow of short-circuit fault current. Should, however, an accidental ground subsequently develop on the other conductor, a short circuit will occur with possible disastrous consequences, such as ignition of ether vapors by arc or a lethal shock to personnel.

FIG. 57—Installation rules for swimming pools
(Sections 680-4 & 5)

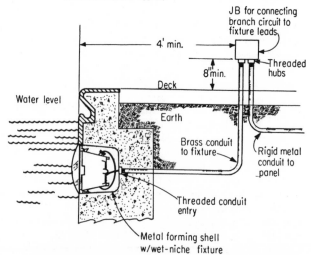

Note: Transformer-enclosure locations are same as shown for JB, except min. vertical clearance is 12 in. Transformer-enclosures or JBs are not permitted in walkways unless afforded added protection.

FIG. 58—Grounding & bonding for swimming pools

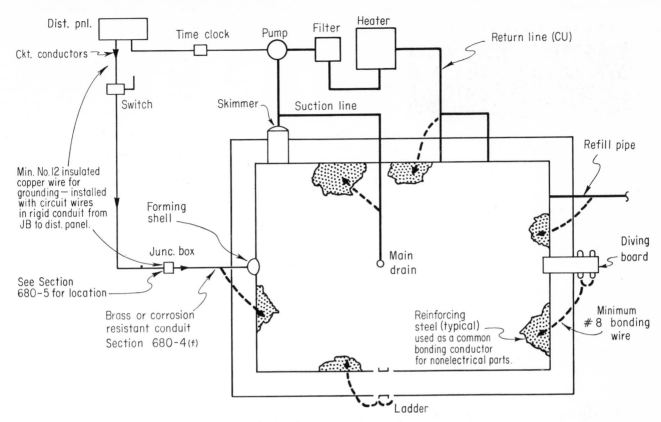

4. Shall include, adjacent to the green lamp, a red signal lamp and an audible alarm signal which will be energized should any ground occur on the system.

5. Shall not be installed within a hazardous area.

6. Should be tested at least weekly for proper operation by successively grounding each conductor of the system through a suitable meter or resistor.

NFPA Pamphlet No. 56 covers the "Code for the use of Flammable Anesthetics 1965."

Swimming pools

Electrification of swimming pools has been the subject of extensive design and code development over recent years. Details on circuit design and equipment layout are covered in NE Code Article 680. Careful reference to this Article should be made in connection with any design work on pools. Fig. 57 illustrates some of the details required by the code in mounting lighting fixtures.

In addition to specifying that underwater lighting fixtures and lighting fixture housings shall be grounded, Section 689-7 states that all metallic conduit and piping, reinforcing steel and other noncurrent-carrying metal components, located in or near a pool, must likewise be bonded together and grounded to a common ground.

These references are all-inclusive. For example, conduit and piping may relate to power circuitry, intercom or telephone wiring, supply and return water, or to gas lines serving nonelectric heaters. Reinforcing steel refers to that which is installed in deckslabs and walkways, as well as to pool structures which are poured in place, cast in forms or "gunnited." Similarly, the phrase "other noncurrent-carrying components" includes metal parts of ladders, diving boards, platforms and supports, scuppers, strainers, filters,

pump and transformer housings, etc. All of these items must be bonded together with a copper conductor not smaller than No. 8 and connected to a common electrode. Fig. 58 shows the basic rules.

Voltage drop

In laying out circuits, the loading and lengths of home runs and runs between outlets must be related to voltage drop and the need for spare capacity in the circuit for possible future increases in load. Each lamp, appliance or other utilization device on the circuit was designed for best performance at a particular operating voltage. Although such devices will operate at voltages on either side of the design value, there will be generally adverse effects due to operation at voltages lower than the specified value.

A 1% drop in voltage to an incandescent lamp produces about a 3% decrease in light output; a 10% voltage drop will decrease the output about 30%. In heating devices of the resistance element type, voltage drop has a similar effect on heat output. In motor operated appliances, low voltage to the device will affect the starting and pullout torque, and the current drawn from the line increases with drop in voltage. Heat rise in the motor windings will be above normal as a result.

Of course, voltage drop in the conductors is due to resistance of the conductors plus, in ac circuits, reactance. And the heat developed by the dissipation of power in the wiring, which itself costs money, deteriorates the conductor insulation. To prevent poor equipment performance and the other bad effects, branch-circuit conductors should generally be sized to keep voltage drop in the circuit under 1%.

Although the recommended 50% loading of circuits offers substantial protection against excessive voltage

Fundamentals of Voltage Drop and Copper Loss

Unity Load Power Factor, Negligible Reactance in Conductors

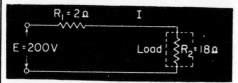

where E = circuit voltage

    R_1 = total resistance
of circuit conductors

    R_2 = resistance of non-inductive (unity pf) load

    I = circuit current

$$I = \frac{E}{R_1 + R_2} = \frac{200}{2 + 18} = 10 \text{ amps}$$

Voltage drop
in conductors = $I \times R_1$ =

    $10 \times 2 = 20$ volts

Copper loss
in conductors = $I^2 \times R_1$ =

    $(10)^2 \times 2$ =

    $100 \times 2 = 200$ watts

% Voltage drop $= \frac{20}{200} = 10\%$

Voltage delivered to load $= 200-20 = 180$ volts
Wattage delivered to load $= I^2 \times R_2 = 100 \times 18 = 1800$ watts

◄ **PF = 100%**

When the load power factor is unity and the conductor reactance due to self-induction is negligible, calculation of voltage drop in the circuit and copper loss due to heating effect of current in the conductors follows the standard relations between current and voltage. The supply voltage is equal to the arithmetic sum of the voltage drop in the conductors and the voltage across the load. Copper loss in watts is a straight "I-squared R" loss.

Less Than Unity Power Factor of Load, Negligible Reactance in Conductors

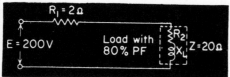

where E = circuit voltage

    R_1 = total resistance of circuit conductors

    R_2 = resistive component of load

    X_L = reactive component of load

    Z = impedance of load

    I = circuit current

$$Z = \sqrt{(R_2)^2 + (X_L)^2}$$
$$Z^2 = (R_2)^2 + (X_L)^2$$
$$(20)^2 = 400 = (R_2)^2 + (X_L)^2$$

but, pf $= 0.8 = \frac{R_2}{Z}$

then, $R_2 = 20 \times 0.8 = 16$ ohms

and, $(X_L)^2 = 400 - (16)^2 = 144$
    $X_L = 12$ ohms

Total Z
of circuit $= \sqrt{(R_1 + R_2)^2 + (X_L)^2}$
    $= \sqrt{(18)^2 + (12)^2}$
    $= 21.6$ ohms

then, $I = \frac{200v}{21.6} = 9.3$ amps

Voltage drop
in conductors = $I \times R_1$ =
    $9.3 \times 2 = 18.6$ volts

Copper loss
in conductors = $I^2 \times R_1$ =
    $86.5 \times 2 = 173$ watts

Apparent %
voltage drop $= \frac{18.6}{200} = 9.3\%$

◄ **PF < 100%**

When the load power factor is less than unity and the conductor reactance is negligible, the straight arithmetic relations among the circuit conditions no longer obtain. It should be noted that although a conductor voltage drop of 18.6 volts exists, the load voltage is equal to 9.3 amps times 20 ohms or 186 volts. The real loss (or drop) in voltage to the load is only 14 volts (200 volts minus 186 volts). The 18.6-volt drop is only the voltage across the resistive conductor load, which differs in phase from the voltage across the reactive load device fed by the circuit. Although the arithmetic sum of the two voltages is 204.6 volts (186 volts plus 18.6 volts), correct vectorial addition of the two voltages gives the 200-volt value of the supply. The significant percent voltage drop is therefore different from the apparent value. Copper loss, however, remains a simple "I-squared R" loss.

Voltage delivered to load $= I \times Z = 9.3 \times 20 = 186$ volts

Significant % voltage drop $= \frac{14}{200} = 7\%$

(Values used in these examples were assumed and chosen to make simple calculations)

When current flows in a conductor in which the reactance due to self induction is negligible, the voltage drop is equal to the product of the current in amps and the total resistance of the conductor in ohms. But when the reactance of the conductor is not negligible, the voltage drop is equal to the product of the current in amps and the total *impedance* of the conductor, which is determined from the formula

$$Z = \sqrt{R^2 + X^2}$$

in which, Z = total impedance in ohms
R = total ac resistance of the conductor in ohms
X = reactance of the conductor in ohms

The voltage drop in such a conductor is

$$V = IZ$$

in which, V = voltage drop (volts)
I = current flowing in conductor (amperes)
Z = total impedance of the conductor (ohms)

(see manufacturers' bulletins and catalogs for
conductor impedance values in ohms per 1000 ft)

Resistance and reactance data on wires and cables are given in literature made available by the manufacturers. Tables and graphs for quickly and easily computing voltage drop in large, heavily-loaded feeders operating at less than unity power factor and with considerable conductor reactance are also available.

NOTES:

1. Reactance in conductors carrying ac power depends upon the size of the conductor, spacing between it and other conductors carrying current, the position of the conductor with respect to conductors close to it, the frequency of the alternating current and the presence of magnetic materials close to the conductor. In an ac circuit, the reactance of the conductors may be reduced by placing the conductors close together and/or by placing them in non-magnetic raceway instead of steel conduit or raceway. In many large size or long ac circuits, the voltage drop due to impedance is often far greater than the drop due simply to resistance of the conductors.

2. Alternating current flow in conductors is subject to "skin effect" which is an apparent increase in resistance over the resistance value which would obtain for direct-current flow. This is due to a reduction in effective conductor cross section because alternating current tends to flow close to the surface (or "skin") of the conductor. Generally, this increase in resistance to ac is of little consequence in conductors smaller than 500 MCM.

---

drop, size of conductors for long runs should always be carefully determined to assure that the spare capacity provision has not been removed by the limit of voltage drop. For this reason, when the design intent is to use 50% loading to provide spare capacity in the circuit, conductors used in long runs should be sized for voltage drop on the basis of the maximum possible loading.

For lighting and appliance branch circuits, calculations of voltage drop should be made on a single-phase, 2-wire basis. That is, voltage drop in the wires should be limited to some percentage of the voltage from the hot leg to the neutral—whether the circuit is 2-wire, 3-wire, single-phase or 4-wire, 3-phase. Since most branch-circuit loads are connected hot-leg-to-neutral, the major concern should be directly with the voltage delivered to the loads, rather than the phase-to-phase voltage when that voltage is not supplied to any load device. Of course, 2-wire circuits made up of ungrounded legs of single-phase or 3-phase systems should be designed for a voltage drop of some percentage of the voltage between them when they supply loads at other than phase-to-neutral.

The voltage drop of any 2-wire circuit, whether it is phase-to-neutral or phase-to-phase, can be taken simply as the I × R drop of the conductors. This is the total dc resistance of the two circuit wires. For conductors up to No. 3 AWG—which covers the conductors of the vast majority of branch circuits—the ac resistance of the wire is equal to the dc resistance, which is readily obtained from Table 8 in Chapter 9 of the NE Code. And in such wire sizes, the inductive reactance of the circuit is negligible. Thus for branch circuits, voltage drop is a relatively simple matter.

A variety of graphs of the type shown in Fig. 59 is available for branch-circuit voltage drop analysis and add speed and ease to the design task. Further discussion of voltage drop is presented in the section on "Feeders."

Layout on plans

Actual design procedure for lighting and appliance branch circuits involves working on a set of plans for the building. Such plans are usually available or can be made. The design work consists of using the

AVERAGE CIRCUIT LENGTHS (FEET) FOR 1% VOLTAGE DROP

TABLE I. SINGLE-PHASE AC LOADS
115/230 Volts, 60 Cycles, 100% PF

AMPERE LOAD	WIRE SIZE—CIRCULAR MILS					WIRE SIZE—B & S or A.W.G.									
	500	400	350	300	250	4/0	3/0	2/0	1/0	1	2	3	4	6	8
40	1106	898	788	669	558	475	378	299	239	188	150	119	94	59	38
50	885	719	630	535	447	380	303	240	191	150	120	91	75	47	30
60	737	599	525	446	372	317	252	200	159	125	100	79	62	39	
70	632	513	450	382	319	271	216	171	136	107	86	68	53	34	
80	553	449	394	334	279	238	189	150	119	94	75	59	47		
90	491	399	350	297	248	211	168	133	106	83	67	53	42		
100	442	359	315	267	223	190	151	120	95	75	60	47			
110	402	327	286	243	203	173	138	109	87	68	55				
120	369	299	263	223	186	158	126	100	79	63					
130	340	276	242	206	172	146	116	92	73	58					
140	316	257	225	191	159	136	108	86	68						
150	295	240	210	178	149	127	101	80	64						
160	276	225	197	167	140	119	95	75	60						
170	260	211	185	157	131	112	89	70							
180	246	200	175	148	124	106	84	66							
190	233	189	166	140	117	100	80								
200	221	180	157	134	112	95	76								
210	211	171	150	127	106	90									
220	201	163	143	122	101	86									
230	192	156	137	116	97	83									
240	184	150	131	111	93										
250	177	144	126	107	89										
260	170	138	121	103	80										
270	164	133	117	99											
280	158	128	112	96											
290	152	124	109	92											
300	147	120	105												
310	143	116	102												
320	138	112													
330	134	109													
340	130	106													

Calculations based on copper resistance of 12.5 ohms per CM-ft at 50C (122F).

Reactance and impedance losses calculated for each wire.

Conductors closely grouped in metallic conduit.

TABLE II. 3-PHASE DELTA AC LOADS
230 Volts, 60 Cycles, 85% PF

AMPERE LOAD	WIRE SIZE—CIRCULAR MILS					WIRE SIZE—B & S or A.W.G.									
	500	400	350	300	250	4/0	3/0	2/0	1/0	1	2	3	4	6	8
40	710	625	584	530	475	429	364	303	253	208	173	139	113	75	49
50	568	500	467	424	380	343	291	242	203	167	139	111	90	60	39
60	473	417	389	353	317	286	243	202	169	139	115	93	75	50	
70	406	357	333	303	271	245	208	173	145	119	99	79	64	43	
80	355	312	292	265	238	214	182	151	127	104	87	69	56		
90	316	278	259	235	211	191	162	134	113	93	77	62	45		
100	284	250	233	212	190	172	146	121	101	83	69	55			
110	258	227	212	193	173	156	132	110	92	76	63				
120	237	208	195	177	158	143	121	101	84	69	58				
130	218	192	180	163	146	132	112	93	78	64					
140	203	179	167	151	136	123	104	86	72						
150	189	168	156	141	127	114	97	81	67						
160	177	156	146	132	119	107	91	76							
170	167	147	137	125	112	101	86	71							
180	158	139	130	118	106	95	81	67							
190	149	132	123	112	100	90	77								
200	142	125	117	106	95	86	73								
210	135	119	111	101	90	82									
220	129	114	106	96	86	78									
230	123	109	101	92	83	75									
240	118	104	97	88	79										
250	114	100	93	85	76										
260	109	96	90	81	73										
270	105	93	86	78											
280	101	89	83	76											
290	98	86	80	73											
300	95	83	78												
310	92	81	75												
320	89	78													
330	86	76													
340	83	73													
350	81														
360	79														
370	77														
380	75														

Calculations based on copper resistance of 12.5 ohms per CM-ft at 50C (122F).

Reactance and impedance losses calculated for each wire.

Conductors closely grouped in metallic conduit.

TABLE III. BALANCED LIGHTING LOADS
3- and 4-Wire, 115 Volts 1% drop from supply cabinet to first outlet supplying permanently connected appliance or fixture.

MAXIMUM OVERCURRENT CIRCUIT PROTECTION	AMPERES (A), WATTS (W), WITH CONDUIT CONDUCTOR (C), FILLS (F)					
	INTERMITTENT LOADS			CONTINUOUS LOADS		
	100% F 2-3 C	80% F 4-6 C	70% F 7-9 C	100% F 2-3 C	80% F 4-6 C	70% F 7-9 C
15 A	15 A 1725 W	12 A 1380 W	10.5 A 1207 W	12 A 1380 W	9.6 A 1104 W	8.4 Amps 966 Watts
20 A	20 A 2300 W	16 A 1840 W	14 A 1610 W	16 A 1840 W	12.8 A 1472 W	11.2 A 1288 W

LOADS AND LENGTHS IN FEET FOR 1% DROP ON 3 AND 4 WIRE 115 V. CIRCUITS

AMPERE LOAD	#10 WIRE	#12 WIRE	#14 WIRE
1	946	596	374
2	474	298	188
3	316	198	124
4	236	148	94
5	190	120	76
6	158	100	62
7	136	86	54
8	118	74	46
9	106	66	42
10	94	60	38
11	86	54	34
12	78	50	32
13	72	46	28
14	68	42	26
15	64	40	24
16	60	38	
17	56	36	
18	52	34	
19	90	32	
20	48	30	
21	46		
22	44		
23	42		
24	40		
25	38		
26	36		
27	36		
28	34		
29	32		
30	32		

Calculations based on copper resistance of 13 ohms per CM-ft at 60C (140F).

NOTES:

TABLE I:

Balanced 3-Wire Loads: Drop is 1.15 volts for given length.

2-Wire, 230-Volt Loads: Drop is 2.3 volts for given length.

TABLE II:

For 208-volt, 4-wire "Y" feeders multiply given length by 0.9

For 230-volt, single-phase feeders multiply given length by 0.85

For 460-volt, 3- or 4-wire feeders multiply given lengths by 2.

For aluminum wire multiply given lengths by 0.7 or use length of copper wire which is 2 sizes smaller than the aluminum size under consideration.

TABLE III:

For 2-phase, 3-wire circuits tapped off a 3-phase, 4-wire "Y" service, multiply given lengths by 0.67.

FIG. 59—Branch-circuit voltage drop and current capacities for 600-volt, Type RHW conductors

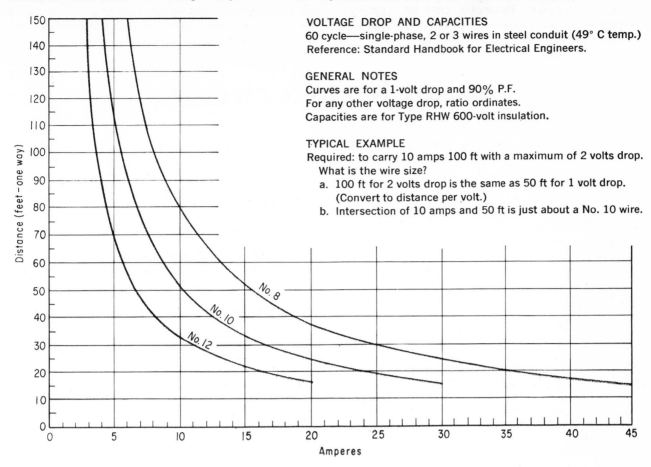

VOLTAGE DROP AND CAPACITIES
60 cycle—single-phase, 2 or 3 wires in steel conduit (49° C temp.)
Reference: Standard Handbook for Electrical Engineers.

GENERAL NOTES
Curves are for a 1-volt drop and 90% P.F.
For any other voltage drop, ratio ordinates.
Capacities are for Type RHW 600-volt insulation.

TYPICAL EXAMPLE
Required: to carry 10 amps 100 ft with a maximum of 2 volts drop.
What is the wire size?
a. 100 ft for 2 volts drop is the same as 50 ft for 1 volt drop.
(Convert to distance per volt.)
b. Intersection of 10 amps and 50 ft is just about a No. 10 wire.

foregoing information and whatever other data is known in laying out the outlets, circuit runs and control legs. Of course, this step depends upon a decision having been made as to the general type of distribution and characteristics and voltage of the feeders from which the branch circuits will be supplied.

The first step in circuit design is to indicate locations of general lighting outlets on floor plans. This layout of general lighting outlets is part of overall lighting design. As follow-up to this first part of the work, the wattage of each outlet is determined, the total load is determined and the number of circuits is selected.

Then the local or special lighting outlets are indicated. These include: corridor lights, exit lights, entrance lights, washroom lights, closet lights, stockroom lights, emergency lights and/or other known lighting outlet requirements. Fig. 60 shows a typical layout of special lighting outlets for continuous operation of emergency lights which also serve as night lights in a hospital corridor. Circuiting arrangement for 2-lamp corridor lighting fixtures throughout hospital provides separate conduit and conductors for normal-circuit lighting with 150-watt lamp in each fixture and emergency-circuit lighting with 25-watt night lamp in each fixture. In this diagram, "D" circuits 12 and 14 supply the 150-watt lamps and may be switched off at night by means of the wall switch at upper left. Panel D is fed from the normal (or nonessential) section of bus in the main switchboard. The 25-watt night lamps are fed from panel 1 EM (circuits 3, 5 and 7 shown here) and operate day and

night, with no local switching available. Panel 1 EM is fed from the section of main switchboard bus which is fed from the normal supply and from the emergency generator when normal supply fails.

In the design of many commercial and industrial buildings, the specifics of lighting requirements may not be known until after it is known what type of work will be performed and tenants decide upon their working layout. In such cases, provision of sufficient capacity and circuits in the panelboard is the initial limit of circuit design work, pending determination of loads.

After laying out lighting outlets, the next usual

FIG. 60—Layout of emergency lighting

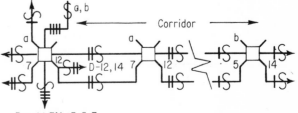

Panel 1 EM –3, 5, 7

Legend:
a — Square recessed incandescent with 150-watt lamp on normal circuit and 25-watt night lamp on emergency circuit. Numbers at bottom show circuits in fixture, letter indicates switch.

step is to indicate convenience and special receptacle outlets on the plans. Depending upon the occupancy, receptacle circuits may be run in conduit to wall-mounted or column-mounted outlet boxes, fed up from the floor slab or down from the ceiling, or the circuits may be run in underfloor raceway or a cellular metal floor system. These latter are the common ways of handling receptacle circuits in office areas.

Motor branch circuits

Motor loads vary widely in size and electrical characteristics, but all motor circuits require careful wiring and protection of conductors and equipment to assure safe and reliable operation. In any plant or building, of course, the problem of providing maximum safety and reliability must be solved along with other problems—minimizing voltage drop, avoiding excessive copper loss, providing sufficient flexibility for changing locations of equipment, designing for ease and economy of maintenance of the motors and equipment and providing spare capacity in the equipment for increased loads in the future.

Although effective application of motor controllers is based primarily on thorough engineering analysis, careful consideration should also be given to the NE Code which sets forth minimum safety provisions for the control of motors.

Basically, Article 430 of the code covers the requirements for motor circuits. This article contains the general requirements; other articles contain specific references to motor applications—in cranes, hoists, elevators, machine tools, hazardous locations and in such occupancies as garages, service stations, bulk storage plants and other industrial areas.

In no way is the code a substitute for intelligent design of motor control circuits suited to the particular characteristics of each individual application. However, because the code does represent the accumulation of years and years of experience with motor circuits, it presents an excellent general outline of motor circuit design. Within this basic framework, the designer can add specific equipment features and circuit techniques to meet his needs.

Fig. 61 shows the five basic elements which the code requires the designer to account for in any motor circuit. Although these elements are shown separately here, there are certain cases where the code will permit a single device to serve more than one function. For instance, in some cases, one switch can serve as both disconnecting means and controller. In other cases, short-circuit protection and overload protection can be combined. In the number order shown in Fig. 61, basic code requirements on these elements are as follows:

1. Sizing circuit conductors

The basic code rule says that the conductors supplying a single motor used for continuous duty must have a current-carrying capacity of not less than 125% of the motor full-load current rating. In the case of a multispeed motor, the selection of branch-circuit conductors on the line side of the controller must be based on the highest of the full-load current ratings shown on the motor nameplate. Selection of branch-circuit conductors between the controller and the motor, which are energized for that particular speed, must be based on the current rating for that speed. Fig. 62 shows the sizing of branch-circuit conductors to four different motors fed from a panel. (Sizing is also shown for branch-circuit protection and running overload protection, as discussed in following sections. Refer to NE Code Table 430-150 for motor full-load currents and Table 430-153 for maximum ratings of fuses.)

Conductors supplying two or more motors must have a current rating not less than 125% of the full-load current rating of the largest motor supplied plus the sum of the full-load current ratings of the remainder of the motors supplied. Of course, these are minimum conductor ratings based on temperature rise only and do not take into account voltage drop or power loss in the conductors. Such considerations frequently require increasing the size of branch-circuit conductors.

Section 430-22(a) of the code also includes re-

FIG. 61—Every motor branch circuit must account for each of these elements

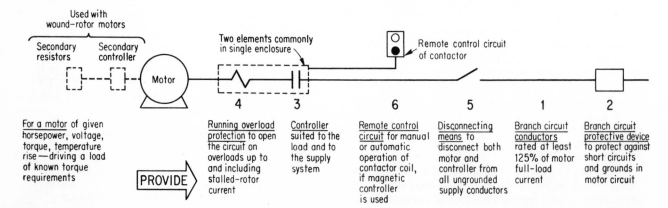

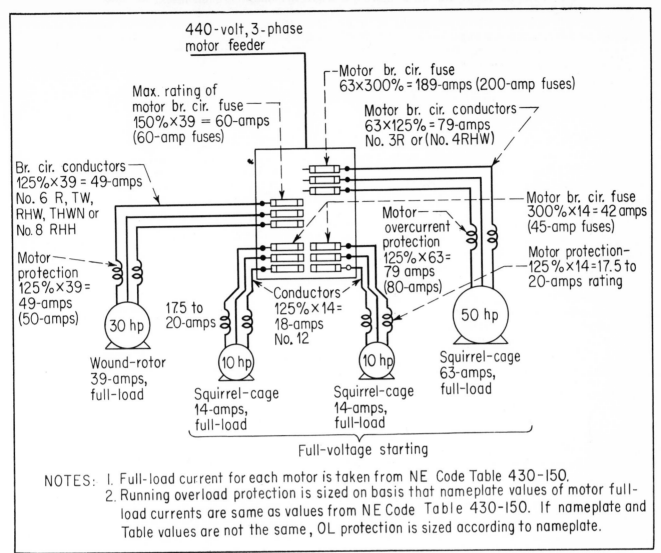

440-volt, 3-phase motor feeder

Max. rating of motor br. cir. fuse 150%×39 = 60-amps (60-amp fuses)

-Motor br. cir. fuse 63×300% = 189-amps (200-amp fuses)

Motor br. cir. conductors 63×125% = 79-amps No. 3R or (No. 4RHW)

Br. cir. conductors 125%×39 = 49-amps No. 6 R, TW, RHW, THWN or No. 8 RHH

Motor overcurrent protection 125%×63= 79 amps (80-amps)

Motor br. cir. fuse 300%×14 = 42 amps (45-amp fuses)

Motor protection 125%×39= 49-amps (50-amps)

Motor protection— 125%×14=17.5 to 20-amps rating

17.5 to 20-amps

Conductors 125%×14= 18-amps No. 12

30 hp

50 hp

10 hp

10 hp

Wound-rotor 39-amps, full-load

Squirrel-cage 14-amps, full-load

Squirrel-cage 14-amps, full-load

Squirrel-cage 63-amps, full-load

Full-voltage starting

NOTES: 1. Full-load current for each motor is taken from NE Code Table 430-150.
2. Running overload protection is sized on basis that nameplate values of motor full-load currents are same as values from NE Code Table 430-150. If nameplate and Table values are not the same, OL protection is sized according to nameplate.

quirements for sizing individual branch-circuit wires serving motors used for short-time, intermittent, periodic or other varying duty. In such cases, frequency of starting and duration of operating cycles impose varying heat loads on conductors. Conductor sizing, therefore, varies with the application. But, it should be noted that any motor is considered to be for continuous duty unless the nature of the apparatus which it drives is such that the motor will not operate continuously with load under any condition of use.

Conductors connecting the secondary of a wound-rotor induction motor to the controller must have a carrying capacity at least equal to 125% of the motor's full-load secondary current if the motor is used for continuous duty. If the motor is used for less than continuous duty, the conductors must have capacity not less than the percentage of full-load secondary current given in the table of Section 430-22. Conductors from the controller of a wound-rotor induction motor to its starting resistors must have a capacity rating in accordance with Table 430-23.

IT SHOULD BE NOTED THAT THE CODE MAKES CERTAIN PROVISIONS FOR DETERMINING CURRENT-CARRYING CAPACITIES:

1. For general motor applications (excluding applications of sealed hermetic-type refrigeration compressor motors), whenever the current rating of a motor is used to determine the current-carrying capacity of conductors, switches, branch-circuit overcurrent devices or circuit breakers, the values given in Tables 430-147, 430-148, 430-149 and 430-150 shall be used instead of the actual current rating marked on the motor nameplate. However, selection of motor running overcurrent protection MUST be based on the actual motor nameplate current rating.

2. For sealed (hermetic-type) refrigeration compressor motors, the actual nameplate full-load running current of the motor must be used in determining the current rating of branch-circuit conductors, short-circuit protection and running overload protection.

2. Protecting against grounds and shorts

The code requires that branch-circuit protection for motor circuits must protect the circuit conductors, the control apparatus and the motor itself against overcurrent due to short circuits or ground.

The first, and obviously necessary, rule is that the branch-circuit protection device for an individual branch circuit to a motor must be capable of carrying the starting current of the motor with-

FIG. 63—Conditions for supplying two or more motors from a single branch circuit

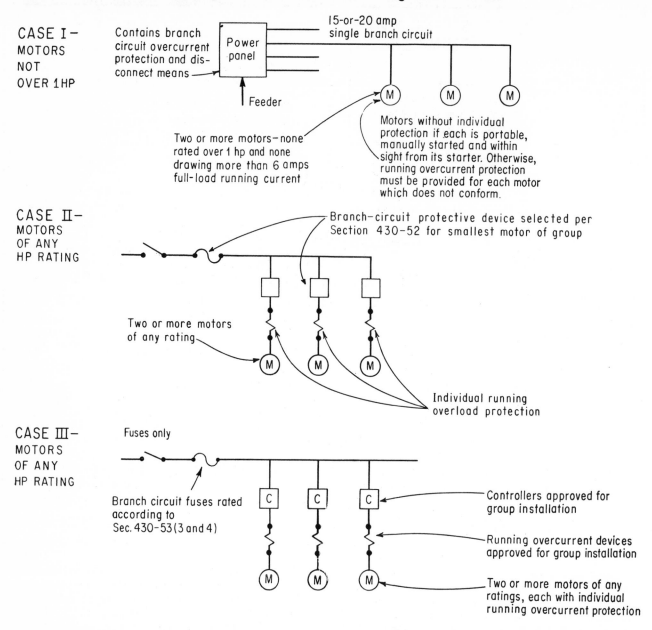

CASE I—
MOTORS
NOT
OVER 1 HP

Contains branch circuit overcurrent protection and disconnect means

Power panel

Feeder

15-or-20 amp single branch circuit

Two or more motors—none rated over 1 hp and none drawing more than 6 amps full-load running current

Motors without individual protection if each is portable, manually started and within sight from its starter. Otherwise, running overcurrent protection must be provided for each motor which does not conform.

CASE II—
MOTORS
OF ANY
HP RATING

Branch-circuit protective device selected per Section 430-52 for smallest motor of group

Two or more motors of any rating

Individual running overload protection

CASE III—
MOTORS
OF ANY
HP RATING

Fuses only

Branch circuit fuses rated according to Sec. 430-53 (3 and 4)

Controllers approved for group installation

Running overcurrent devices approved for group installation

Two or more motors of any ratings, each with individual running overcurrent protection

out opening the circuit. Then the code proceeds to place maximum values on the ratings or settings of such overcurrent devices. It says that such devices must not be rated in excess of the values given in Tables 430-152 or 430-153, except that, where absolutely necessary for motor starting, the device may be rated up to 400% of the motor full-load running current. But for sealed hermetic compressor motors of 400-kva locked rotor or less, the protection must not exceed a rating of 225% of the motor full-load current.

For a multispeed motor, a single short-circuit and ground-fault protective device may be used for one or more windings of the motor provided the rating of the protective device does not exceed the above applicable percentage of the nameplate rating of the smallest winding protected.

Table 430-146 presents a wide range of data on the makeup of motor branch circuits and should be thoroughly familiar to circuit designers. Fig. 62 shows sizing of branch-circuit fuses in accordance with Tables 430-153 (and 430-146).

It should be noted that the code establishes maximum values for branch-circuit protection, setting the limit of safe applications. However, use of smaller sizes of branch-circuit protective devices is obviously permitted by the code and does offer opportunities for substantial economies in selection of circuit breakers, fuses and the switches used with them, panelboards, etc. In any application, it is only necessary that the branch-circuit device which is smaller than the usual 300% of motor current must have sufficient time delay in its operation to permit the motor starting current to flow without opening the circuit.

But a circuit breaker for branch-circuit protection must have a continuous current rating of not less than 115% of the motor full-load current.

A single branch circuit may be used to supply two or more motors as follows (see Fig. 63):

1. Two or more motors, each rated not more than 1 hp and each drawing not over 6 amps full-load current, may be used on a branch circuit protected at not more than 20 amps at 125 volts or less, or 15

FIG. 64—Typical example of expanded use of several motors on one circuit
(1965 NE Code Section 430-53)

THIS IS NOW PERMITTED . . .

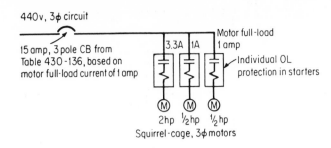

440v, 3φ circuit

15 amp, 3 pole CB from Table 430-136, based on motor full-load current of 1 amp

3.3A | 1A

Motor full-load 1 amp

Individual OL protection in starters

2hp | ½hp | ½hp
Squirrel-cage, 3φ motors

PRIOR TO 1965 NE CODE THIS COULD NOT BE DONE, BECAUSE—

1. Section 430-53(a) only applied to motors rated not over 1 hp.
2. Section 430-53(b) [now Section 430-53(c)] limited use of several motors on single circuit to controllers and running overload devices which were "approved for group installation" and recognized only fuses (not circuit breakers) for branch-circuit protection—with fuses rated not over four times the current rating of the smallest motor on the circuit.

FIG. 65—An actual job problem in connecting several motors on one circuit

Problem: A factory has 100 1½-hp, 3-phase motors, with individual motor starters incorporating overcurrent protection, rated for 440 volts. Provide circuits.

Solution by 1962 NE Code
Section 430-53 would not permit several motors on one branch circuit fed from a 3-pole CB in panel. Each of the 100 motors had to have its own individual 3-phase circuit fed from a 15-amp, 3-pole CB in a panel. As a result, a total of 300 CB poles were required, calling for seven panels of 42 circuits each plus a smaller panel (or special panels of greater numbers than 42 poles per panel).

Solution by 1965 NE Code [Section 430-53(b)]
Depending upon the starting torque characteristics and operating duty of the motors and their loads, with each motor rated for 2.5 amps, three or four motors could be connected on each 3-phase, 15-amp circuit —greatly reducing the number of panelboards, overcurrent devices and the amount of wire involved in the total system. Time-delay of CB influences number of motors on each circuit.

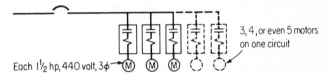

Each 1½ hp, 440 volt, 3φ

3, 4, or even 5 motors on one circuit

---

amps at 600 volts or less. Individual running overcurrent protection is necessary in such circuits, unless: the motor is not permanently installed, is manually started and is within sight from the controller location; the motor has sufficient winding impedance to prevent overheating due to stalled rotor current; or the motor is part of an approved assembly which does not subject the motor to overloads and which incorporates protection for the motor against stalled rotor.

2. Two or more motors of any rating, each having individual running overcurrent protection, may be connected to a branch circuit which is protected by a short-circuit protective device selected in accordance with the maximum rating or setting of a device which could protect an individual circuit to the motor of the smallest rating. This may be done only where it can be determined that the branch-circuit device so selected will not open under the most severe normal conditions of service which might be encountered.

This foregoing permission for use of two or more motors of any rating on one branch circuit is a very important addition to Section 430-53 in

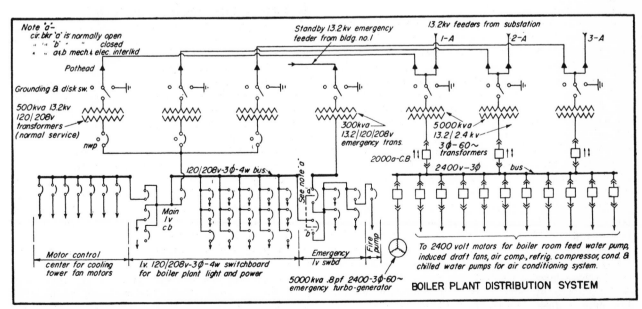

MOTOR BRANCH CIRCUITS shown in this distribution diagram of the boiler plant of a large medical research building are derived from 3-phase, 4-wire 120/208-volt motor control center for fan motors, from a 120/208-volt switchboard for general purpose motor applications and from a 2400-volt, 3-phase circuit breaker switchboard supplying 2400-volt circuits to motors for pumps, compressors, air conditioning system, etc.

FIG. 66—Effective short-circuit protection

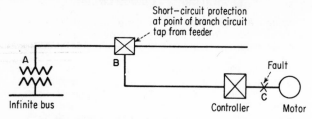

A short-circuit fault at C will draw current until the circuit is opened by the protection at B. The value of the short-circuit current available at C depends upon the kva rating of the supply transformer, A, percent reactance of the transformer, the secondary voltage and the effective impedance of the current path from the transformer to the point of fault. Application of motor controllers must, therefore, be coordinated with branch-circuit overcurrent protection which must be able to safely interrupt the short-circuit current. And not only must the device be rated to interrupt the fault current, it must act quickly enough to open the circuit before let-through current can damage the controller.

FIG. 67—Effective protection eliminates this

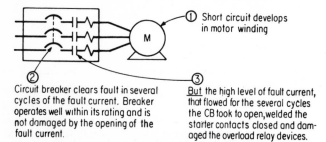

① Short circuit develops in motor winding

② Circuit breaker clears fault in several cycles of the fault current. Breaker operates well within its rating and is not damaged by the opening of the fault current.

③ But the high level of fault current, that flowed for the several cycles the CB took to open, welded the starter contacts closed and damaged the overload relay devices.

Solution: The damage to the motor controller could have been avoided by use of a faster-operating CB (a current-limiting CB) or by fast-acting fuses which would limit fault current to a value safe for the controller to withstand.

FIG. 68—A controller for a motor must be one of these

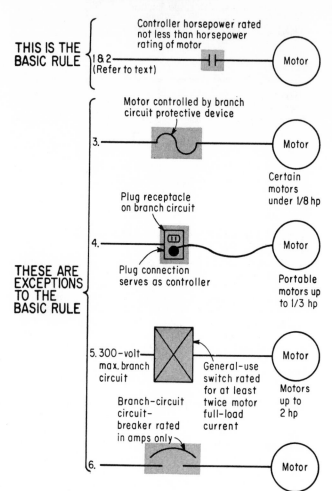

the 1965 NE Code. This new permission greatly expands the use of more than one motor on a single circuit, particularly the use of fractional-hp and small integral-hp motors on 440-volt, 3-phase systems. See Figs. 64 and 65.

3. Two or more motors of any rating may be connected to one branch circuit if each motor has running overcurrent protection, the overcurrent devices and controllers are approved for group installation and the branch-circuit fuse rating is in accordance with Tables 430-152 or 430-153 for the largest motor plus the sum of the full-load current ratings of the other motors. The branch-circuit fuses must not be larger than four times the rating of the smallest motor of the group, unless the thermal device is approved for group installation with a given maximum size of the short-circuit protective device.

Fig. 66 calls attention to the fact that branch-circuit protection must always be capable of interrupting the amount of short-circuit current which might flow through it. And the speed of clearing the circuit must be compared to the abilities of the various circuit elements to withstand the damaging effects of short-circuit current flow during the time it does take the protective device to operate. Fig. 67 shows a typical example of the problem that arises when the operating speed of the branch-circuit overcurrent device does not protect other circuit elements from the effects of let-through current. Short-circuit protection must be coordinated with the controller and other apparatus.

3. Controlling motor operation

As used in the code, the term "controller" includes any switch or device normally used to start and stop a motor, in addition to motor controllers as such. The basic requirements for sizes and types of motor controllers are as follows (refer to Fig. 68):

1. A controller must be capable of starting and stopping the motor which it controls, and for an ac motor must be able to interrupt the stalled-rotor current of the motor.

2. A controller must have horsepower rating not lower than the rating of the motor, except—

3. The branch-circuit protective device may serve as the controller for motors under ⅛ hp which are normally left running and are not subject to damage from overload or failure to start. Clock motors are typical of this application.

4. A plug and receptacle connection may serve as the controller for portable motors up to ⅓ hp.

5. A general-use switch rated at not less than twice the full-load motor current may be used as the controller for stationary motors up to 2 hp, rated for operation at 300 volts or less.

On ac circuits, a general-use snap switch suitable only for use on ac may be used to control a motor

FIG. 69—Example of motor controller not opening all circuit legs

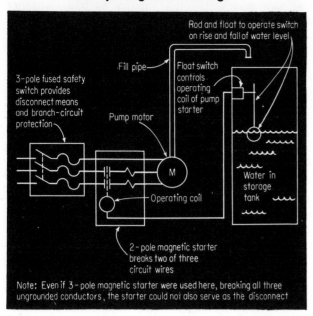

3-pole fused safety switch provides disconnect means and branch-circuit protection

Fill pipe

Pump motor

Rod and float to operate switch on rise and fall of water level

Float switch controls operating coil of pump starter

M

Operating coil

Water in storage tank

2-pole magnetic starter breaks two of three circuit wires

Note: Even if 3-pole magnetic starter were used here, breaking all three ungrounded conductors, the starter could not also serve as the disconnect

having a full-load current rating not over 80% of the ampere rating of the switch.

6. A branch-circuit circuit breaker rated in amperes only, may be used as a controller. If the same circuit breaker is used to provide overcurrent protection for the motor circuit, it must be rated accordingly.

For sealed (hermetic-type) refrigeration compressor motors, selection of the size of controller is slightly more involved than it is for standard applications. Because of their low-temperature operating conditions, hermetic motors can handle heavier loads than general-purpose motors of equivalent size and rotor-stator construction. And because the capabilities of such motors cannot be accurately defined in terms of horsepower, they are rated in terms of full-load current and locked-rotor current for polyphase motors and larger single-phase motors. Selection of controller size is accordingly different than in the case of a general-purpose motor where horsepower ratings must be matched.

For controllers rated in horsepower, selection of the size required for a particular hermetic motor can be made after the full-load and locked-rotor currents

FIG. 70—Can one device serve as both controller and disconnect?

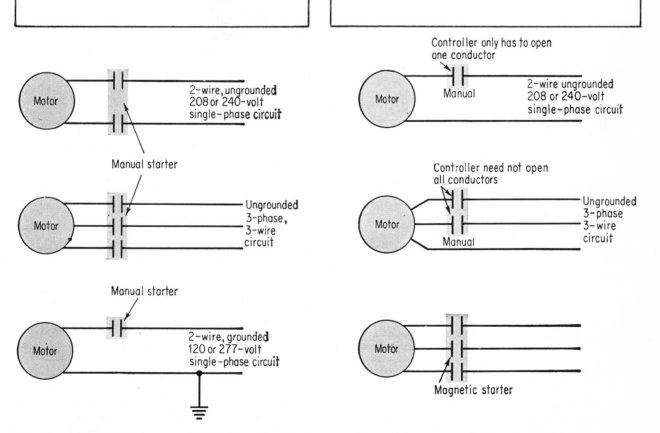

YES—If a manual starter opens all ungrounded wires to motor, it may serve as both controller and disconnect.

NO—If starter is a manual starter which does not open all ungrounded wires or if starter is magnetic, a separate disconnect is required.

Motor — Manual starter — 2-wire, ungrounded 208 or 240-volt single-phase circuit

Motor — Manual starter — Ungrounded 3-phase, 3-wire circuit

Motor — Manual starter — 2-wire, grounded 120 or 277-volt single-phase circuit

Controller only has to open one conductor

Motor — Manual — 2-wire ungrounded 208 or 240-volt single-phase circuit

Controller need not open all conductors

Motor — Manual — Ungrounded 3-phase 3-wire circuit

Motor — Magnetic starter

Note: The word "ungrounded" above refers to the condition that none of the circuit conductors is grounded. These may be the ungrounded conductors of grounded systems.

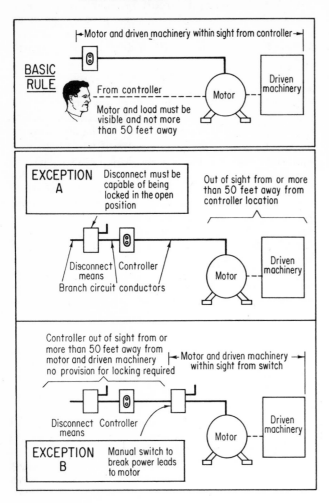

of the motor have been converted to an equivalent horsepower rating. To get this equivalent horse-power rating, which is the required size of controller, the tables in Article 430 must be used. First, the nameplate full-load current of the motor is found in Tables 430-148, 430-149 or 430-150 and the horsepower rating which corresponds to it noted. Then the nameplate locked-rotor current of the motor is found in Table 430-151 and again the corresponding horsepower is noted. In both tables, if the exact value of current is not listed, the next higher value should be used. If the two horsepower ratings obtained in this way are not the same, the larger value is taken as the required size of controller. A typical example is as follows:

Given: a 220-volt, 3-phase, squirrel-cage induction motor in a compressor.
Nameplate full-load current ....25.8 amps
Nameplate locked-rotor current ....90 amps

From Table 430-150, Article 430, 27 amps is the next higher current to the nameplate current of 25.8, and the corresponding horsepower rating for a 220-volt, 3-phase motor is 10 hp.

From Table 430-151, Article 430, a locked-rotor current rating of 90 amps for a 220-volt, 3-phase motor requires a controller rated at 5 hp. The two values of horsepower obtained are not the same, so the higher rating is selected as the acceptable unit for the conditions. A 10-hp motor controller must be used in this case.

Some controllers may be rated not in horsepower but in full-load current and locked-rotor current. For use with a hermetic motor, such a controller must have current ratings equal to or greater than the nameplate full-load current and locked-rotor current of the motor.

It is interesting to note that the NE Code says that a controller need not open all conductors to a motor, except when the controller serves also as the required disconnecting means. For instance a 2-pole starter could be used for a 3-phase motor as shown in Fig. 69. The controller must interrupt only enough conductors to be able to start and stop the motor.

However, when a manual starter is used, the starter can also serve as the disconnect means if it opens all ungrounded conductors to the motor. This eliminates the need for another switch or CB to serve as the disconnecting means. But it should be noted that only a manually operated switch or circuit breaker may serve such a dual function. A magnetic starter cannot also serve as the disconnecting means even if it does open all ungrounded conductors to the motor. These conditions are shown in Fig. 70.

Still another code requirement on motor controllers concerns the installed location. Basically, the code requires that the motor and its driven machinery be within sight from the controller for the motor. When the controller is out of sight (and the code considers a distance of 50 ft to be equivalent to "out of sight," even though the motor and its load might actually be visible from the controller location), the controller must comply with one of the following conditions:

A. The controller disconnecting means must be capable of being locked in the open position, or

B. A manually operable switch, which will provide disconnection of the motor from its power supply conductors, must be placed within sight from the motor location. And this switch may not be a switch in the control circuit of a magnetic starter.

These requirements are shown in Fig. 71. Specific layouts of the two exceptions are shown in Fig. 72. (NOTE: Code provisions shown in these sketches are minimum safety requirements. Additional use of disconnects, with and without lock-open means, may be made necessary or desirable by actual job conditions.)

Generally, an individual motor controller is required for each motor. However, for motors rated not over 600 volts, a single controller may be used with a group of motors in any one of the following cases:

1—If a number of motors drive several parts of a single machine or piece of apparatus—metal-and woodworking machines, cranes, etc.

2—If two or more motors are under protection of one overcurrent device as in the case of small motors supplied from a single branch circuit. This use of single controller applies only to cases involving motors of one hp or less, as in Section 430-53.

3—If a group of motors is located in one room and all are within sight from the controller location.

On the subject of motor controllers, the code further requires that speed-limiting devices be used with separately excited dc motors, with series motors and with motor-generators and converters which can be driven at excessive speed from the direct-current end, as by a reversal of current or decrease in load. Exceptions to this general requirement are allowed in cases where the machine, the system or the connection to the load and the load itself safely limits the speed or where an operator has constant manual control of the machine.

4. Protection against operating overloads

The code makes specific requirements on motor running overcurrent (overload protection) intended to protect the elements of the branch circuit—the motor itself, the motor control apparatus and the branch-circuit conductors—against excessive heating due to motor overloads. Such overload is considered to be operating overcurrent up to and including stalled-rotor current. When overcurrent persists for sufficient length of time, it will cause damage or dangerous overheating of the apparatus. Overcurrent does not include fault currents due to shorts or grounds.

Typical code requirements for running overcurrent protection, shown in Fig. 73, are as follows:

1. For motors of more than 1 hp, if used for continuous duty, running overcurrent protection must be provided. This may be an external overcurrent device actuated by the motor running current and set to open at not more than 125% of the motor full-load current for sealed (hermetic-type) refrigeration compressor motors and for motors with a temperature rise not over 40C or 115% of the motor full-load current for all other motors.

2. Motors of 1 hp or less which are not permanently installed but are manually started are considered protected against overcurrent by the branch-circuit protection if the motor is within sight from the starter. Running overcurrent devices are not required in such cases. A distance of over 50 ft is considered out of sight.

3. It should be noted that any motor of 1 hp or less which is not portable, is not manually started and/or is not within sight from its starter location must have specific running overcurrent protection. Automatically started motors of 1 hp or less must be protected against running overcurrent in the same way as motors rated over 1 hp. That is, a separate overcurrent or integral device must be used.

Basic code requirements are concerned with the rating or setting of the devices. However, the code

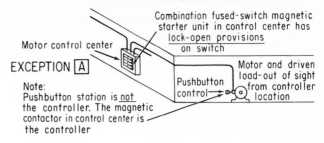

FIG. 72—These conditions are OK, with controller out-of-sight of motor and load

Combination fused-switch magnetic starter unit in control center has lock-open provisions on switch

Motor control center

EXCEPTION [A]

Note:
Pushbutton station is <u>not</u> the controller. The magnetic contactor in control center is the controller

Pushbutton control

Motor and driven load-out of sight from controller location

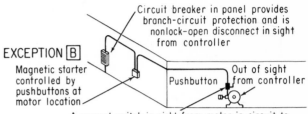

Circuit breaker in panel provides branch-circuit protection and is nonlock-open disconnect in sight from controller

EXCEPTION [B]

Magnetic starter controlled by pushbuttons at motor location

Pushbutton

Out of sight from controller

A <u>manual switch in sight from motor</u> in circuit to motor windings, eliminates need for lock-open disconnect. But this is an additional switch and is not needed if disconnect ahead of starter is lock-open type

permits the use of thermal protectors integral with motors, provided such devices are approved for their particular applications and that they do prevent dangerous overheating of the motors.

Under certain conditions, no specific running overload protection need be used. The motor is considered to be properly protected if it is part of an approved assembly which does not normally subject the motor to overloads and which has controls to protect against stalled rotor. Or if the impedance of the motor windings is sufficient to prevent overheating due to failure to start, the branch-circuit protection is considered adequate.

A motor used for a condition of service which is inherently short-time, intermittent, periodic or varying duty (see Table 430-22), is considered as protected against overcurrent by the branch-circuit overcurrent device. Motors are considered to be for continuous duty unless the motor cannot operate continuously with load under any condition of use.

FIG. 73—Rules on running overload protection

Protective device set for not more than 125% of motor full-load current for motors having a temperature rise not over 40 C, or set for not more than 115% for motors of other types

1.

Over 1 hp, under 1500 hp and without integral thermal protector

Motor

CB or fuses in panel or busway tap

The branch circuit overcurrent device is sufficient running overcurrent protection

2.

Portable motor 1 hp or less, manually started and within sight from the starter

Motor

(Plug connection may be starter) or (Manual starter may be on the machine)

For motors without integral thermal protectors, protective device set for not more than 125% of motor full-load current for motors having a temperature rise not over 40 C, or set for not more than 115% for motors of other types

3.

Motor

1. Motor of 1 hp or less, automatically started or
2. Motor of 1 hp or less, out of sight from starter or
3. Motor of 1 hp or less, not portable

FIG. 74—Number of OL units must meet local code ruling

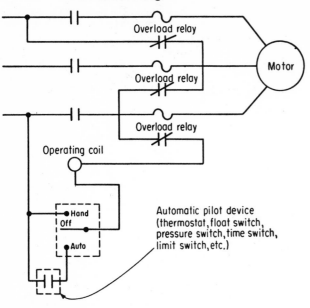

Overload relay

Overload relay

Overload relay

Motor

Operating coil

Hand
Off
Auto

Automatic pilot device
(thermostat, float switch,
pressure switch, time switch,
limit switch, etc.)

**THREE OL RELAYS—
WIDER USE BY 1965 NE CODE?**

Complete data on the number and location of over-current devices is given in Table 430-37 of the code.

Consistent with the engineering basis for code requirements, motor starters are generally provided with one overload relay in 2-pole starters and with two relays in 3- and 4-pole starters. However, in recent years, increasing experience with motors on rural or otherwise isolated electrical systems has clearly indicated the need, under certain conditions, for an overload protective device in each hot leg of a 3-phase motor circuit.

It has been found that primary single-phasing can cause burnouts of motors connected to secondary distribution systems supplied from wye-delta or delta-wye transformers (with the wye neutral point in the primary ungrounded or not connected to the circuit). The problem is particularly applicable to motors in isolated rural pumping stations where only a motor is supplied from a pole-mounted transformer stepping primary voltage power to secondary voltage level. For this reason, the use of three relays on a 3-phase starter is required by the note to Table 430-37: "Three running overcurrent units shall be used where 3-phase motors are installed in isolated, inaccessible or unattended locations, unless the motor is protected by other approved means. UNATTENDED (Definition): Lacking the presence of a person capable of exercising responsible control of the motor under consideration."

The addition of the definition for the word "unattended" has caused a difference in interpretation among inspection agencies. Some inspectors contend that the intent of the definition is to require the use of three OL relays in all starters for motors that are controlled by automatic pilot devices like thermostats, humidistats, pressure switches, time switches, float switches, etc. They contend that any motor which has its ON-OFF operation governed by a sensing device or other control which actuates the motor starter automatically (i.e., without interven-

tion of a person) is operating "unattended" and must be protected by three OL relays. According to this interpretation, two OL units may be used only for a motor which has its ON-OFF operations controlled by an operator in attendance at the motor—as an operator at a lathe or other machine tool. If this is truly the intent of the Note added in the 1965 NE Code, then this is a radical change and the vast majority of 3-phase motor applications will require three OL units.

There is, however, opinion among other inspectors that the "Note" does not have the above meaning and that there is no change in the code intent. These inspectors hold that use of three OL units is required only in the same cases where it has long been required—that is for automatically operated motors installed miles away from any attendant and checked only periodically. Typical examples would be motors in isolated, rural pump houses on irrigation or water supply systems.

Because of the differing opinions on this matter of the number of overload relays required, every motor circuit design should be arranged to conform to the local interpretation of this new code ruling. Fig. 74. This is frequently made a specification requirement by engineers. Such additional protection can usually be added to starters and some starters are made with three overload relays as standard.

Fig. 75 points up the need for correcting the size of running overload protection in motor controllers when power-factor capacitors are used on the load side of the controller.

5. Disconnecting motor and controller

The code specifically requires that a disconnecting means—basically, a motor-circuit switch rated in hp or a CB—be provided in each motor circuit to disconnect both the motor and its controller from all ungrounded supply conductors. In a motor branch circuit, every switch in the circuit in sight from the controller must satisfy the requirements. And the disconnect switch must be able to carry at least 115% of the nameplate current rating of the motor. Fig. 76 sets forth basic code requirements on types of disconnect.

As shown in Fig. 76, the NE Code makes a basic requirement that the disconnecting means for a motor and its controller be a motor-circuit switch rated in horsepower. For motors rated up to 50 hp, this is readily complied with, inasmuch as the UL lists motor-circuit switches up to 50 hp, NEMA standards cover hp ratings of enclosed switches up to 50 hp, and the manufacturers mark switches to conform. But for motors rated over 50 hp, the code does not require that the disconnect have a hp rating. It makes an exception to the basic rule and permits the use of ampere-rated switches or isolation switch, provided the switch has a carrying capacity of at least 115% of the nameplate current rating of the motor.

Example:

Provide a disconnect for a 100-hp, 3-phase, 440-volt motor. Use a nonfusible switch inasmuch as short-circuit protection is provided at the supply end of the branch circuit.

The full-load running current of the motor is 123 amps. A suitable disconnect must have a continuous carrying capacity of 123×1.15 or 142 amps.

FIG. 75—OL setting must be corrected when capacitors are at motors

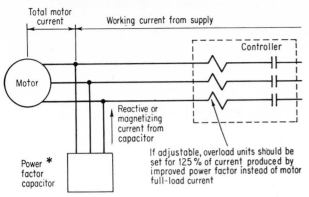

Total motor current

Working current from supply

Controller

Motor

Reactive or magnetizing current from capacitor

Power factor capacitor *

If adjustable, overload units should be set for 125% of current produced by improved power factor instead of motor full-load current

TOTAL MOTOR CURRENT = VECTOR SUM OF REACTIVE AND WORKING CURRENTS

EXAMPLE: Motor with 70% power factor has full-load current of 143 amps. Capacitor corrects to 100% PF.

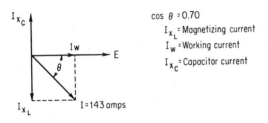

$\cos\theta = 0.70$

I_{X_L} = Magnetizing current
I_W = Working current
I_{X_C} = Capacitor current

I_{X_C} cancels I_{X_L} leaving only working current to be supplied from circuit. Working current = 143 × cos θ = 143 × 0.70 = 100

OVERLOAD RELAYS SHOULD BE SET FOR 125% OF 100 AMPS

* The rating of such capacitors should not exceed the value required to raise the no-load power factor of the motor to unity. Capacitors of these maximum ratings usually result in a full-load power factor of 95 to 98%.

FIG. 76—A motor disconnect must be one of these

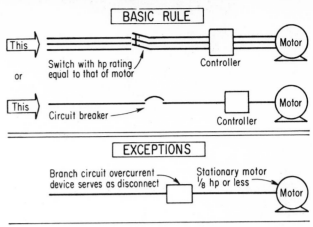

BASIC RULE

This or

Switch with hp rating equal to that of motor

Controller

Motor

This

Circuit breaker

Controller

Motor

EXCEPTIONS

Branch circuit overcurrent device serves as disconnect

Stationary motor ⅛ hp or less

Motor

For stationary motors rated at 2 hp or less and 300 volts or less the disconnecting means may be a general-use switch with an ampere rating at least twice that of the full-load current of the motor

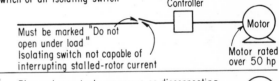

General-use switch rated twice motor amperes

Motor rated 2 hp or less

Or, on ac circuits only, an ac general-use snap switch may be used as a disconnecting means for a motor with full-load current not in excess of 80% of the ampere rating of the switch

For stationary motors rated at more than 50 hp, the disconnecting means may be a motor-circuit switch rated also in amperes, a general-use switch or an isolating switch

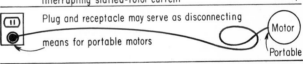

Controller

Motor

Must be marked "Do not open under load" Isolating switch not capable of interrupting stalled-rotor current

Motor rated over 50 hp

Plug and receptacle may serve as disconnecting means for portable motors

Motor

Portable

This calls for a 200-amp, 3-pole switch rated for 480 volts. The switch may be a general-use switch or a current-and-hp marked motor-circuit switch or an isolation switch. A motor-circuit switch with the required current and voltage rating for this case would be marked for 50 hp, but the horsepower rating is of no concern.

The code requires that isolation switches for such applications be marked "Do Not Open Under Load."

If the 50-hp switch were of the heavy-duty type, it would have an interrupting rating of 10 × 63 amps (the full-load current of a 440-volt, 50-hp motor) or 630 amps. But the locked-rotor current of the 100-hp motor might run as high as 8 × 123 amps or about 1000 amps. In such a case, the switch should be marked "Do Not Open Under Load."

If a fusible switch had to be provided for the above motor to provide disconnect and short-circuit protection, the size of the switch would be determined by the size and type of fuses used. Using a maximum fuse rating of 300% of motor current (Table 430-152 or 430-153) for standard NE Code fuses, the application would call for 400-amp fuses in a 400-amp switch. This switch would certainly qualify as the motor disconnect. However, if time-delay fuses are used, a 200-amp switch would be large enough to take the time-delay fuses and could

be used as the disconnect (because it is rated at 115% of motor current).

In the foregoing, the 400-amp switch might have an interrupting rating high enough to handle the locked-rotor current of the motor. Or the 200-amp switch might be of the type that has an interrupting rating up to 12 times the rated load current of the switch itself. In either of these cases, there would probably be no need for marking "Do Not Open Under Load."

A switch which satisfies the code on rating for use as a motor controller may also provide the required disconnect means—the two functions being performed by the one switch—provided it opens all ungrounded conductors to the motor, is protected by an overcurrent device (which may be the branch-circuit protection or may be fuses in the switch itself) and is a manually operated air-break switch or an oil switch not rated over 600 volts or 100 amps.

As described under "Controllers," a manual starting switch—capable of starting and stopping a given motor, capable of interrupting the stalled-rotor current of the motor and having the same hp rating as the motor—may serve the functions of controller and disconnecting means in many motor circuits, if the switch opens all ungrounded conductors to the motor. A circuit breaker may also serve as

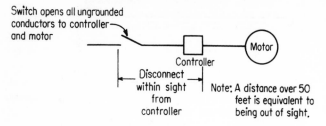

Switch opens all ungrounded conductors to controller and motor

Controller

Motor

Disconnect within sight from controller

Note: A distance over 50 feet is equivalent to being out of sight.

controller and disconnect. This is permitted by Section 430-111. An important exception to this allowance, however, is made in the case of a compensator type of controller. Such controllers must be provided with a separate means for disconnecting controller and the motor.

The acceptability of a single switch for both the controller and disconnecting is based on the single switch satisfying the code requirements for a controller and for a disconnect. It finds application where general-use switches or horsepower-rated switches are used, as permitted by the code, in conjunction with time-delay fuses which are rated low enough to provide both running overload protection and branch-circuit (short-circuit) protection. In such cases, a single fused switch may serve a total of four functions. And it is possible for a single circuit breaker to also serve four functions. Such application, however, requires extreme care in matching the time-current heating curve of the motor and the starting characteristics of the motor and its load to the operating curve of the protective device.

For sealed refrigeration compressors, Section 430-110 gives the procedure for determining disconnect capacity.

In general, each motor is provided with a separate disconnecting means. However, for motors under 600 volts, a single disconnect sometimes may serve a group of motors. Such a disconnect must have a rating sufficient to handle a single load equal to the sum of the horsepower ratings or current ratings. The single disconnect may be used for a group of motors driving different parts of a single piece of apparatus, for several motors on one branch circuit or for a group of motors in a single room within sight from the disconnect location.

An important requirement in motor circuits is that the disconnect be within sight from the controller location except that the disconnect for a "stationary" motor-driven appliance over ⅛ hp may

be located out-of-sight from the controller if the disconnect is capable of being locked in the open position. Fig. 77. But for all other motor loads, a disconnect means must be located in-sight from the controller—even if the out-of-sight disconnect is a lock-open type. NE Code Section 430-102 no longer contains the phrase it had prior to 1965 edition, "or be arranged to be locked in the open position." See Fig. 78.

6. Designing remote control circuits

The elements of a control circuit include all of the equipment and devices concerned with the function of the circuit: conductors, raceway, contactor operating coil, source of energy supply to the circuit, overcurrent protective devices and all switching devices which govern energization of the operating coil.

The NE Code covers application of control circuits in Article 725 and in Sections 240-5 and 430-71 to 430-74. Design and installation of control circuits are basically divided into two classes (in Article 725) according to the energy available in the circuit. Class 2 control circuits have low energy-handling capabilities; and any circuit, to qualify as a Class 2 control circuit, must have its open-circuit voltage and overcurrent protection limited to one of the set of conditions given in code Section 725-31.

The vast majority of control circuits for magnetic starters and contactors could not qualify as Class 2 circuits because of the relatively high energy required for operating coils. And any control circuit rated over 150 volts (such as 220- or 440-volt coil circuits) can never qualify as Class 2, regardless of energy. Even where a contactor coil is within the voltage and energy rating for Class 2—such as a Size 00 contactor with a 110-volt operating coil, which draws 0.7 amp inrush and only 0.14 amp for holding—design must meet the specific requirement that the 110-volt supply to the coil be made from a Class 2 approved transformer rated not over 100 volt-amps and the requirement that current-limiting means other than overcurrent protection must be provided to limit current to a maximum of one amp in the event of any fault in the circuit.

Class 1 control circuits include all operating coil circuits for magnetic starters which do not meet the requirements for Class 2 circuits. Class 1 circuits must be wired in accordance with Sections 725-11 to 725-21. Fig. 79 illustrates the major requirements. It should be noted in part 4 of Fig. 79 that there is no code limitation on the number of control circuit wires permitted in a raceway. As many wires as can safely be installed, without damaging the wires, may be installed. And in parts 6 and 7, it should be noted that there is a general code rule prohibiting the use of control circuit wires in raceways for power and light wiring. BUT, in Section 300-3 (e) and (f), it is made clear that control wires may occupy the same raceway with power supply wires to the motor or other load controlled by the control wires. This is repeated in the last sentence of Section 725-16 and is illustrated in B of part 7 of Fig. 79.

In general, remote control conductors must be protected against overcurrent. Section 240-5 of the code states that such conductors can be satisfactorily protected by overcurrent devices which are not of

FIG. 78—A nonfusible-switch combination starter provides in-sight disconnect

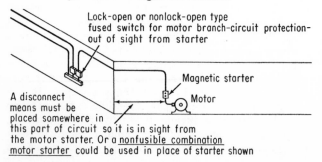

Lock-open or nonlock-open type fused switch for motor branch-circuit protection—out of sight from starter

Magnetic starter

Motor

A disconnect means must be placed somewhere in this part of circuit so it is in sight from the motor starter. Or a nonfusible combination motor starter could be used in place of starter shown the time-lag type and are rated at not more than 500% of the carrying capacity of the control circuit conductors. Section 430-72, however, modifies this requirement for motor control circuits as follows: In Fig. 80, the remote control conductors (A) may be properly protected by the branch-circuit overcurrent devices (B) if these devices are rated or set at not more than five times the current rating of the control conductors. If the branch-circuit overcurrent devices were rated or set at more than five times the rating of the control conductors, the control conductors would have to be protected by separate protective devices located "at the point where the conductor to be protected receives its supply" (C). And in the case of motor control circuits, the branch-circuit protective devices may be of the time-lag type and still qualify as protection for the control conductors. It should be noted that the overcurrent protection is required for the control conductors and not for the operating coil. Because of this, the size of control conductors can be selected to allow application without separate overcurrent protection.

Careful attention should be given to design of control circuits for operating coils. It should be borne in mind that available equipment and skillful installation techniques can afford safe use of control circuits at the same voltage rating as motors up to 600 volts. And this fact should be related to consideration of the voltage drop in long remote-control circuits, in which higher coil currents at lower coil voltages may produce objectionable voltage-drop.

Control circuits may be supplied directly from the conductors of the load circuit being controlled or can be fed from a control transformer which is supplied either from the load circuit or from a separate circuit. There is also the possibility of taking control voltage from a separate system of lower voltage than the voltage of the circuit to the controlled load. Such might be the case of a control circuit from a 120-volt panelboard for a contactor or starter controlling a 440-volt load circuit. Or batteries or a rectifier supply might be used to provide direct-current control circuits.

Accidental motor starting

An important addition to the 1965 NE Code is the mandatory rule of Section 430-73:

"Control circuits *shall* be so arranged that an accidental ground in the remote control devices will not start the motor."

The 1962 NE Code contained this same sentence in Section 430-73 except that the word *should* was used instead of *shall*. As a result, the 1965 NE Code makes it mandatory to design control circuits so that an accidental ground in the control circuit will not start the motor. The previous code, through the use of the word *should*, only *recommended* such arrangement of control circuit.

As shown in Fig. 81, any magnetic motor controller used on a 3-phase, 3-wire ungrounded system always presents the possibility of accidental starting of the motor. If, for instance, an undetected ground fault exists on one phase of the 3-phase system—even if this system ground fault is a long distance from the controller—a second ground fault in the remote control circuit for the operating coil of the starter can start the motor. This circuit presents a possibility which the 1965 NE Code requires to be eliminated.

If Fig. 81 is a violation of the new code rule,

FIG. 79—Wiring coil circuits of starters and contactors

1. In general, wiring of Class I control systems must be the same as general-purpose power and light wiring.
2. Conductors are generally limited to minimum of No. 14, but No. 18 or No. 16 may be used if installed in raceway or approved cable or flexible cord and protected at not more than 20 amps.
3. Wires larger than No. 16 must be Type R, T or other approved type. Fixed No. 18 or No. 16 must have insulation at least equal to Type RF-2 or TF. Other conductors with specific approval for the purpose may be used.
4. The number of Class I control circuit conductors in a conduit **may** be determined from Table 1, Chapter 9. There is no code limit on number of wires permitted in a raceway.

Conduit or EMT

Number of conductors per Table I, Chapter 9— no derating for occupancy

5. Class I control circuit conductors do not have to be derated according to number in a raceway.
6. When Class I control conductors are run in raceway with power and light conductors, all conductors must be derated in accordance with Note 8 of Tables 310-12 through 310-15—determining the derating factor on the basis of the number of power and light conductors only.
7. Conductors for two or more Class I control circuits may be run in the same raceway—ac and/or dc circuits—if all conductors are insulated for the maximum voltage of any conductor in the raceway. Other permitted installations are as follows:

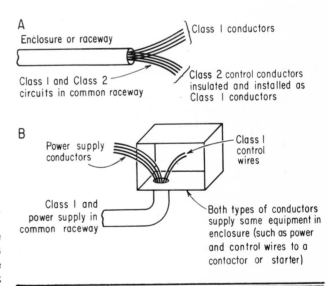

A
Enclosure or raceway
Class I conductors
Class 2 control conductors insulated and installed as Class I conductors
Class I and Class 2 circuits in common raceway

B
Power supply conductors
Class I control wires
Class I and power supply in common raceway
Both types of conductors supply same equipment in enclosure (such as power and control wires to a contactor or starter)

FIG. 80—Overcurrent protection for control circuit conductors

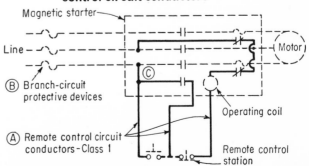

Magnetic starter
Line
Motor
(B) Branch-circuit protective devices
(C)
Operating coil
(A) Remote control circuit conductors-Class 1
Remote control station

FIG. 81—This type of accidental starting must be prevented

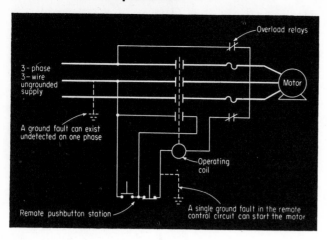

FIG. 82—Control transformer isolates coil against accidental starting

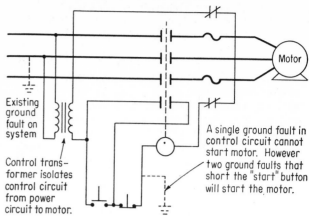

FIG. 83—2-pole "start" button isolates coil from ground-fault starting

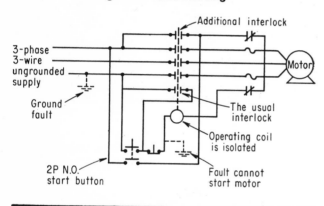

FIG. 84—Switch only in hot leg of grounded coil circuits

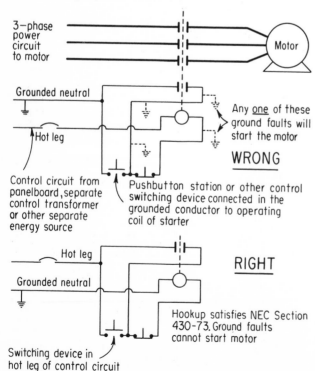

what method or methods will the code accept to produce compliance with the code? How must a control circuit be "arranged" so that a ground in the remote control circuit *will not start* the motor being controlled?

Fig. 82 shows the use of a control transformer to isolate the control circuit from responding to the combination of ground faults shown in Fig. 81. This transformer may be a one-to-one isolating transformer, with the same primary and secondary voltage. Or, the transformer can step the motor circuit voltage down to a lower level for the control circuit.

In the hookup shown in Fig. 83, a 2-pole START button is used in conjunction with two sets of holding contacts in the motor starter. This hookup protects against accidental starting of the motor under the fault conditions shown in Fig. 81. The hookup also provides against accidental starting due to two ground faults in the control circuit simply shorting out the START button and energizing the operating coil. This could happen in the circuit of Fig. 81 or the circuit of Fig. 82 with the coil circuit fed from the secondary of an isolating control transformer, connected to the same line wires.

Fig. 84 shows another example of control circuit installation which involves the new rule in Section 430-73. Whenever the coil is fed from a circuit made up of a hot conductor and a grounded conductor (as when the coil is fed from a panelboard or separate control transformer, instead of from the supply conductors to the motor), care must be taken to place the pushbutton station or other switching control device in the hot leg to the coil and not in the grounded leg to the coil. By switching in the hot leg, the starting of the motor by accidental ground fault (as shown at top of the illustration) can be effectively eliminated.

Control circuit disconnect

When a separate source of energy is used for a control circuit, care must be taken to provide suitable disconnect for the control circuit. Section 430-74 on disconnection of coil control circuits of magnetic motor starters says: "Control circuits shall be so arranged that they will be disconnected from all sources of supply when the disconnecting means is in the open position. The disconnecting means

FIG. 85—Disconnect means for separate control power

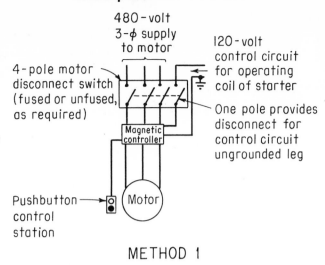

480-volt 3-φ supply to motor

120-volt control circuit for operating coil of starter

4-pole motor disconnect switch (fused or unfused, as required)

One pole provides disconnect for control circuit ungrounded leg

Magnetic controller

Pushbutton control station

Motor

METHOD 1

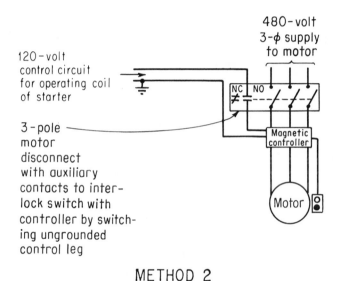

120-volt control circuit for operating coil of starter

480-volt 3-φ supply to motor

3-pole motor disconnect with auxiliary contacts to interlock switch with controller by switching ungrounded control leg

NC NO

Magnetic controller

Motor

METHOD 2

FIG. 86—Application of power-factor capacitors

Power-factor capacitors can be connected across electric lines to neutralize the effect of lagging power-factor loads, thereby reducing the current drawn for a given kilowatt load. In a distribution system, small capacitor units may be connected at the individual loads or the total capacitor kilovolt-amperes may be grouped at one point and connected to the main. Although the total kvar of capacitors is the same, the use of small capacitors at the individual loads reduces current all the way from the loads back to the source and thereby has greater PF corrective effect than the one big unit on the main, which reduces current only from its point of installation back to the source.

Calculating Size of Capacitor:
Assume it is desired to improve the power factor a given amount by the addition of capacitors to the circuit.

Then $kvar_R = kw \times (\tan \theta_1 - \tan \theta_2)$

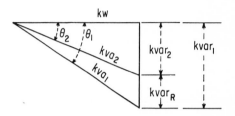

where $kvar_R$ = rating of required capacitor
$kvar_1$ = reactive kilovolt-amperes at original PF
$kvar_2$ = reactive kilovolt-amperes at improved PF
θ_1 = original phase angle
θ_2 = phase angle at improved PF
kw = load at which original PF was determined.

NOTE: The phase angles θ_1 and θ_2 can be determined from a table of trigonometric functions using the following relationships:
θ_1 = The angle which has its cosine equal to the decimal value of the original power factor (e.g., 0.70 for 70% PF; 0.65 for 65%; etc.).
θ_2 = The angle which has its cosine equal to the decimal value of the improved power factor.

may consist of two separate devices, one of which disconnects the motor and the controller from the source of power supply for the motor, and the other, the control circuit from its power supply. Where the two separate devices are used, they should be located immediately adjacent one to the other. Fig. 85 shows two methods of providing for disconnect of separate control power without the use of additional switch device. The alternative to these methods is to use a suitable switch in an enclosure, adjacent to the power disconnect.

METHOD 1 shows use of a power disconnect with one more pole than required for the power circuit. The extra pole then switches the control circuit, assuring complete absence of power on load side.

METHOD 2 shows the use of a power disconnect switch which contains auxiliary contacts (as a typical case, one normally closed and one normally open contact) to interlock the starter control circuit with the disconnect. The mechanical arrangement is such that when the handle of the disconnect switch is moved from the ON to the OFF position, the

auxiliary contacts in the control circuit open to kill the control power and open the starter before the contacts in the power circuit of the switch actually open. Such interlocking puts the load-break task on the starter. To provide that feature, the interlock can be used even when the control power is taken from the motor-controller line terminals.

Voltage regulation

To assure proper and efficient operation of motors, the matter of voltage regulation must be considered carefully. Many factors—number of motors, sizes and types of motors, duty cycles, load densities, type of distribution system, loading of various feeders, power factor—are related to the design problem of assuring necessary level and stability of voltages for motors. The matter of voltage regulation follows through every step in design and must be accounted for in sizing conductors.

Voltage drop from the source of voltage supply to any motor in the system must not exceed 5%. Normally, the proper power feeder design will limit

TABLE FOR 3-PHASE MOTORS

(Induction-Type, Full-Voltage Starting)
Code Letters F to V, and No Code Letters

HP	F. L. C. in Amps 220/440V	Min. AWG/MCM Wire Sizes Conduit *CU 220/440V	Min. AWG/MCM Wire Sizes Conduit **AL 220/440V	Running Protection Non-Adjustable Types 220/440V	Running Protection Adjustable Types 220/440V	Branch-Circuit Protection Switch-Fuse Max. Size for Standard Fuses 220/440V	CB (Max. Size) 220/440V
½	2/1	14/½ / 14/½	12/½ / 12/½	3/2	2.5/1.25	30–15/30–15	15/15
¾	2.8/1.4	14/½ / 14/½	12/½ / 12/½	4/3	3.5/1.75	30–15/30–15	15/15
1	3.5/1.8	14/½ / 14/½	12/½ / 12/½	5/3	4.37/2.25	30–15/30–15	15/15
1½	5/2.5	14/½ / 14/½	12/½ / 12/½	8/4	6.25/3.12	30–15/30–15	15/15
2	6.5/3.3	14/½ / 14/½	12/½ / 12/½	10/6	8.12/4.12	30–20/30–15	20/15
3	9/4.5	14/½ / 14/½	12/½ / 12/½	12/8	11.25/5.62	30–30/30–15	30/15
5	15/7.5	12/½ / 14/½	10/¾ / 12/½	20/10	18.75/9.37	60–45/30–25	40/20
7½	22/11	10/¾ / 14/½	8/¾ / 12/½	30/15	27.5/13.75	100–70/60–35	70/30
10	27/14	8/¾ / 12/½	8/¾ / 10/¾	35/20	33.75/17.5	100–90/60–45	70/40
15	40/20	6/1 / 10/¾	6/1 / 10/¾	50/25	50/25	200–125/60–60	100/50
20	52/26	6/1 / 8/¾	4/1¼ / 8/¾	70/35	65/32.5	200–175/100–80	150/70
25	64/32	4/1¼ / 8/¾	2/1¼ / 8/¾	80/40	80/40	200–200/100–100	175/100
30	78/39	3/1¼ / 6/1	1/1½ / 6/1	100/50	97.5/48.75	400–250/200–125	200/100
40	104/52	1/1½ / 6/1	00/2 / 4/1¼	150/70	130/65	400–350/200–175	300/150
50	125/63	00/2 / 4/1¼	0000/2½ / 2/1¼	175/80	156.5/78.7	400–400/200–200	350/175
60	150/75	000/2 / 2/1¼	250/2½ / 1/1½	200/100	187.5/93.7	600–450/400–225	400/200
75	185/93	250/2½ / 1/1½	350/3 / 0/2	250/125	231/116.25	600–600/400–300	500/250
100	246/123	350/3 / 00/2	500/3 / 000/2	350/175	307.5/153.7	800–800/400–400	700/350

* 60°C wire, 14–8; 75°C wire No. 6 and larger
** 60°C wire, 12–10; 75°C wire No. 8 and larger

Data compiled from following 1965 NE Code tables: 310–12, 310–14, 430–146, 430–150, 430–152, 430–153, & Table 1, Ch. 9

voltage drop to 3%, leaving a maximum permissible voltage drop of 2% in any motor branch circuit under full-load conditions. However, a 1% maximum circuit voltage drop is recommended.

Power factor should be taken into consideration in all calculations, using the known value of PF or an 80% assumed value.

Depending upon the results of study of the vol-tage drop and power-factor relationship, use of cor-rective measures for improving power factor may be designed into motor branch circuits. At individual motor locations, power-factor-correcting capacitors offer improved voltage regulation. Power-factor ca-pacitors installed at terminals of motors provide maximum relief from reactive currents, reducing the required current-carrying capacities of conduc-

Typical Arrangement for PF Capacitor at Motor Terminals

(See NEC Article 460)

6-500 MCM RH conductors (2 per phase) divided between 2-3"C

500-hp motor

Motor starter

Power circuit

Overcurrent protection provided by fuses

Pullbox

3-250 MCM RH conductors in 2½"C

80-kvar enclosed capacitor unit is ceiling suspended at location of 500-hp motor

Discharge resistors

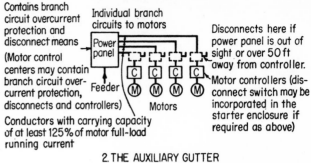

FIG. 87—Layout of motor branch circuits

1. THE CONTROL CENTER LAYOUT

Contains branch circuit overcurrent protection and disconnect means (Motor control centers may contain branch circuit overcurrent protection, disconnects and controllers)

Individual branch circuits to motors

Power panel

Feeder

Motors

Disconnects here if power panel is out of sight or over 50 ft away from controller.

Motor controllers (disconnect switch may be incorporated in the starter enclosure if required as above)

Conductors with carrying capacity of at least 125% of motor full-load running current

2. THE AUXILIARY GUTTER

Feeder or subfeeder

Branch circuit overcurrent and disconnect means

Branch circuit conductors

Motors

Branch circuit tap conductors with same carrying capacity as feeder or ⅓ feeder capacity if not more than 25 feet long (for taps not more than 10 feet long, tap capacity same as branch circuit conductors)

Controllers

3. THE BUSWAY TAP-SWITCH METHOD

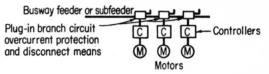

Busway feeder or subfeeder

Plug-in branch circuit overcurrent protection and disconnect means

Controllers

Motors

tors from their point of application all the way back to the supply system. Such application also eliminates extra switching devices, since each capacitor can be switched with the motor it serves. When motors are small, numerous and operated intermittently, however, it is often economically more desirable to install required capacitor kvar at the motor loadcenter.

Fig. 86 outlines the procedure for applying capacitors for power-factor correction.

Layout of circuits

Laying out wiring to serve two or more motors may be made according to several plans. Fig. 87.

1. **Each motor** may be served by a separate branch circuit from a panel or distribution center. Branch-circuit protective devices for motor circuits are grouped, sometimes with required controller and disconnect equipment. Grouping may be made in one enclosure—power panel or control center assembly —or may consist of a number of individual enclosures· at one location fed from a gutter.

2. **Individual circuits** to motors may be tapped from a feeder in an auxiliary gutter without individual overcurrent protection for the taps, provided they are carried direct to the disconnecting means or controller for each motor. Such taps must have the

same carrying capacity as the feeder if they are over 25 ft long. If they are under 25 ft long, they must have a carrying capacity at least equal to one-third the carrying capacity of the feeder. In such cases, the motor branch-circuit protection is included with the disconnect means (switch and fuses, or CB) or in a combination starter, and the branch circuit originates at that point. Taps not over 10 ft long need have only the same capacity of the branch circuit wires.

3. **Individual branch circuits** to motors may originate at disconnects fed directly by a feeder or subfeeder (e.g., tap units on a busway) with disconnect and branch-circuit protection provided by the tap switch (with fuses) or CB.

Feeders to distribution centers

Supply of electric energy from the source or sources of energy to the branch circuits which feed the loads is made by the distribution system. This system is a layout of equipment in various configurations designed to provide the right amount of current at the right voltage to each utilization outlet. The distribution system carries power to lighting panelboards, power panelboards, motor control centers and to the branch-circuit protective devices for individual motor or power loads.

A distribution system may operate at a single voltage level or may involve one or more transformations of voltage. A distribution system might also incorporate change in frequency of ac power or rectification from ac to dc power.

Design of a distribution system is a matter of selecting circuit layouts and equipment to accomplish electrical actions and operations necessary for the conditions of voltage, current and frequency required by the loads. This means relating such factors as service voltage, distribution voltage or voltages, conductors, transformers, converters, switches, protective devices, regulators and power-factor corrective means to economy, load conditions, continuity of service, operating efficiency and future power requirements. The factors of capacity, accessibility, flexibility and safety, which were discussed previously, must be carefully included in design considerations for distribution.

Basic rules for distribution design are as follows:

1. Determine the magnitude and characteristics of all individual loads and load groupings.

2. Locate the one or more electrical supply points as near as possible to building loadcenters.

3. Select and arrange feeders and other distribution equipment to provide power continuity required by the commercial or industrial functions of the building.

4. Constantly relate the building's electrical requirements to the system characteristics of flexibility, accessibility and regulation.

5. Provide a calculated amount of spare capacity in all system components from the supply to load devices, carefully correlating feeder and subfeeder spare capacities to realistic demand expectations.

6. Use modern loadcenter layouts where possible.

7. In design calculations, observe minimum and maximum code figures for conductors, conduit, protective devices, switches and control equipment. But exceed code standards to obtain required convenience, flexibility, effectiveness and greater safety.

Distribution voltage levels

Distribution systems are basically classified according to voltage levels used to carry the power either directly to the branch circuits or to loadcenter transformers or substations at which feeders to branch circuits originate.

1. 120/240-volt, 3-wire, single-phase combination light and power distribution (also called "115/230-volt").

This type of system is restricted to applications where the total load is small and is primarily lighting and receptacle circuits. It operates with the neutral wire grounded.

The most common application is in residential occupancies—individual homes or multifamily dwellings. Stores, small schools and other small commercial occupancies also use this system. In most cases of small commercial buildings, however, the use of

FIG. 88—120/208-volt distribution

Power and light feeders in 60,000-sq-ft factory

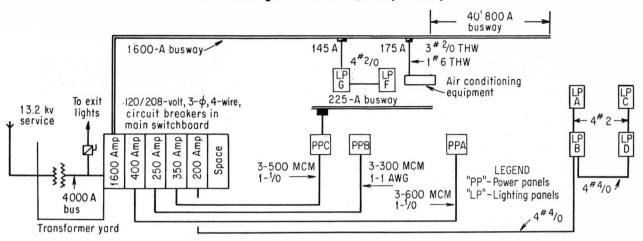

Transformation to utilization voltage is made in the outdoor transformer yard. Here a Y-Y connection of three 167-kva, oil-filled distribution transformers steps the incoming supply to a 120/208-volt utilization level. The 120/208-volt level was dictated by the ratings of existing motor loads on all of the production machinery which had been moved from the old building. As a result of this, there was no opportunity to take advantage of the distribution economies of 480/277-volt circuits for lighting and motor loads.

Subdistribution for vital hospital circuits

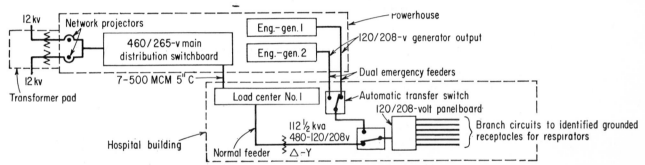

Plan shows three alternative circuits for supplying essential circuits to "iron lungs" in a research hospital. The 120/208-volt panelboard may be fed from: a step-down transformer fed by the 480-volt distribution system, supplied from a dual-primary network hookup; from Eng. Gen. 1; or from Eng. Gen. 2. Although not shown here, the panelboard for emergency lighting and the panelboard for isolated, ungrounded circuits in surgical areas are supplied from the same normal-and-emergency hookup, with the ungrounded circuits transformer-isolated.

120/208-volt, 3-phase distribution offers greater economy due to higher operating efficiency of 3-phase circuits.

In those cases where 120/240-volt feeders are used as the basic distribution method, the service to the premises is made at that voltage. Of course, 120/240-volt distribution is frequently an effective and economical system for lighting-subfeeder distribution in electrical systems which use a higher-voltage basic distribution system with loadcenter step-down to utilization voltages for local and incidental lighting and receptacle circuits.

2. 120/208-volt, wye 3-phase, 4-wire light and power distribution.

This is the most common type of system used in commercial buildings, in institutional occupancies and in industrial shops with limited electrical loads. Such a system operates with the neutral conductor grounded and offers substantial economy over the 120/240-volt system in the amount of conductor material required to carry a given amount of power to a load. This combination system provides 120 volts phase-to-neutral for lighting and single-phase loads and 208 volts phase-to-phase for single- or 3-phase motor or other power loads.

The system is used as the basic distribution in those occupancies in which the service to the building is of the same voltage. It is also the most common subdistribution system for lighting and receptacle circuits in those occupancies using higher-voltage distribution to loadcenter. See Fig. 88.

3. 240-volt, 3-phase, 3-wire distribution.

This is a common system for power loads in commercial and industrial buildings. It may operate ungrounded or with one of the phase legs grounded—in which case it is called a "corner-grounded delta" system. In such cases, service to the premises is made at 240 volts, 3 phase. Feeders carry the power to panelboards or wireways supplying branch circuits for motor loads. Lighting loads are then handled by a separate single-phase service to the building or through a step-down transformer.

This system offers economic application where the power load is large compared to the lighting load.

FIG. 89—480-volt, 3-phase, 3-wire ungrounded

Power feeders for modernized distribution in existing plant

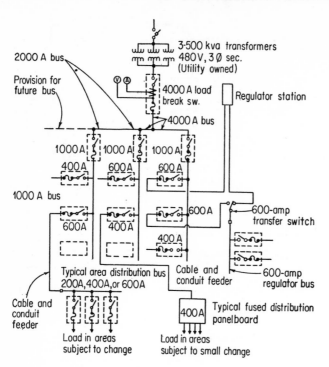

The outdoor enclosure houses a 4000-amp, load-break, 480-volt, 3-pole disconnect switch.

A 4000-amp bus-stub on the line side of the switch provides connection to the utility owned substation. The 4000-amp busway on the load side feeds into the building at the same elevation as the system inside.

Adequate fault and overcurrent protection is offered by the use of current-limiting fuses in the main and branch feeder circuit bus-plug switches. Proper selection and location in the system of these fuses provides a coordinated protective arrangement that will isolate faulted circuits without affecting the operation of equipment on other circuits in the system.

Plug-in busway distribution centers have not been used exclusively throughout this plant. In areas of fixed load, such as air conditioning machinery, motor-generator sets and plant lighting transformers, fusible-switch distribution panelboards have been used. These are wall-mounted types having capacity for future load growth.

Underground feeders for 480-volt mercury-vapor ballasts

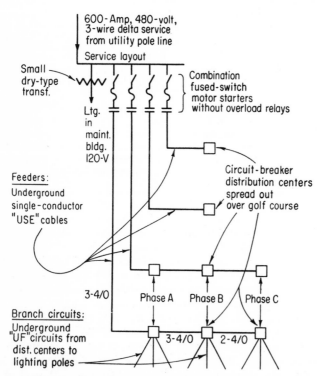

At the main distribution center, combination fused-switch motor starters are used to control and protect the underground feeder runs to the branch-circuit panels. These combination starters are used without overload relay elements and each functions simply as a fused switch and magnetic contactor. Each of two of the distribution feeders supplies three single-phase, 2-wire, 480-volt branch-circuit loadcenters. Each of the other two 480-volt distribution feeders supplies one 3-phase CB distribution center.

At each branch-circuit distribution center, a two-pole circuit breaker is used to control and protect Type UF branch-circuit conductors run underground to the lighting poles.

tap on one of the phases is brought out as a neutral to provide 120 volts for lighting and receptacle circuits, forming a 4-wire system.

4. 480-volt, 3-phase, 3-wire distribution.

This system is commonly used in commercial and industrial buildings with substantial motor loads. It is generally operated ungrounded but it can be operated with one phase leg grounded—as a corner-grounded delta. Service to the building may be made

at this voltage, and the 480-volt feeders carried to motor loads and to step-down transformers for lighting and receptacle circuits.

In many cases, 480-volt feeders will be derived from loadcenter substations within the building and carried to motor loads or power panels. See Fig. 89.

5. 480Y/277-volt (460Y/265-volt), 3-phase, 4-wire combination power and light distribution.

This is a very popular basic system for use in com-

FIG. 90—480/277-volt distribution plus 2400-volt delta

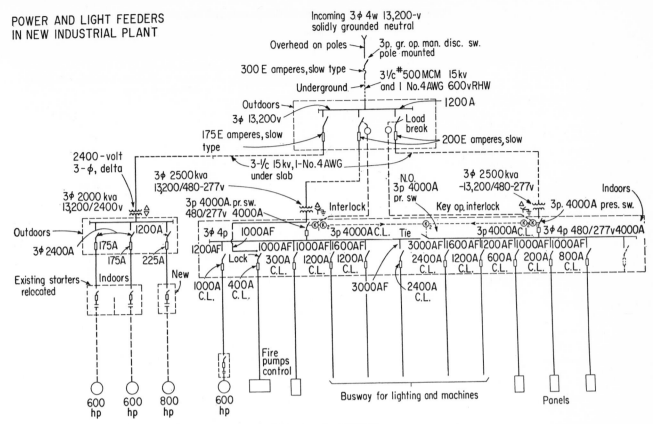

POWER AND LIGHT FEEDERS
IN NEW INDUSTRIAL PLANT

Two of the transformers in the outdoor substation step 13.2 kv down to 480/277.
The third outdoor transformer steps 13.2 down to 2400 volts, 3-phase, 3-wire delta for circuits to three large machine motors.

mercial buildings and industrial buildings. In office and other commercial buildings, the 480-volt, 3-phase, 4-wire feeders are carried to each floor where 480-volt, 3-phase, 3-wire power is tapped to a power panel or to motors; general area fluorescent lighting using 277-volt ballasts is connected between each phase leg and the neutral.

And 120/208-volt, 3-phase, 4-wire circuits are derived from step-down transformers for local lighting, appliance and receptacle circuits.

Application of this system offers economic advantage over a 120/208-volt system when less than about half of the load devices require 120- or 208-volt power. Where the 480Y system can be used, it will cost less than the 120/208-volt system due to such savings as—smaller sizes of conductors, lower raceway needs, reduced installation labor and lower cost of system elements due to lower current capacities.

If the required amount of 120- or 208-volt power is over half of the total load in a building, the cost of the step-down transformers to supply these circuits will generally offset the savings in the 480-volt circuiting. Costs of switchgear and panelboards also affect comparison of the two types of systems (i.e., 120/208 and 480/277).

The 480Y system is generally more advantageous in multifloor buildings than in buildings of only a few floors and more advantageous in large or long single-level areas than in small areas. The savings are directly related to reducing the sizes of long feeders, getting more kva delivered per pound of installed system. See Figs. 90 and 91.

6. 2400-volt, 3-phase delta distribution.

This is an industrial type system used to feed heavy motor loads directly and motor and lighting loads through loadcenter substations and lighting transformers.

7. 4160Y/2400-volt, 3-phase, 4-wire distribution with a grounded neutral.

This is a more common system than the above 2400-volt, delta-connected system. Originally developed primarily for industrial applications, this system of high-voltage distribution has gained widespread use for large-area, spread-out commercial and institutional buildings, such as shopping centers, schools, motels.

The 4160Y/2400-volt system also appears to have become the most popular high-voltage system for inside distribution. Economies in the use of cables and switchgear seem to be highest for this particular primary system. In many installations, this system offers the advantages of loadcenter primary distribution for power and light loads with direct connection of heavy motor loads operating at 4160 volts.

This system is widely used to supply loadcenter substations in which the voltage is stepped to 480 to feed motors and lighting transformers for 120/240-volt and/or 120/208-volt circuits. It may also be used in distribution to substations stepping the voltage directly to 120/208. See Figs. 92 and 93.

8. 4800-volt distribution.

This is a delta-connected industrial system for layouts of substations supplying motors and lighting transformers.

FIG. 91—480/277 plus 13.8-kv distribution

Distribution layout for multibuilding computer center

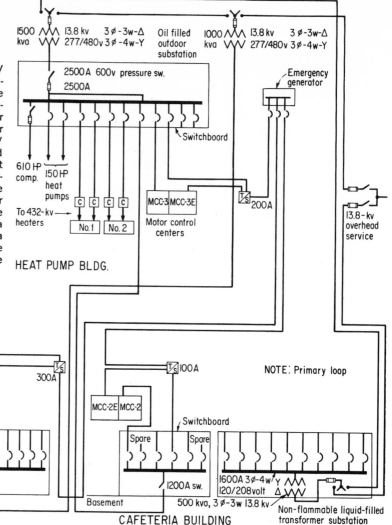

One of the 13.8-kv feeders is routed to the 120/208-volt unit substation in the basement of the cafeteria building, and the second feeder is routed to the outdoor transformer mat for the 1000-kva and 1500-kva transformers rated for 480/277 volts on their secondary. Although the major lighting and power load in the cafeteria building was designed for 480/277 volts, 3-phase, 4-wire, the very substantial load of electric kitchen cooking equipment was rated at 120/208 volts, which would require large, high-current circuits with large conductor sizes to minimize voltage drop in the very long runs from the outdoor transformer mat to the cafeteria building. To eliminate the costly runs of secondary feeders for the cafeteria cooking equipment, the plan called for installing a 13.8-kv-to-120/208-volt transformer substation in the basement of the cafeteria building to supply the kitchen loads.

9. 7200-volt, 3-phase distribution.

This is another industrial system used with substations for stepping voltage to lower levels for power and lighting.

10. 13.2Y/7.2-kv (or 13.8-kv), 3-phase, 4-wire distribution.

This is a modern, widely used distribution system for large industrial plants. Power at this voltage is delivered to substations which step the voltage to 480 for motor loads and which supply 480-to-120/240-volt or 480-to-120/208-volt transformers for lighting. Or 480Y/277-volt substations may be used to supply motor loads and 277-volt incandescent, fluorescent or mercury vapor lighting for office and industrial areas. Lighting transformers are then used to supply 120 volts for lighting and receptacles. See Fig. 94.

The voltage values given for these distribution systems are subject, of course, to the usual variation or spreads due to distance of transmission and distribution, local conditions of utility supply and settings of transformer taps. There are certain times when selection of distribution secondary voltages other than those described offers better application, or is required. See Fig. 95. Other high-voltage systems may operate at 6.6 kv, 8.3 kv, 11 kv and 12 kv.

System voltage designations

Of the high-voltage (over 600 volts) distribution systems, 4160 volts and 13,200 volts are the most common and represent good design selection and economy of application for most cases. However, selection of primary depends upon size and layout of load and the supply voltages which the utility makes available. Consultation with the utility must precede any design for high-voltage distribution.

The trend today is toward the use of the 13-kv systems over other high-voltage distribution systems for large industrial plants and the use of 4160/2400-volt systems for spread-out commercial and institutional buildings.

For any given system voltage configuration, the industry has more or less standardized on three different values of voltage by which the system may be described—1.) the transformer voltage; 2.) the nominal system voltage; and 3.) the utilization voltage. These three levels for any given system account for voltage drop from the source to the load. As shown in Fig. 96, for instance, the 480/277-volt system has 480 volts at the source or transformer; 460 volts is the nominal system voltage; and 440 volts is delivered to the 440-volt rated motor loads.

FIG. 92—4160-volt distribution

Feeders to basement and roof vaults in high-rise apartment building

The basement vault supplies basement loads—oil burners, air-conditioning equipment, a 75-hp fire pump, garage loads, pool loads, laundry equipment, etc.—and risers to apartment panels, up to and including the first 21 floors of the building. The roof vault supplies typical roof loads, elevator motors, exhaust fans, cooling tower fans and mechanical auxiliary motors—and feeders running down to apartment panels from the 33rd floor down to, and including, the 22nd floor. Thus, the entire building load is clearly divided between the two vaults. The only secondary-voltage connection between the basement service and the roof service consists of two small conduit circuits—one to connect the secondary-voltage electric meter on the roof to a totalizing meter at the basement service, and one control conduit between air-conditioning equipment in the basement and the cooling tower on the roof.

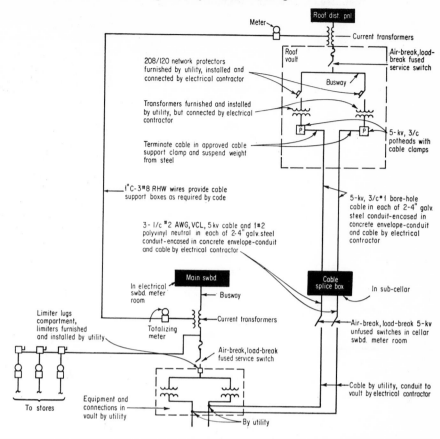

FIG. 93—4160-volt risers to loadcenter transformers

Primary selective system in office building

4160-volt feeders are carried upwards in pairs to serve 500-kva 4160-480/277-volt substations located at 3-floor intervals on both sides of building core. Primary selector switches can connect with alternate feeders which in turn connect through 1200-amp circuit breakers to opposite sides of split bus in main switchboard. Each 480/277-volt substation carries half the fluorescent lighting load of three floors, and also serves a 480-208/120-volt substation located above it.

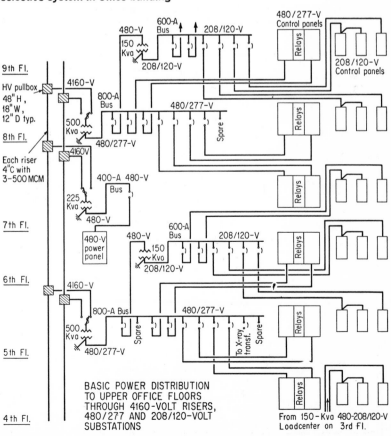

FIG. 94—13.2-kv distribution

Top and bottom feed for 776-unit apartment building

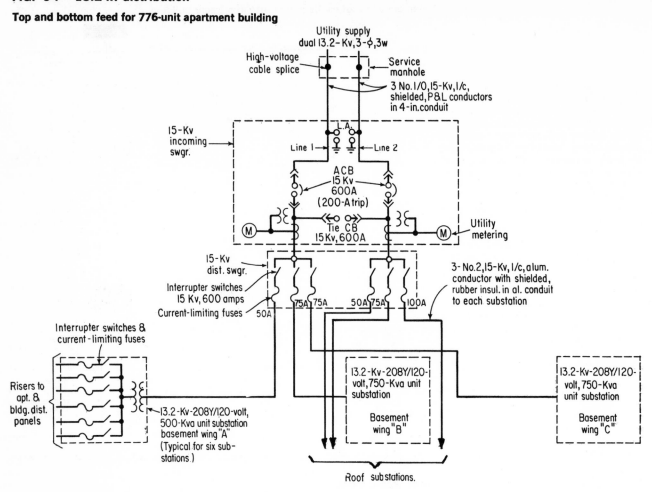

To provide high reliability of service, a dual 13.2-kv supply is provided. If service is interrupted on either utility line, a tie circuit breaker in incoming switchgear allows the alternate feeder to power entire building. Six high-voltage feeders carry 13.2-kv to unit substations, which are located in the basement and on the roof of each building wing Total substation transformer capacity is 4250 kva. Basement subs supply bottom ten floors of building. Roof subs supply top ten floors.

Primary Distribution from Secondary Service

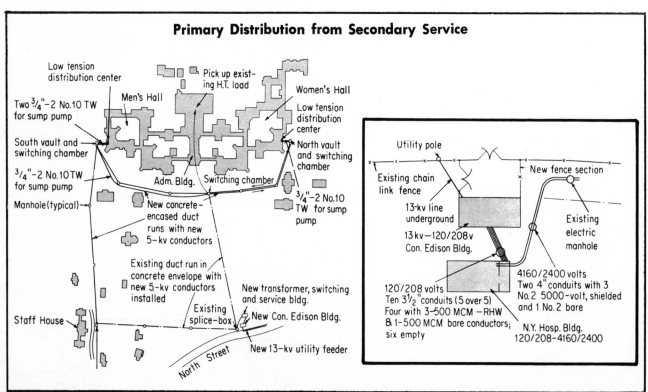

FIG. 95—Special distribution voltage levels

240-volt, 3-phase underground circuits for isolation in hospital

Two-stage step-down transformer hookup serves the ungrounded circuits required in a hospital operating room. The NE Code generally requires that circuits in areas used for anesthetizing—operating rooms, delivery rooms, anesthesia rooms and corridors and utility rooms used for administering flammable anesthetics—must be supplied from an ungrounded distribution system which is isolated from any distribution system supplying areas other than anesthetizing locations [NE Code Section 517-6(a)]. Such isolation is generally provided by means of two-winding transformers with no electrical connection between primary and secondary (that is, primary to secondary energy transfer must be made only by magnetic induction). It would seem, just from this, that the circuits could be provided by simply installing single-phase transformers for 480 to 120/240 volts or 3-phase transformers for 480-volt delta to 120/208-volt wye. But there is a further complication.

Section 517-6(b) of the NE Code states that: "Circuits supplying primaries of isolating transformers [as required by Section 517-6(a)] shall operate at not more than 300 volts between conductors. . . ." This rules out the use of any transformer with a 480-volt primary for stepping down to the ungrounded distribution system for anesthetizing areas. As a result, a two-stage transformation is necessary to obtain the ungrounded system from the 480-volt delta system. This transformation is made in one of the roof penthouses where a 480-volt 3-wire feeder from the main switchboard comes into a hookup of three 5-kva, single-phase transformers connected for 480-volt delta down to 240-volt delta. The secondary conductors are brought into a trough from which single-phase, 2-wire subfeeds are tapped to single-phase transformers (2 and 3 kva sizes) connected for 240 volts down to 120 volts. These small transformers provide required isolation of their secondary, 2-wire ungrounded subfeeds to panels for the ungrounded

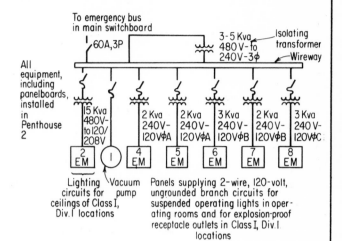

branch circuits. The small single-phase transformers are divided among the three phases of the 240-volt delta secondary of the 3-phase transformer bank.

Output of emergency generator was selected at 600 volts to obtain the advantages of 600-volt distribution for the long feeder runs to widespread distribution centers. Use of 600-volt, 3-phase, 3-wire makeup permits use of smaller wires (due to reduced current) and smaller conduits than would be needed to deliver the same power at 208 volts or even 480 volts.

600-volt circuit for emergency feeders at multibuilding hospital

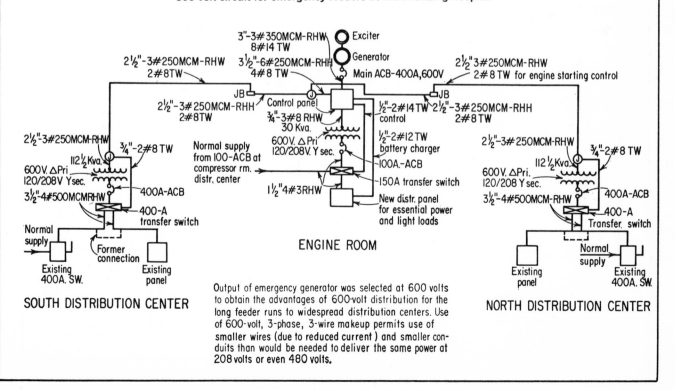

Output of emergency generator was selected at 600 volts to obtain the advantages of 600-volt distribution for the long feeder runs to widespread distribution centers. Use of 600-volt, 3-phase, 3-wire makeup permits use of smaller wires (due to reduced current) and smaller conduits than would be needed to deliver the same power at 208 volts or even 480 volts.

EQUIPMENT FOR MODIFYING ELECTRICAL CHARACTER OF DISTRIBUTION

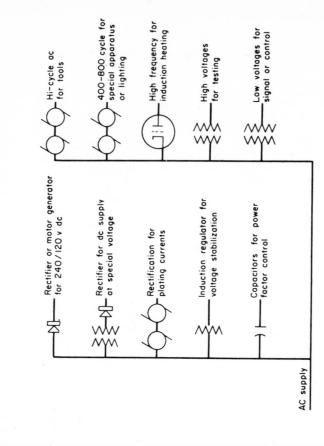

- Rectifier or motor generator for 240/120 v dc
- Rectifier for dc supply at special voltage
- Rectification for plating currents
- Induction regulator for voltage stabilization
- Capacitors for power factor control

- Hi-cycle ac for tools
- 400-800 cycle for special apparatus or lighting
- High frequency for induction heating
- High voltages for testing
- Low voltages for signal or control

AC supply

Modification or refinement of the characteristics of the distribution voltage often have to be made for such purposes as those indicated in the above diagram. In such cases, the designer must analyze the load served from the various types of equipment shown and determine the magnitude and characteristics of each load as it is reflected back into the distribution system. Manufacturers' instructions should be carefully followed, and engineering assistance of the manufacturer should be sought in extensive or complex installations.

LOAD-CENTER LAYOUTS FOR LIGHTING

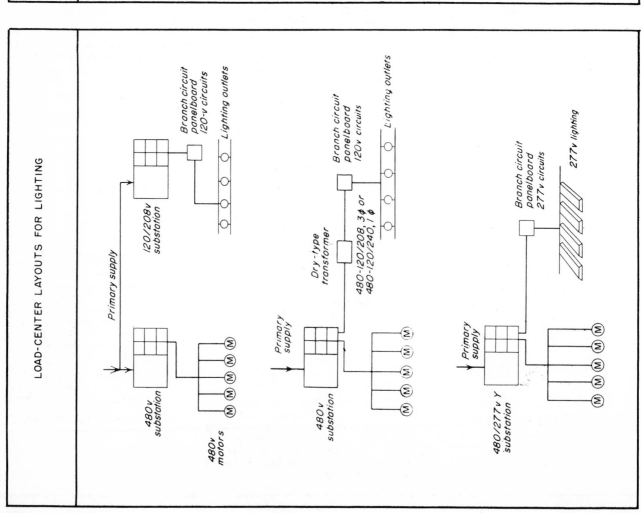

- Primary supply
- 120/208v substation
- Branch circuit panelboard 120-v circuits
- Lighting outlets
- 480v substation
- 480v motors

- Primary supply
- 480v substation
- Dry-type transformer
- 480-120/208, 3 ϕ or 480-120/240, 1 ϕ
- Branch circuit panelboard 120v circuits
- Lighting outlets

- Primary supply
- 480/277v Y substation
- Branch circuit panelboard 277v circuits
- 277v lighting

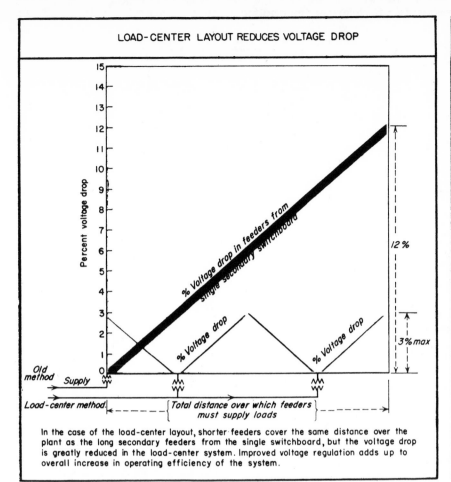

In the case of the load-center layout, shorter feeders cover the same distance over the plant as the long feeders from the single switchboard, but the voltage drop is greatly reduced in the load-center system. Improved voltage regulation adds up to overall increase in operating efficiency of the system.

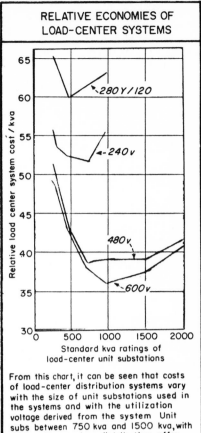

RELATIVE ECONOMIES OF LOAD-CENTER SYSTEMS

From this chart, it can be seen that costs of load-center distribution systems vary with the size of unit substations used in the systems and with the utilization voltage derived from the system Unit subs between 750 kva and 1500 kva, with 480 - volt secondary distribution, offer the greatest economy overall.

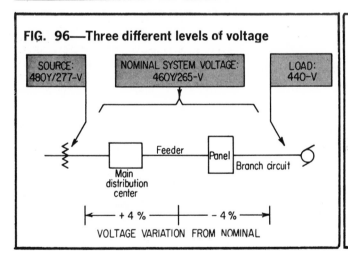

FIG. 96—Three different levels of voltage

Code Definitions of "Location"

Dry Location: A location not normally subject to dampness or wetness. A location classified as dry may be temporarily subject to dampness or wetness, as in the case of a building under construction.

Damp Location: A location subject to a moderate degree of moisture, such as some basements, some barns, some cold storage warehouses, and the like.

Wet location: A location subject to saturation with water or other liquids, such as—
1. locations exposed to weather,
2. locations like garage washrooms,
3. underground installations,
4. installations in concrete slabs or masonry in direct contact with the earth.

Power and lighting feeders

"Feeders" are the conductors which carry electrical power from the service equipment (or generator switchboard where power is generated on the premises) to the overcurrent protective devices for branch circuits supplying the various loads.

In some systems, feeder runs may be made directly from a main switchboard to lighting panels, power panels and/or directly to motor circuits. In other systems, feeders may be carried from a main distribution switchboard to subdistribution switchboards or panelboards from which subfeeders originate to feed branch-circuit panels or motor branch circuits. In still other systems, either or both of the two foregoing feeder layouts may be incorporated with transformer substations to step the distribution voltage to utilization levels. Fig. 97 shows the wide

FIG. 97—These are typical components of electrical distribution

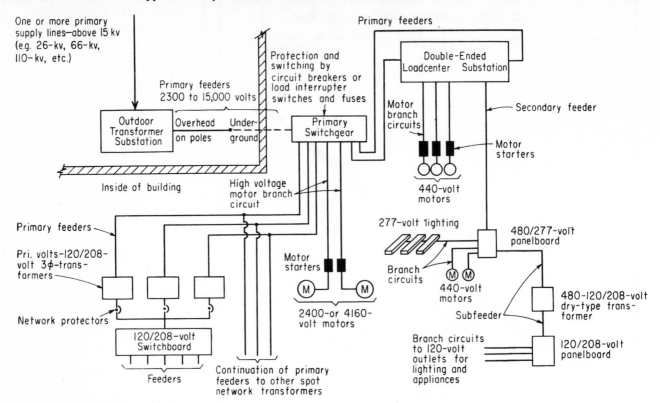

FIG. 98—Unit loads to determine minimum feeder and branch-circuit capacities required for any area

Table 220–2(a). General Lighting Loads by Occupancies

Type of Occupancy	Unit Load Per Sq Ft (Watts)
Armories and Auditoriums	1
Banks	2
Barber Shops and Beauty Parlors	3
Churches	1
Clubs	2
Court Rooms	2
*Dwellings (other than hotels)	3
Garages—Commercial (storage)	½
Hospitals	2
*Hotels and Motels, including apartment houses without provisions for cooking by tenants	2
Industrial and Commercial (loft) Buildings	2
Lodge Rooms	1½
Office Buildings	5
Restaurants	2
Schools	3
Stores	3
Warehouses, Storage	¼
In any of the above occupancies except single-family dwellings and individual apartments of multifamily dwellings:	
Assembly Halls and Auditoriums	1
Halls, Corridors, Closets	½
Storage Spaces	¼

*All receptacle outlets of 15-amp or less rating in single-family and multifamily dwellings and in guest rooms of hotels and motels [except those connected to the receptacle circuits specified in Section 220-3 (b)] may be considered as outlets for general illumination, and no additional load need be included for such outlets. The provisions of Section 220-2(b) shall apply to all other receptacle outlets.

range of elements which can be involved in a distribution system and presents the basic terminology applied to system parts.

The following discussion covers a detailed analysis of feeder requirements for various types of distribution systems. Because descriptive terms referring to distribution systems and their elements are frequently misused and misunderstood, the following definitions are given to clarify the discussion throughout this section:

MAINS are the conductors extending from the utility service terminals at the building wall (or generator or converter bus) to the service switch or to the main distribution center.

FEEDER is a set of conductors originating at a main distribution center and feeding one or more subdistribution centers, one or more branch-circuit distribution centers, one or more branch circuits (as in the case of plug-in busway or motor circuit taps to a feeder) or a combination of these. It may be a primary or secondary voltage circuit but its function is always to deliver a block of power from one point to another point at which the power capacity is apportioned among a number of other circuits.

LIGHTING FEEDER is a feeder to a load which is primarily made up of lighting circuits.

POWER FEEDER is a feeder to a load of branch circuits for motors, heating or other power loads.

SUBFEEDER is a set of conductors originating at a distribution center other than the main distribution center and supplying one or more other distribution panelboards, branch-circuit panelboards or branch circuits.

SWITCHBOARD is a large single panel, frame or assembly of panels, with switches, overcurrent and other protective devices and usually instruments mounted on the front and/or the back. Switchboards are generally accessible from the back as well as from the front and are not intended to be installed in cabinets.

PANELBOARD is a single panel or group of panel units assembled in the form of a single panel. It contains busses tapped by fuse holders, with or without switches, or by circuit breakers, providing protection and, if switches or circuit breakers are used, it also provides control of circuits for light, heat or power. These circuits may be branch circuits or subfeeders. A panelboard is designed to be placed in a cabinet or cutout box placed in or against a wall or partition and accessible only from the front.

Calculating feeder load

Feeders and subfeeders are sized to provide sufficient power to the circuits they supply. For the given circuit voltage, they must be capable of carrying the amount of current required by the load, plus any current which may be required in the future. Selection of the size of a feeder depends upon the size and nature of the known load computed from branch-circuit data, the anticipated future load requirements and voltage drop. This represents one of the most important engineering tasks in electrical design work. Economy and efficiency of system operation and maintenance depend heavily on the selection of the proper size of feeders.

Experience with today's electrical modernization work has revealed feeder capacity as the big bottleneck in rewiring old buildings and even some that are not so old. In those buildings, the cost of bringing the capacity of the electrical systems up to meet modern load requirements would be considerably less if original design of feeders had been based on sound study of known and anticipated future loads. All of this experience confirms the importance of careful sizing of feeders, utilizing calculations related to the particular conditions of the job and not just a mechanical procedure of adding up load watts and dividing by volts to get required current-carrying capacity.

Minimum feeder capacity

According to the code, feeders are sized to carry a computed load current which is not less than the sum of all branch-circuit load currents supplied by each feeder, with certain qualifications:

1. For general illumination, a feeder must have capacity to carry the total load of lighting branch circuits determined as part of the lighting design or a minimum branch-circuit load determined on a watts-per-sq-ft basis from the table given in Section 220-2(a) of the code, shown in Fig. 98. And these watts-per-sq-ft values must be increased by 25% where branch-circuit loads are to operate continuously for long periods of time—such as general lighting. The demand factors given in Table 220-4(a), shown in Fig. 99 may be applied to the total branch-circuit load to get required feeder capacity for lighting (but must never be used in providing branch-circuit capacity).

2. If show-window lighting is supplied by the feeder, capacity must be included in the feeder to handle 200 watts/lin ft of show-window length.

3. In single-family dwellings, in individual apart-

Table 220-4(a). Calculation of Feeder Loads by Occupancies

Type of Occupancy	Portion of Lighting Load to which Demand Factor Applies (wattage)	Feeder Demand Factor
Dwellings—other than hotels	First 3000 or less at	100%
	Next 3001 to 120,000 at	35%
	Remainder over 120,000 at	25%
*Hospitals	First 50,000 or less at	40%
	Remainder over 50,000 at	20%
*Hotels and Motels— including apartment houses without provision for cooking by tenants	First 20,000 or less at	50%
	Next 20,001 to 100,000 at	40%
	Remainder over 100,000 at	30%
Warehouses (storage)	First 12,500 or less at	100%
	Remainder over 12,500 at	50%
All Others	Total Wattage	100%

*The demand factors of this table shall not apply to the computed load of subfeeders to areas in hospitals and hotels where entire lighting is likely to be used at one time; as in operating rooms, ballrooms, or dining rooms.

ments of multi-family dwellings with provisions for cooking by tenants or in a hotel suite with a serving pantry, at least 1500 watts for each 2-wire, 20-amp small appliance circuit (to handle the small appliance load in kitchen, pantry, laundry and dining areas) must be added to the general lighting load on each feeder. The total load of lighting and small appliance load may be reduced by the demand factors given in Table 220-4(a).

4. In other than dwelling occupancies (where receptacle outlets of 15 amps or less are considered to be outlets for general lighting), the branch-circuit load for receptacle outlets for which not more than 1½ amps were allowed per outlet may be added to the general lighting load, and may also be reduced by the demand factors in Table 220-4(a).

5. Feeder capacity must be allowed for electric cooking appliances rated over 1¾ kw, in accordance with Table 220-5 of the code. Feeder demand loads for a number of cooking appliances on a feeder may be obtained from Table 220-5 of the code.

6. For fixed appliances other than ranges, clothes dryers, air conditioning equipment and space heating equipment, feeder capacity must be provided for the sum of these loads and the total load of four or more such appliances may be reduced by a demand factor of 75%, NE Code Section 220-4(j).

7. If motor loads are supplied by a feeder which also supplies lighting and appliance loads as described above, Article 430 of the code (Sections 430-24, 430-25 and 430-26) gives the required capacity which the feeder must include to handle such loads. Feeder capacity for motor loads is usually taken at 125% of the full-load current rating of the largest motor supplied, plus the sum of the full-load currents of the other motors supplied.

8. Capacity of a feeder supplying fixed electrical space heating equipment is determined on the basis of a load equal to the total connected load on all branch circuits served from the feeder. Under conditions of intermittent operation or where all units cannot operate at the same time, permission may be

STANDARD LOADS FOR GENERAL LIGHTING IN INDUSTRIAL OCCUPANCIES

Watts/Sq Ft

AISLES, STAIRWAYS, PASSAGEWAYS
10 watts per running foot.

ASSEMBLY
a. Rough	3.0
b. Medium	4.5
c. Fine	*4.5
d. Extra Fine	*4.5

AUTOMOBILE MANUFACTURING
a. Assembly Line	*4.5
b. Frame Assembly	3.0
c. Body Assembly	4.5
d. Body Finishing and Inspecting	*4.5

BAKERIES 4.0

BOOK BINDING
a. Folding, Assembling, Pasting	3.0
b. Cutting, Punching, Stitching, Embossing	4.0

BREWERIES
a. Brew House	3.0
b. Boiling, Keg Washing, etc.	3.0
c. Bottling	4.0

CANDY MAKING 4.0

CANNING AND PRESERVING 4.0

CHEMICAL WORKS
a. Hand Furnaces, Stationary Driers and Crystallizers	2.0
b. Mechanical Driers and Crystallizers, Filtrations, Evaporators, Bleaching	2.0
c. Tanks for Cooking, Extractors, Percolators, Nitrators, Electrolytic Cells	3.0

CLAY PRODUCTS AND CEMENTS
a. Grinding, Filter Presses, Kiln Rooms	2.0
b. Moldings, Pressing, Cleaning, Trimming	2.0
c. Enameling	3.0
d. Glazing	4.0

CLOTH PRODUCTS
a. Cutting, Inspecting, Sewing	
(1) Light Goods	4.5
(2) Dark Goods	*4.5
b. Pressing, Cloth Treating (Oil Cloth, etc.)	
(1) Light Goods	3.0
(2) Dark Goods	6.0

COAL BREAKING, WASHING, SCREENING 2.0

DAIRY PRODUCTS 4.0

ENGRAVING *4.5

FORGE SHOPS
a. Welding	2.0

FOUNDRIES
a. Charging Floor, Tumbling, Cleaning, Pouring, Shaking Out	2.0
b. Rough Molding and Core Making	2.0
c. Fine Molding and Core Making	4.0

GARAGES
a. Storage	2.0
b. Repair and Washing	*3.0

GLASS WORKS
a. Mixing and Furnace Rooms, Pressing and Lehr Glass Blowing Machines	3.0
b. Grinding, Cutting Glass to Size, Silvering	4.5
c. Fine Grinding, Polishing, Beveling, Etching, Inspecting, etc.	*4.5

GLOVE MANUFACTURING
a. Light Goods	
(1) Cutting, Pressing, Knitting, Sorting	4.5
(2) Stitching, Trimming, Inspecting	4.5
b. Dark Goods	
(1) Cutting, Pressing, etc.	*4.5
(2) Stitching, Trimming, etc.	*4.5

HANGARS— AEROPLANE
a. Storage—Live	2.0
b. Repair Department	*3.0

HAT MANUFACTURING
a. Dyeing, Stiffening, Braiding, Cleaning and Refining	
(1) Light	2.0
(2) Dark	4.5
b. Forming, Sizing, Pouncing, Flanging, Finishing and Ironing	
(1) Light	3.0
(2) Dark	6.0
c. Sewing	
(1) Light	4.5
(2) Dark	*4.5

ICE MAKING
a. Engine and Compressor Room	2.0

INSPECTION
a. Rough	3.0
b. Medium	4.5
c. Fine	*4.5
d. Extra Fine	*4.5

JEWELRY AND WATCH MANUFACTURING

LAUNDRIES AND DRY CLEANING

LEATHER MANUFACTURING
a. Vats	2.0
b. Cleaning, Tanning and Stretching	2.0
c. Cutting, Fleshing and Stuffing	3.0
d. Finishing and Scarfing	4.5

LEATHER WORKING
a. Pressing, Winding and Glazing	
(1) Light	2.0
(2) Dark	4.5
b. Grading, Matching, Cutting, Scarfing, Sewing	
(1) Light	4.5
(2) Dark	*4.5

LOCKER ROOMS 2.0

MACHINE SHOPS
a. Rough Bench and Machine Work	3.0
b. Medium Bench and Machine Work, Ordinary Automatic Machines, Rough Grinding, Medium Buffing and Polishing	4.5
c. Fine Bench and Machine Work, Fine Automatic Machines, Medium Grinding, Fine Buffing and Polishing	*4.5
d. Extra Fine Bench and Machine Work, Grinding	
(1) Fine Work	*4.5

MEAT PACKING
a. Slaughtering	2.0
b. Cleaning, Cutting, Cooking, Grinding, Canning, Packing	4.5

MILLING—GRAIN FOODS
a. Cleaning, Grinding and Rolling	2.0
b. Baking or Roasting	4.5
c. Flour Grading	4.5

OFFICES
a. Private and General	
(1) No close work	3.0
(2) Close work	4.5
b. Drafting Rooms	7.0

The figures given in this table are average design loads for general lighting. In those cases marked with an asterisk (*), the load values provide only for large area lighting applications. Local lighting must then be provided as an additional load.

The figures given are based on the use of fluorescent and mercury vapor equipment of standard design. Adjustments may be made for use of higher or lower efficiency equipment. For equal lighting intensities from incandescent units, the figures must be at least doubled.

STANDARD LOADS FOR GENERAL LIGHTING IN INDUSTRIAL OCCUPANCIES

Watts/Sq Ft

PACKING AND BOXING 3.0

PAINT MANUFACTURING 3.0

PAINT SHOPS
a. Dipping, Spraying, Firing, Rubbing, Ordinary Hand Painting and Finishing — 3.0
b. Fine Hand Painting and Finishing — *3.0
c. Extra Fine Hand Painting and Finishing (Automobile Bodies, Piano Cases, etc.) . — *3.0

PAPER BOX MANUFACTURING
a. Light — 3.0
b. Dark — 4.0
c. Storage of Stock — 2.0

PAPER MANUFACTURING
a. Beaters, Grinding, Calendering — 2.0
b. Finishing, Cutting, Trimming — 4.5

PLATING 2.0

POLISHING AND BURNISHING 3.0

POWER PLANTS, ENGINE ROOMS, BOILERS
a. Boilers, Coal and Ash Handling, Storage Battery Rooms — 2.0
b. Auxiliary Equipment, Oil Switches and Transformers — 2.0
c. Switchboards, Engines, Generators, Blowers, Compressors — 3.0

PRINTING INDUSTRIES
a. Matrixing and Casting — 2.0
b. Miscellaneous Machines — 3.0
c. Presses and Electrotyping — 4.5
d. Lithographing — *4.5
e. Linotype, Monotype, Typesetting, Imposing Stone, Engraving — *4.5
f. Proof Reading — *4.5

RECEIVING AND SHIPPING 2.0

RUBBER MANUFACTURING AND PRODUCTS
a. Calendars, Compounding Mills, Fabric Preparation, Stock Cutting, Tubing Machines, Solid Tire Operations, Mechanical Goods Building, Vulcanizing — 3.0
b. Bead Building, Pneumatic Tire Building and Finishing, Inner Tube Operation, Mechanical Goods Trimming, Treading — 4.5

SHEET METAL WORKS
a. Miscellaneous Machines, Ordinary Bench Work — 3.0
b. Punches, Presses, Shears, Stamps, Welders, Spinning, Medium Bench Work — 4.5
c. Tin Plate Inspection — *4.5

SHOE MANUFACTURING
a. Hand Turning, Miscellaneous Bench and Machine Work — 2.0
b. Inspecting and Sorting Raw Material, Cutting and Stitching
(1) Light — 4.5
(2) Dark — *4.5
c. Lasting and Welting — 4.5

SOAP MANUFACTURING
a. Kettle Houses, Cutting, Soap Chip and Powder — 3.0
b. Stamping, Wrapping and Packing, Filling and Packing Soap Powder — 4.5

STEEL AND IRON MILLS, BAR, SHEET AND WIRE PRODUCTS
a. Soaking Pits and Reheating Furnaces. — 2.0
b. Charging and Casting Floors — 2.0
c. Muck and Heavy Rolling, Shearing (Rough by Gauge), Pickling and Cleaning — 2.0
d. Plate Inspection, Chipping — *4.5
e. Automatic Machines, Light and Cold Rolling, Wire Drawing, Shearing (fine by line) — 4.5

STONE CRUSHING AND SCREENING
a. Belt Conveyor Tubes, Main Line Shafting Spaces, Chute Rooms, Inside of Bins — 2.0
b. Primary Breaker Room, Auxiliary Breakers under Bins — 2.0
c. Screens — 3.0

STORAGE BATTERY MANUFACTURING
a. Molding of Grids — 3.0

STORE AND STOCK ROOMS
a. Rough Bulky Material — 2.0
b. Medium or Fine Material requiring care — 3.0

STRUCTURAL STEEL FABRICATION 3.0

SUGAR GRADING 5.0

TESTING
a. Rough — 3.0
b. Fine — 4.5
c. Extra Fine Instruments, Scales, etc. — *4.5

TEXTILE MILLS
a. Cotton
(1) Opening and Lapping, Carding, Drawing, Roving, Dyeing — 3.0
(2) Spooling, Spinning, Drawing, Warping, Weaving, Quilling, Inspecting, Knitting, Slashing (over beam end) — 4.5
b. Silk
(1) Winding, Throwing, Dyeing — 4.5
(2) Quilling, Warping, Weaving, Finishing
Light Goods — 4.5
Dark Goods — 6.0
c. Woolen
(1) Carding, Picking, Washing, Combing — 3.0
(2) Twisting, Dyeing — 3.0
(3) Drawing-in, Warping—
Light Goods — 4.5
Dark Goods — 6.0
(4) Weaving—
Light Goods — 4.5
Dark Goods — 6.0
(5) Knitting Machines — 4.5

TOBACCO PRODUCTS
a. Drying, Stripping, General — 3.0
b. Grading and Sorting — *4.5

TOILETS AND WASH ROOMS 2.0

UPHOLSTERING
a. Automobile, Coach, Furniture — 4.5

WAREHOUSE 2.0

WOODWORKING
a. Rough Sawing and Bench Work — 2.0
b. Sizing, Planing, Rough Sanding, Medium Machine and Bench Work, Gluing, Veneering, Cooperage — 4.5
c. Fine Bench and Machine Work, Fine Sanding and Finishing — 6.0

Use of these figures in computing number and loading of circuits and feeders should always be checked against the conditions and requirements of the particular area. The figures are not substitutes for lighting design.

In any case, need for particular color quality of light or special intensities or control of light must be determined as part of the lighting design, and wattages and circuit requirements must be provided accordingly.

STANDARD LOADS FOR LIGHTING IN COMMERCIAL BUILDINGS

Watts/Sq Ft

Armories
Drill Sheds and Exhibition Halls   5
This does not include lighting circuits for demonstration booths, special exhibit spaces, etc.

Art Galleries
a. General   3
b. On Paintings—50 watts per running foot of usable wall area.

Auditoriums   4

Automobile Show Rooms   6

Banks
a. Lobby   4
b. Counters—50 watts per running foot including service for signs and small motor applications, etc.
c. Offices and Cages   5

Barber Shop and Beauty Parlors   5
This does not include circuits for special equipment.

Billards
a. General   3
b. Tables—450 watts per table.

Bowling
a. Alley Runway and Seats   5
b. Pins—300 watts per set of pins.

Churches
a. Auditoriums   2
b. Sunday School Rooms   5
c. Pulpit or Rostrum   5

Club Rooms
a. Lounge   2
b. Reading Rooms   5
The above two uses are so often combined that the higher figure is advisable. It includes provision for convenience outlets.

Court Rooms   5

Dance Halls   2
No allowance has been included for spectacular lighting, spots, etc.

Drafting Rooms   7

Fire Engine Houses   2

Gymnasiums
a. Main Floor   5
b. Shower Rooms   2
c. Locker Rooms   2
d. Fencing, Boxing, etc.   5
e. Handball, Squash, etc.   5

Halls and Interior Passageways
—20 watts per running foot.

Hospitals
a. Lobby, Reception Room   3
b. Corridors—20 watts per running foot.
c. Wards   3
Including allowance for convenience outlets for local illumination.

d. Private Rooms   5
Including allowance for convenience outlets for local illumination.
e. Operating Room   5
f. Operating Tables or Chairs
Major Surgeries—3000 watts per area.
Minor Surgeries—1500 watts per area.
This and the above figure include allowance for directional control. Special wiring for emergency systems must also be considered.
g. Laboratories   5

Hotels.
a. Lobby   5
Not including provision for conventions, exhibits.
b. Dining Room   4
c. Kitchen   5
d. Bed Rooms   3
Including allowance for convenience outlets.
e. Corridors—20 watts per running foot.
f. Writing Room   5
Including allowance for convenience outlets.

Library
a. Reading Rooms   6
This includes allowance for convenience outlets.
b. Stack Room—12 watts per running foot of facing stacks.

Motion Picture Houses and Theatres
a. Auditoriums   2
b. Foyer   3
c. Lobby   5

Museums
a. General   3
b. Special exhibits—supplementary lighting   5

Office Buildings
a. Private Offices, no close work   4
b. Private Offices, with close work   5
c. General Offices, no close work   4
d. General Offices, with close work   5
e. File Room, Vault, etc.   3
f. Reception Room   2

Post Office
a. Lobby   3
b. Sorting, Mailing, etc.   5
c. Storage, File Room, etc.   3

Professional Offices
a. Waiting Rooms   3
b. Consultation Rooms   5
c. Operating Offices   7
d. Dental Chairs—600 watts per chair.

Railway
a. Depot—Waiting Room   3
b. Ticket Offices—General   5
On Counters 50 watts per running foot.
c. Rest Room, Smoking Room   3
d. Baggage, Checking Office   3
e. Baggage Storage   2
f. Concourse   2
g. Train Platform   2

Restaurants, Lunch Rooms and Cafeterias
a. Dining Areas   3
b. Food Displays—50 watts per running foot of counter (including service aisle.)

Schools
a. Auditoriums   3
If to be used as a study hall—5 watts per sq. ft.
b. Class and Study Rooms   5
c. Drawing Room   7
d. Laboratories   5
e. Manual Training   5
f. Sewing Room   7
g. Sight Saving Classes   7

Show Cases—25 watts per running foot.

Show Windows
a. *Large Cities
Brightly Lighted District—700 watts per running foot of glass.
Secondary Business Locations—500 watts per running foot of glass.
Neighborhood Stores—250 watts per running foot of glass.
b. *Medium Cities
Brightly Lighted District—500 watts per running foot of glass.
Neighborhood Stores—250 watts per running foot of glass frontage.
c. *Small Cities and Towns—300 watts per running foot of glass frontage.
d. Lighting to Reduce Daylight Window Reflections—1000 watts per running foot of glass.

*Wattages shown are for white light with incandescent filament lamps. Where color is to be used, wattages should be doubled.

Stores, Large Department and Specialty
a. Main Floor   6
b. Other Floors   6

Stores in Outlying Districts   5

Wall Cases—25 watts per running foot.

NOTE: Figures based on use of fluorescent equipment for large-area application, incandescent for local or supplementary lighting.

granted for use of less than 100% demand factor in sizing the feeder.

9. When space heating and air cooling in dwelling occupancies are supplied by the same feeder, the smaller of the two loads may be omitted from the total capacity required for the feeder if it is unlikely that the two loads will operate at the same time.

It should be noted that all of the foregoing are general requirements of the code and cover minimum load conditions. This is particularly true of the watts-per-sq-ft unit loads given in the table, which are based on 100% power factor. Determination of feeder size solely on the basis of code requirements provides no relation to particular operating conditions in an occupancy, such as voltage stability and power losses, or any allowance for future growth in the load served by the feeder.

Although there are certain feeder applications which can be satisfactorily sized by use of the indicated code method of sizing, modern feeder design practice carefully incorporates such factors as voltage drop, power factor, detailed analysis of watts-per-sq-ft loads, realistic and studied application of demand factors and provision of substantial spare capacity as required in each case.

Adding branch-circuit loads

Based on the foregoing code rules on minimum feeder capacity, the required load capacity of any feeder can be determined by adding up the branch-circuit loads supplied by the feeder. In the section on "Branch Circuits," procedures were given for determining branch-circuit loads—general lighting, fixed appliance, special receptacle circuits and general-use convenience receptacles—and for determining the number and characteristics of circuits to handle the loads.

Whether general lighting circuits were determined on a watts-per-sq-ft basis or from a lighting design layout, the amount of load for general illumination was established, and capacity for this load must be designed into the feeder, modified by the applicable demand factor from Table 220-4(a). Other circuit loads—such as local and/or special lighting, motor loads, electric cooking appliances and fixed appliances—are also generally known loads and can be accounted for in a feeder. Loads for convenience receptacle circuits and spare circuits in the panelboard, however, are not known and must be estimated in sizing a feeder.

From the known and estimated branch-circuit loads, the minimum capacity for a feeder to a number of branch circuits can be determined as follows:

1. **For each multioutlet branch circuit supplying general lighting, allow watts equal to the load on the circuit.**

2. **For each multioutlet plug receptacle branch circuit, allow watts equal to half the watts rating of the circuit, if such circuits were loaded to 50% of capacity, or allow watts equal to the load value of such circuits as used in branch-circuit design.** The minimum watts allowance for each receptacle circuit must equal the number of outlets times 1½ amps, times 120 volts.

Where multioutlet assemblies (plug-in strip or raceway) are used, each 5 ft or fraction thereof of each separate and continuous length is taken as a

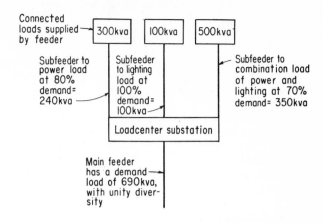

FIG. 100—Typical application of demand and diversity factors

load equal to 1½ amps. And when such assemblies are used where a number of appliances are likely to be used simultaneously, each 1 ft or fraction is taken as a load of 1½ amps to prevent overloading of the circuits.

3. **For each multioutlet branch circuit supplying heavy-duty lampholders, allow watts equal to the load on the circuit as used in branch-circuit design.** The minimum watts allowance for each heavy-duty circuit must equal the number of outlets times 5 amps, times the circuit volts.

4. **For each multioutlet branch circuit supplying local or special lighting, allow watts equal to the load on the circuit.**

5. **For each individual branch circuit supplying a fixed appliance, allow watts equal to the rating of the appliance.**

6. **For the sum of the loads of individual branch circuits supplying electric cooking appliances, allow kilowatts equal to the values given in Table 220-5 for the particular number and sizes of cooking appliances.**

7. **For each individual branch circuit supplying a motor, allow watts equal to 1.25 times the motor full-load current (from Table 430-147 to 430-150 according to the horsepower of the motor), times the circuit voltage.** For 3-phase motors, the foregoing product must be multiplied by 1.732 to get the correct watts. Actually, the result of these calculations is not a watts value but a volt-ampere product, due to the lower-than-unity power factor of the motor. However, when sizing conductors to meet required load currents, the volt-ampere load should always be used for devices operating at less than unity pf, to assure required current capacity which is greater than would be required to supply only the watts—or effective power—represented by such loads.

8. **For each branch circuit supplying more than one motor, allow watts equal to the following product:** take 1.25 times the full-load current rating of the highest rated motor; add to this the sum of the full-load current ratings of the other motors; then multiply the total sum by the circuit volts. Again, this product must be multiplied by 1.732 to get the correct volt-ampere product for 3-phase motors.

9. **For each branch circuit supplying show-window lighting, allow watts equal to 200 times the horizontal linear footage of show window served by the circuit.**

By adding up these ratings, a total of watts is obtained which is the initial minimum feeder load. Of course, the majority of feeders used in commercial, institutional and industrial buildings will serve only a few of the above described loads. And feeders in different buildings will handle different combinations of loads.

For each spare branch circuit supplied by a feeder, watts equal to the values given above for multioutlet general lighting branch circuits should be added to the feeder load.

Although the table in Section 220-4(a) allows limited use of demand factors for general lighting circuits and multioutlet plug receptacle circuits, reducing the feeder design load, most occupancies require a demand factor of 100% applied to the total load obtained by adding up the circuit loads.

Using demand factors

Two terms constantly used in the literature of modern electrical design are Demand Factor and Diversity Factor. Because there is a very fine difference between the meanings for the words, the terms are often confused.

DEMAND FACTOR is the ratio of the maximum demand of a system, or part of a system, to the total connected load on the system, or part of the system, under consideration. This factor is always less than unity.

DIVERSITY FACTOR is the ratio of the sum of the individual maximum demands of the various subdivisions of a system, or part of a system, to the maximum demand of the whole system, or part of the system, under consideration. This factor generally varies between 1.00 and 2.00.

Demand factors and diversity factors are used in system design. For instance, the sum of the connected loads supplied by a feeder is multiplied by the demand factor to determine the load which the feeder must be sized to serve. This load is termed the maximum demand of the feeder. The sum of the maximum demand loads for a number of subfeeders divided by the diversity factor for the subfeeders will give the maximum demand load to be supplied by the feeder from which the subfeeders are derived.

Tables of demand and diversity factors have been developed from experience with various types of load concentrations and various layouts of feeders and subfeeders supplying such loads. Table 220-4(a) of the NE Code presents common demand factors for feeders to general lighting loads in various types of buildings. See Fig. 99.

It is common and preferred practice in modern electrical design to take unity as the diversity factor in main feeders to loadcenter substations to provide a measure of spare capacity. Main secondary feeders are also commonly sized on the full value of the sum of the demand loads of the subfeeders supplied.

From power distribution practice, however, basic diversity factors have been developed. These provide general indication of the way in which main feeders can be reduced in capacity below the sum of the demands of the subfeeders they supply. On a radial feeder system, diversity of demands made by a number of transformers reduces the maximum load which the feeder must supply to some value less than the sum of the transformer loads. Typical diversity factors for main feeders are as follows:

LIGHTING FEEDERS—1.10 to 1.50
POWER AND LIGHT FEEDERS—1.50 to 2.00 (or higher).

Selection of a diversity factor for any particular case must be based on study of load characteristics and operating cycles. Very accurate data on diversity of demands is recorded by operating personnel in many types of commercial and industrial buildings.

Another factor used to analyze systems is—
LOAD FACTOR, which is the ratio of the average load over a particular period of time to the peak load occurring in that period of time.

Fig. 100 illustrates the use of demand and diversity factors in sizing system components. It should be noted that the kva-rating required for each of the subfeeders must have a minimum value as described in the text of this section. And any feeder or subfeeder (even the main feeder in this diagram) can be sized directly by totalling all connected loads fed by that particular circuit, applying demand factors where conditions make it necessary or desirable.

Feeder spare capacity for growth

The total feeder load obtained from foregoing summation of all branch-circuit loads fed by the feeder represents only the provision for initial branch-circuit loads. Future utilization of the spare capacity designed into the branch circuits (they are loaded only to 50%) has not yet been accounted for in the feeder. And no provision has been designed into the feeder to meet the future possibility of exceeding the maximum capacity of the panelboard itself, requiring additional panelboard capacity—either a second panel or one new larger panel.

Certainly, in the light of present experience with electrical modernization, there are many cases in which a little forethought and study would reveal the advisability of making spare capacity provisions in feeder capacity. Not in all cases, or even in most cases, but there is such a possibility. And only careful consideration of the nature of electrical utilization in a particular occupancy will accurately indicate possible future load requirements. But certainly in all cases of electrical design, some spare capacity must be provided in the feeders.

Allowance for load growth in feeders should begin with the spare capacity designed into the branch circuits. For all circuits loaded to 50% of capacity, it can be assumed that there is an allowance for growth of each circuit load by an amount equal to 30% of the circuit capacity. This allowance is based on the code limitation of 80% load on circuits which are in operation for long periods of time or on circuits which supply motor-operated appliances in addition to other appliances and/or lighting. **The 30% growth allowance in each branch circuit should be converted to total watts figure and added to the total load on the feeder as calculated above.**

This grand total then represents the required feeder capacity to handle the full circuit load on the panelboard. The next step is to provide capacity in the feeder for anticipated load growth (plus some amount for possible unforeseen future requirements).

From experience, modern design practice dictates the sizing of feeders to allow increase of 25 to 50% in load on a feeder where analysis reveals any load growth possibilities. Analysis of spare capacity allowances for feeders depends upon the type of building, the work performed, the plans or expectations of management with respect to expansion of facilities or growth of business, the type of distribution system used, locations of centers of loads, permanence of various load conditions and particular economic conditions.

Depending upon thorough study of all pertinent factors, the advisability of spare capacity can be determined for each feeder in a distribution system. But where study demands extra capacity in a feeder, substantial growth allowance—50%—is generally essential to realize the sought-after economy of future electrical expansion. Skimpy upsizing of feeder conductors or raceways has proved a major shortcoming of past electrical design work. This is particularly true in tall office buildings, apartment houses and other commercial buildings in which elimination of riser bottlenecks represents a large part of the total modernization cost.

Provision of spare capacity in feeders may be provided in one or more of several ways. If the anticipated increase in feeder load is to be made in the near future, the extra capacity should usually be included in the conductor size and installed as part of the initial electrical system. In many small office or commercial buildings and apartment houses, extra capacity should automatically be included in the initial size of the feeder conductors for load growth.

Here are other ways of providing for growth in feeder loads:

1. Selection of raceways larger than required by the initial size and number of feeder conductors. With this provision, the conductors can be replaced with larger sizes if required at a later date. The advisability of this step should be carefully considered in the case of risers or underground or concealed feeder raceway runs and similar cases of permanent installation where it will be very costly to add conduit runs at a later date. In some cases, a compromise can be made between providing spare capacity in the feeder conductor size and increasing the size of feeder raceway.

2. Including spare raceways in which conductors may be installed at a later date to obtain capacity for load growth. Such arrangements of multiple raceways must be carefully laid out and related to the existing overall system. The types of feeder distribution centers or main switchboards and the layout of local branch-circuit panelboards must be able to accommodate future expansion of distribution capacity based on the use of spare raceways, with modification and regrouping of feeder loads.

Selecting conductor sizes

When total design watts, including all of the foregoing provisions, have been determined, this value is then used with the voltage and other electrical characteristics of the feeder (or the total load in amperes can be used) to obtain the required current-carrying capacity of the conductors. In addition to circuit voltage, feeder conductor size for a particular total load will depend upon the power factor and the voltage drop in the conductors.

Fig. 101 covers the necessary calculations for sizing feeders. In these calculations, and in the determination of the feeder design load, care should be taken to distinguish between circuit load values in "watts" and those in "volt-amperes." When load val-

FIG. 101—Formulas to determine required current rating of feeder conductors

$$I = \frac{\text{Load Watts}}{K \times E \times PF} = \frac{\text{Load Volt-Amperes}}{K \times E}$$

K = 1 for 2-wire dc single-phase ac
= 1.73 for 3-wire, 3-phase ac
= 2 for 3-wire dc or single-phase ac
= 3 for 4-wire, 3-phase ac
E = voltage between outside wire and neutral or, if no neutral exists, between any two line wires (volts)
I = current in any line wire except neutral (amperes), which feeder must be rated to carry (check tables of conductor current ratings)

Calculating power loss in circuit conductors

Assuming resistivity of conductor metal to be as follows:
K = 12 for circuits loaded to more than 50% (copper)
K = 11 for circuits loaded to less than 50% (copper)
K = 18 for aluminum conductors

For a 2-wire circuit (direct-current or single-phase):

$$P = \frac{2 \times K \times L \times I^2}{CM}$$

For a 3-wire, 3-phase circuit (assuming balanced load):

$$P = \frac{3 \times K \times L \times I^2}{CM}$$

in which, P = power lost in the circuit (watts)
K = resistivity of conductor metal (circular mil-ohms/foot)
I = current in each wire of the circuit (amps)
L = one-way length of the circuit (ft)
CM = cross-section area of each of the wires in circular mils

When the resistance of conductors is determined from a table, the power loss is calculated from the relation

$$P = I^2 R$$

ues are in watts, power factor must be taken into consideration.

The size of conductors is related to total current values and must have capacity to carry the current at the given value of power factor. Of course, at low power factor, the conductors must have more current-carrying capacity to supply a particular load wattage than at high power factor.

Minimizing voltage drop

Voltage drop must be carefully considered in sizing feeder conductors, and calculations should be made for peak load conditions. Size of feeder conductors should be such that voltage drop up to the branch-circuit panelboards or point of branch-circuit origin is not more than 1% for lighting loads or combined lighting, heating and power loads and not more than 2% for power or heating loads. Local codes may impose lower limits of voltage drop. Voltage-drop limitations are shown in Fig. 102, as follows:

1. For combinations of lighting and power loads on feeders and branch circuits, use the voltage drop percentages for lighting load (at left in Fig. 102).

2. The word feeder here refers to the overall run of conductors carrying power from the source to the point of final branch-circuit distribution, including feeders, subfeeders, sub-subfeeders, etc.

FIG. 104—Feeder voltage drop and current capacities for 600-volt, Type RHW conductors

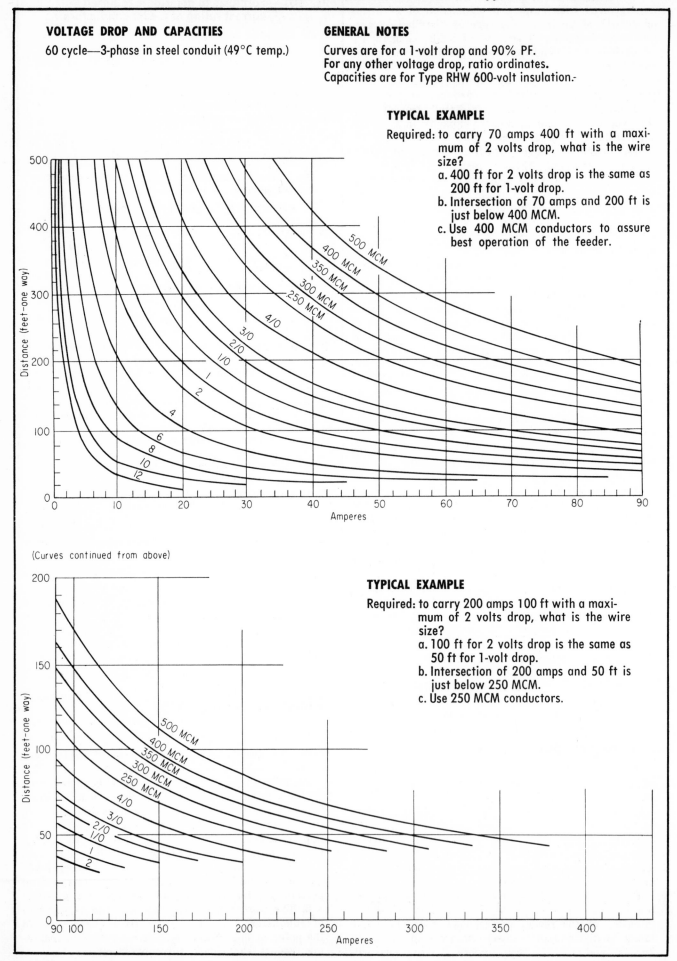

VOLTAGE DROP AND CAPACITIES

60 cycle—3-phase in steel conduit (49°C temp.)

GENERAL NOTES

Curves are for a 1-volt drop and 90% PF.
For any other voltage drop, ratio ordinates.
Capacities are for Type RHW 600-volt insulation.

TYPICAL EXAMPLE

Required: to carry 70 amps 400 ft with a maximum of 2 volts drop, what is the wire size?
a. 400 ft for 2 volts drop is the same as 200 ft for 1-volt drop.
b. Intersection of 70 amps and 200 ft is just below 400 MCM.
c. Use 400 MCM conductors to assure best operation of the feeder.

(Curves continued from above)

TYPICAL EXAMPLE

Required: to carry 200 amps 100 ft with a maximum of 2 volts drop, what is the wire size?
a. 100 ft for 2 volts drop is the same as 50 ft for 1-volt drop.
b. Intersection of 200 amps and 50 ft is just below 250 MCM.
c. Use 250 MCM conductors.

3. The voltage drop percentages are based on nominal circuit voltage at the source of each voltage level Indicated limitations should be observed for each voltage level in the distribution system.

Calculation of voltage drop in any set of feeders can be made in accordance with the formulas given in Fig. 103. From this calculation, it can be determined if the conductor size initially selected to handle the load will be adequate to maintain voltage drop within given limits. If it is not, the size of the conductors must be increased (or other steps taken where conductor reactance is not negligible) until the voltage drop is within prescribed limits. Fig. 104 shows a set of curves correlating size of conductor, ampere load and voltage drop for 3-phase circuits in steel conduit. Many such graphs and tabulated data on voltage drop are available in handbooks and from manufacturers.

In application, the loading and lengths of feeders can be adjusted to accommodate voltage drop considerations, with additional advantages, as shown in Fig. 105 for a modern office building. A total of nine risers supply lighting and receptacle circuits in all of the building's office space—floors 2 through 22. Each of these floors has three electric closets. At each feeder-riser location, one feeder supplies the bottom eight floors, the second feeder supplies seven floors in the middle of the building's height and the third feeder supplies the top six floors. With the design demand load the same for each of the electric closets, the feeder serving the bottom eight closets has a heavier load than the one serving the middle seven closets, which in turn is more heavily loaded than the feeder to the top six closets. In designing each feeder to deliver its kva capacity with only 2% drop in voltage from the switchboard to any panel, the unbalanced loading of the feeders made it possible to use a single makeup—four 500 MCM, RHW conductors in 3½-in. conduit—for each of the feeders. The one size of feeder can supply a total load of eight closets with a 2% voltage drop for the given distance from the switchboard to the load, but it can only supply a total of six closets with a 2% drop when the feeder has to run to the top of the building.

The use of a basic feeder makeup for all feeders provided two distinct advantages. First, four 500s in 3½-in. conduit is a highly economical and efficient makeup based on kva delivered, voltage drop and cable power loss—measured against installed cost of the feeder. The second reason for selecting a single feeder makeup was to minimize construction costs. With the use of only 500s in 3½-in. conduit, the contractor needed only one wire and conduit size for all of the lighting feeder work, permitting greater standardization and mechanization in installing the conduit, pulling the conductors, coupling to panel enclosures, making taps, installing lugs, etc.

There are many cases in which the above-mentioned limits of voltage drop (1% for lighting feeders, etc.) should be relaxed in the interests of reducing the prohibitive costs of conductors and conduits required by such low drops. In many installations 5% drop in feeders is not critical or unsafe. A recommended plan for apartment houses is shown in Fig. 106.

Voltage regulators

In general, it can be said that when overcabling is needed in order to meet the NE Code or City Codes on voltage drop, the alternative of voltage regulators plus normal cabling should be considered for the most economical method.

Voltage regulators are used wherever it is neces-

FIG. 105—Feeder loads balanced against circuit length for uniform voltage drop and circuit makeup of risers

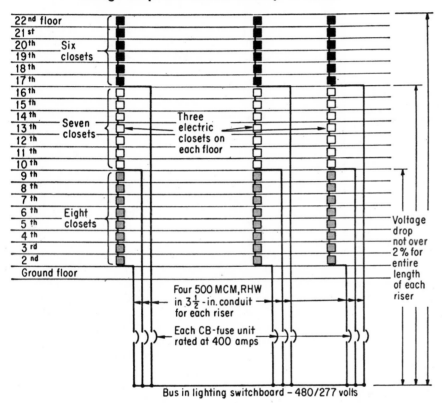

FIG. 102—Recommended limits of voltage drop

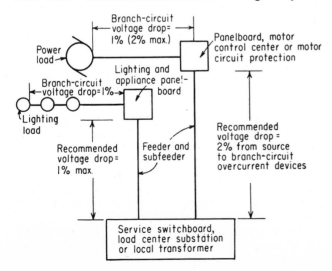

FIG. 103—Basic calculations for voltage drop in feeder circuits

Two-Wire, Single-Phase Circuits: (Inductance Negligible)

$$V = \frac{2k \times L \times I}{d^2} = 2R \times L \times I \qquad d^2 = \frac{2k \times I \times L}{V}$$

V = drop in circuit voltage (volts)
R = resistance per ft of conductor (ohms/ft)
I = current in conductor (amps)

Three-Wire, Single-Phase Circuits: (Inductance Negligible)

$$V = \frac{2k \times L \times I}{d^2}$$

V = drop between outside conductors (volts)
I = current in more heavily loaded outside conductor (amperes)

Three-Wire, Three-Phase Circuits: (Inductance Negligible)

$$V = \frac{2k \times I \times L}{d^2} \times 0.866$$

V = voltage drop of 3-phase circuit

Four-Wire, Three-Phase Balanced Circuits: (Inductance Negligible)
    For lighting loads: Voltage drop between one outside conductor and neutral equals one-half of drop calculated by formula for 2-wire circuits.
    For motor loads: Voltage drop between any two outside conductors equals 0.866 times drop determined by formula for 2-wire circuits.

In above formulas—

L = one-way length of circuit (ft)
d^2 = cross-section area of conductor (circular mils)
k = resistivity of conductor metal (cir mil-ohms/ft) (k = 12 for circuits loaded to more than 50% of allowable carrying capacity; k = 11 for circuits loaded less than 50%; k = 18 for aluminum conductor)

FIG. 106—Realistic voltage drop plan for apartment houses

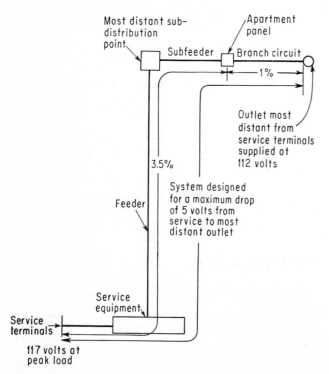

Most distant sub-distribution point

Apartment panel

Subfeeder   Branch circuit

1%

Outlet most distant from service terminals supplied at 112 volts

3.5%

Feeder

System designed for a maximum drop of 5 volts from service to most distant outlet

Service equipment

Service terminals

117 volts at peak load

sary to eliminate objectionable variations in the voltage level of a supply circuit. Overvoltage and undervoltage have undesirable effects on the operation of a wide range of electric and electronic load devices. In particular, electronic equipment like data processing equipment and communication, instrumentation and control devices require fairly constant operating voltage.

A growing application for voltage regulators is in high-ampere (thousands of amperes) distribution circuits for modern commercial and industrial properties where long secondary-voltage runs (typically, 120/208 volts) would require many conductors per phase leg to keep voltage drops within reasonable limits. Voltage regulators provide extremely economical use on long high-ampere circuits with constantly varying load demands (such as apartment houses, schools, hospitals, etc.) permitting use of only the amount of cable necessary for the load current instead of that needed to keep voltage drop down.

Fig. 107 shows the use of a voltage regulator installation on the campus of a university. The university was supplied secondary voltage from the transformer bank at 208Y/120 nominal at plus 5% and minus 2% from the 208 base.

The municipal code limited voltage drop between service-entrance equipment and the final distribution point to 2½% (or 5.2 volts) on a 208-volt base. Calculations to determine the number and size of conductors that would be needed to serve the three buildings assigned approximately half of the allowable voltage drop to the supply feeders and the remaining half to the building distribution feeders.

Since the utility transformer bank was close to the classroom building and the administration building, the supply feeders were relatively short and the allowable voltage drop could be achieved by normal cabling. The library, however, required a 450-ft supply feeder from the transformer bank to the distribution center located in the basement. In addition, the library had an estimated load of 1900 amps.

Using oversizing of feeders, to meet the requirement of half the allowable voltage drop in the supply feeder for a run of 450 ft at 1900 amps, would have required 20 500-MCM conductors per phase. The cost of material and labor, the amount of space required and the difficulty of installation made this method impractical.

Using a voltage regulator at the load end of the library feeder, with the regulators compensating for all the voltage drop in the supply feeder, six 500-MCM conductors per phase were needed since they only had to be selected to carry the load current.

Since the regulators maintain nominal voltage at the distribution center in the library basement, the full 2½% voltage drop allowed by the electrical code could be assigned to the building's distribution feeders. The amount of cabling space was kept to a minimum. The regulators maintained nominal voltage at the distribution center not only when the load was heavy and the utility supply voltage low, but also when the load was light and the utility supply voltage was high. This resulted in the utilization equipment in the library building always operating at peak efficiency with maximum life.

The short-circuit current available from the utility for a 3-phase bolted fault was 116,000 amps symmetrical rms. The impedance introduced by the all-

FIG. 107—Voltage drop problem solved by use of voltage regulators

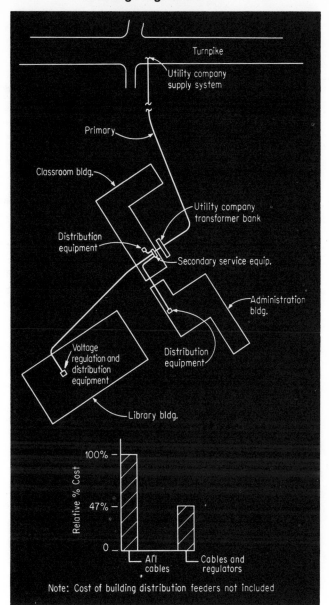

Note: Cost of building distribution feeders not included

FIG. 108—Full-size neutral for feeders to ballast loads

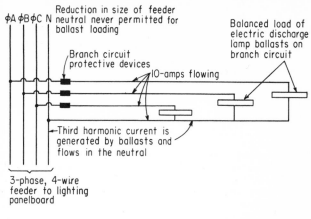

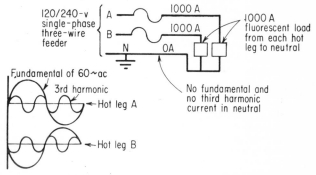

As shown, both the fundamental and harmonic currents are 180° out of phase and both cancel in the neutral. This action is the same as it would be for an incandescent load. Under balanced conditions, the neutral current is zero. But the literal wording of Section 220-4(d) says there can be no reduction in neutral capacity when fluorescent lighting is supplied. As a result, there should be no use of the 70% factor for current over 200 amps as there would be for incandescent loading. Neutral here must be rated for 1000 amps.

cable method would have reduced the short-circuit current at the distribution equipment to approximately 40,000 amps. However, with the regulator-cable method the additional impedance of the smaller cable capacity reduced the short-circuit current to approximately 19,000 amps—which was an added bonus.

Sizing feeder neutral

Section 220-4(d) of the NE Code covers requirements for sizing the neutral conductor in a feeder. It states that "the neutral feeder load shall be the maximum unbalance" of the feeder load.

"The maximum unbalanced load shall be the maximum connected load between the neutral and any one ungrounded conductor. . . ." In a 3-wire, 120-240-volt, single-phase feeder, the neutral must have a current-carrying capacity at least equal to the current drawn by the total 120-volt load connected between the more heavily loaded hot leg and the neutral.

It should be noted that straight 240-volt loads, connected between the two hot legs, do not place any load on the neutral. As a result, the neutral conductor of such a feeder must be sized to make up a 2-wire 120-volt circuit with the more heavily loaded hot leg. Actually, the 120-volt circuit loads on such a feeder would be considered as balanced on both sides of the neutral. The neutral, then, would be the same size as each of the hot legs if only 120-volt loads were supplied by the feeder. If 240-volt loads also were supplied, the hot legs would be sized for the total load, but the neutral would be sized for only half of the total 120-volt load.

Section 220-4(d) contains three other provisions for sizing neutral conductors. The first of these refers to electric range loads of feeders, the second refers to feeders of three or more wires, and the third refers to neutral currents with balanced fluorescent ballast loads:

A. When a feeder supplies electric ranges, the neutral conductor may be smaller than the hot conductors

FIG. 110—Examples of sizing a feeder neutral (NE Code Section 220-4d)

Serving an incandescent load, each phase conductor must be rated for 1000 amps. But neutral only has to be rated for 200 amps plus (70% x 800 amps) or 200 + 560 = 760 amps.

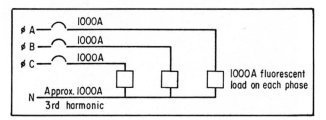

Because load is electric discharge lighting, there can be no reduction in the size of the neutral. Neutral must be rated for 1000 amps, the same as the phase conductors, because the third harmonic currents of the phase legs add together in the neutral. This applies also when the load is mercury-vapor or other metallic-vapor lighting.

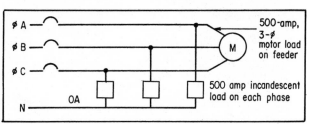

Although 1000 amps flow on each phase leg, only 500 amps is related to the neutral. Neutral, then, is sized for 200 amps plus (70% x 300 amps) or 200 + 210 = 410 amps. The amount of current taken for 3-phase motors cannot be "unbalanced load" and no capacity has to be provided for this in the neutral.

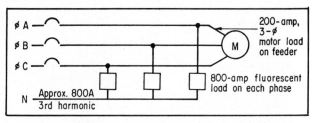

Here again, the only possible load that could flow on the neutral is the 800 amps flowing over each phase to the fluorescent lighting. But because it is fluorescent lighting there can be no reduction of neutral capacity below the 800-amp value on each phase. The 70% factor for that current above 200 amps DOES NOT APPLY in such cases.

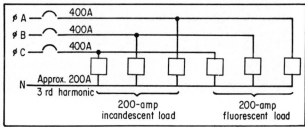

Each phase leg carries a total of 400 amps to supply the incandescent load plus the fluorescent load. But because there can be no reduction of neutral capacity for the fluorescent and because the incandescent load is not over 200 amps, the neutral must be sized for the maximum possible unbalance which is 400 amps.

but must have a carrying capacity at least equal to 70% of the current capacity required in the ungrounded conductors to handle the load (i.e., 70% of the load on the ungrounded conductors). Table 220-5 gives the demand loads to be used in sizing feeders which supply electric ranges and other similar cooking appliances.

B. For feeders of three or more conductors—3-wire, dc; 3-wire, single-phase; and 4-wire, 3-phase—a further demand factor of 70% may be applied to that portion of the unbalanced load in excess of 200 amps. That is, in a feeder supplying only 120-volt loads evenly divided between each ungrounded conductor and the neutral, the neutral conductor must be the same size as each ungrounded conductor up to 200-amp capacity, but may be reduced from the size of the ungrounded conductors for loads above 200 amps by adding to the 200 amps only 70% of the amount of load current above 200 amps in computing

the size of the neutral. It should be noted that this 70% demand factor is applicable to the unbalanced load in excess of 200 amps and not simply to the total load, which in many cases may be made up of balanced 240-volt loads or straight 3-phase loads. Determination of required neutral current-carrying capacity can often be facilitated by vector analysis of the particular conditions involved.

C. The foregoing reduction of the neutral to 200 amps plus 70% of the current over 200 amps does not apply to electric discharge lighting. In a feeder supplying ballasts for electric discharge lamps, there must not be a reduction of the neutral capacity for that part of the load which consists of fluorescent or mercury vapor lighting. In feeders supplying only electric discharge lighting, the neutral conductor must be the same size as the phase conductors no matter how big the total load may be. This exception is based on tests which show that, in a balanced cir-

FIG. 111—Here's how multiple conductors offer wire and conduit economy

The following circuit makeups represent typical considerations in the application of multiple conductor feeders (copper conductors):

Circ. 1

A 3-phase circuit of three 2000 MCM Type R conductors in a 6-in. conduit.
Current rating of each phase = 560 amps.
Cross-section area per phase = 3.2079 sq in.

Circ. 2

A 3-phase circuit of six 400 MCM Type R conductors (two per phase) in a 4-in. conduit.
Current rating of each phase might appear to be = 2 x 280 = 560 amps, but, because of the 80% derating required by Note 8 to Tables 310-12 to 310-15 of the NE Code, current rating of each phase = 560 x 80% = 448 amps.
Cross-section area per phase = 1.6730 sq in. (two conductors).

Circ. 3

A 3-phase circuit of three 1000 MCM Type R conductors in a 4-in. conduit.
Current rating of each phase = 455 amps.
Cross-section area per phase = 1.7531 sq in.

Circ. 4

A 3-phase circuit of six 600 MCM Type R conductors in a 5-in. conduit.
Current rating of each phase might appear to be = 2 x 355 = 710 amps.
But 80% derating must be applied because of the number of conductors in the conduit.
Current rating of each phase = 710 x 80% = 568 amps.
Cross-section area per phase = 2.3880 sq in. (two conductors).

FIG. 112—Conductors protected at supply ends

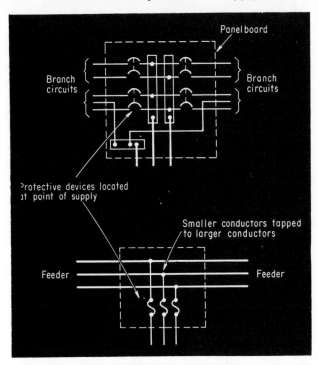

FIG. 113—This is the basic idea behind short-circuit calculations

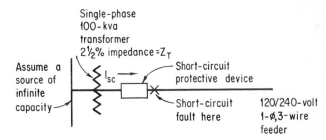

Neglecting line and other impedances between the transformer and the fault—

Transformer full-load secondary current $= \dfrac{100,000 \text{ va}}{240 \text{ v}} = 417$ amps

Maximum short-circuit current based on transformer impedance $= \dfrac{100\%}{\% Z_T} \times$ secondary full-load current

Max. $I_{sc} = \dfrac{100}{2.5} \times 417 = 16,680$ amps symmetrical

---

cuit supplying ballasts, neutral current approximating the phase current is produced by third (and other odd order) harmonics developed by the ballasts, as shown in Fig. 108. For large fluorescent lighting loads, this factor affects sizing of neutrals all the way back to the service. It also affects rating of conductors in conduit since a circuit as above consists of four current-carrying wires, which requires application of 80% reduction factor.

It should be noted that the code wording in Section 220-4(d) prohibits reduction in the size of the neutral when electric discharge lighting is used, even if the feeder supplying the electric discharge lighting load over 200 amps happens to be a 120/240-volt, 3-wire, single-phase feeder. In such a feeder, however, the third harmonic currents in the hot legs are 180° out of phase with each other and, therefore, would not be additive in the neutral as they are in a 3-phase, 4-wire circuit. In the latter type of circuit,

the third harmonic components of the phase currents are in phase with each other and add together in the neutral instead of canceling out. Fig. 109 shows a 120/240-volt circuit.

In the case of a feeder supplying, say, 200 amps of fluorescent lighting and 200 amps of incandescent, there can be no reduction of the neutral below the required 400-amp capacity of the phase legs, because the 200 amps of fluorescent lighting load cannot be used in any way to take advantage of the 70% demand factor on that part of the load in excess of 200 amps.

Fig. 110 shows a number of circuit conditions involving the rules on sizing a feeder neutral.

Using multiple conductors

For makeup of high-current-capacity feeders, there is distinct advantage in the use of multiple conduc-

Multiple Conductors For Feeders

POWER FEEDER SPECIFICATION DATA

P	Cable Size	Cables Per Phase	Conduit Size	Cost in Dollars Per 100 Feet	Ampere Rating NE Code	Dollars Per 100 Feet Per Unit P	Economic Choice
2.0	4	1	1¼	$136.00	70	$68.00	
3.0	2	1	1¼	151.00	95	50.30	
3.7	1	1	1½	189.00	110	51.10	
4.6	0	1	2	237.00	125	51.50	
5.5	2/0	1	2	260.00	145	47.20	
6.6	3/0	1	2	286.00	165	43.40	
7.4	1	2	2½	342.00	176	46.30	B
7.7	4/0	1	2½	356.00	195	46.30	A
8.2	250	1	2½	421.00	255	51.40	B
9.2	0	2	2½	378.00	200	41.10	A
9.5	350	1	3	532.00	310	56.00	C
11.0	2/0	2	3	468.00	232	42.50	A
11.0	500	1	3	622.00	380	56.60	C
11.2	1	3	3	472.00	231	42.20	B
13.2	3/0	2	3	521.00	264	39.50	A
13.8	0	3	3	526.00	262	38.10	A
15.4	4/0	2	3½	586.00	312	38.00	A
16.4	250	2	3½	755.00	408	46.00	B
16.5	2/0	3	3½	634.00	304	38.40	A
19.8	3/0	3	3½	713.00	346	36.00	A
23.1	4/0	3	4	848.00	410	36.70	A
24.5	250	3	4½	1085.00	535	44.30	A

Wiring in steel conduit for up to 600-volt three-phase 30 C ambient NE Code ratings.

Size 250 MCM and above — Heat and moisture resistant rubber type cable insulation with 75C rating.

Below 250 MCM — Thermoplastic cable insulation with 60 C rating.

A — Preferred   B — Second Choice   C — Uneconomical

A suitable unit for comparing the performance of cables is P, which is defined as (1)

$$P = L \times I / dV \times 1000$$

where, L = feeder length in feet

I = load current in amperes

dV = feeder voltage drop

(1000 is included for brevity)

Based on the average value of load power factor, 0.8 to 0.95, it can be assumed that voltage drop in a feeder is equal to the impedance drop, so that dV in Equation (1) becomes $LIZ\sqrt{3}/1000$. Equation (1) then simplifies to $P = 1/(Z\sqrt{3})$

where, Z = ohms to neutral impedance per 1000 feet of feeder.

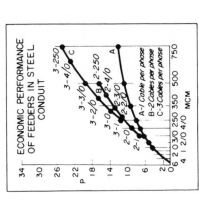

ECONOMIC PERFORMANCE OF FEEDERS IN STEEL CONDUIT

A-1 Cable per phase
B-2 Cables per phase
C-3 Cables per phase

The higher the value of "P," the lower the voltage drop and power losses and the higher the extra capacity.

Common Neutral

EXAMPLE OF COMMON NEUTRAL AND REDUCED NEUTRAL

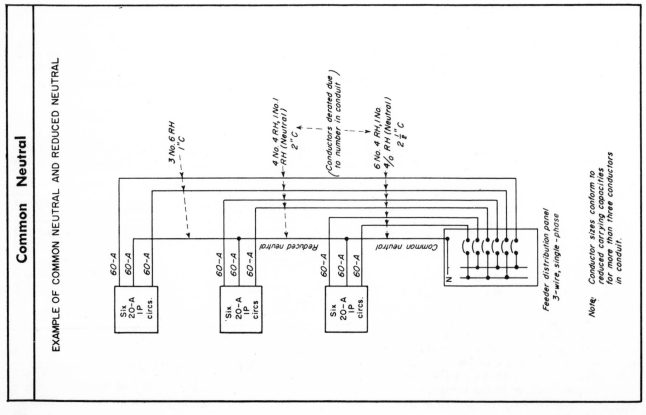

Note: Conductor sizes conform to reduced carrying capacities for more than three conductors in conduit.

tors per leg. This may be done in accordance with Section 310-10, which says, "Conductors in sizes 1/0 and larger may be run in multiple provided the arrangement is such as to assure equal division of total current among all conductors involved. All of the multiple conductors shall be of the same length, of the same conductor material, circular-mil area, same insulation type and terminated in the same manner. Where run in separate raceways or cables, the raceways or cables shall have the same physical characteristics."

From the code tables of current-carrying capacities of various sizes of conductors, it can be seen that small conductor sizes carry more current per circular mil of cross section than do large conductors. This results from rating conductor capacity according to temperature rise. The larger a cable, the less is the radiating surface per circular mil of cross section. Loss due to "skin effect" (apparent higher resistance of conductors to alternating current than to direct current) is also higher in the larger conductor sizes. And larger conductors cost more per ampere than smaller conductors.

All of the foregoing factors point to the advisability of using a number of smaller conductors in multiple to get a particular carrying capacity, rather than using a single conductor of that capacity. In many cases, multiple conductors for feeders provide distinct operating advantages and are more economical than the equivalent-capacity single-conductor makeup of a feeder. But, it should be noted, the reduced overall cross-section of conductor resulting from multiple conductors instead of a single conductor per leg produces higher resistance and greater voltage drop than the same length as a single conductor per leg. Voltage drop may be a limitation.

Fig. 111 shows a typical application of copper conductors in multiple, with the advantages of such use. The following four circuit makeups show:

a. Without derating for conduit occupancy, circuit 2 would be equivalent to circuit 1.

b. A circuit of six 400 MCMs can be made equivalent in current-carrying capacity to a circuit of three 2000 MCMs by dividing the 400's between two conduits (3 conductors/3-in. conduit).

c. Circuit 2 is almost equivalent to circuit 3 in current rating.

d. Circuit 4 is equivalent to circuit 1 in current rating, but uses less conductor copper and a smaller conduit. And the advantages are obtained even with the occupancy derating.

A common neutral conductor

Another frequently discussed code requirement is that of Section 215-5, covering the use of a common neutral with more than one set of feeders. This section says that "A common neutral feeder may be employed for two or three sets of 3-wire feeders, or two sets of 4-wire feeders. . . ." It further states that "When in metal enclosures, all conductors of feeder circuits employing a common neutral feeder shall be contained within the same enclosure. . . ."

A common neutral is a single neutral conductor used as the neutral for more than one set of feeder conductors. It must have current-carrying capacity equal to the sum of the neutral conductor capacities if an individual neutral conductor were used with each feeder set. A common neutral may be used only with feeders. It may never be used with branch circuits.

Protecting against overcurrent

General rules on the application of overcurrent protection to feeder conductors are as follows:

A. Conductors in electric circuits must be protected against conditions of excessive current flow. Such protection must be provided in accordance with the current-carrying capacities of the conductors, except where certain higher settings or ratings of protective devices are required—as in the case of motor branch circuits or motor feeders.

B. An overcurrent device must not be used in a permanently grounded conductor—except where the device simultaneously opens all conductors of the circuit.

C. Overcurrent protection for a conductor must be located at the point where the conductor receives its supply, as in Fig. 112. This means that a conductor run of a particular current-carrying capacity must be protected at the point at which it is fed by a conductor of higher current-carrying capacity. In a feeder run, then, change in conductor size (from larger to smaller) must be accompanied by protection for the smaller conductor. Exceptions to this rule are made in the case of taps, which is discussed later under "Feeder taps." Another exception is where the protection for the larger conductor meets the requirements for protection of the smaller conductor, that is, the rating or setting of the fuse or CB protecting the larger wires is suitable to protect the smaller tap wires. See Fig. 19.

For feeder circuits other than motor feeders, sizing of the overcurrent device which protects against short circuits and grounds can be made as follows:

A. If the allowable current-carrying capacity of a conductor does not correspond to the rating of a standard-size fuse, the next larger rating of fuse may be used only where the rating is 800 amps or less. Over 800 amps, the next smaller fuse must be used.

B. Nonadjustable-trip circuit breakers must be rated in accordance with the current-carrying capacity of the conductors they protect—except that a higher-rated circuit breaker may be used if the carrying capacity of the conductor does not correspond to a standard unit rating. In such a case, the next higher standard rating and setting may be used only where the rating is 800 amps or less. Circuit breakers in the 0- to 30-amp sizes should be of the time-delay type.

C. Adjustable-trip circuit breakers of the thermal-trip, magnetic time-delay trip or instantaneous-trip types must be set to operate at not more than 125% of the allowable current-carrying capacity of the conductor.

There are many other considerations in the selection of the size of a thermal-magnetic circuit breaker. If the CB is of the type calibrated in open air in an ambient temperature of 25°C, it generally will not carry full current without tripping when installed in an enclosure in an ambient of 25°C. It must be derated for such application.

Circuit breakers of the newer types which are calibrated at 40°C in open air, will generally carry their full-load current when installed in an enclosure in an

FIG. 114—Selective coordination minimizes circuit outage

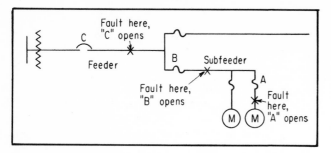

ambient of 25°C. These are sometimes called "enclosure compensated." Another type of CB, called "ambient compensated," is calibrated in open air at 40°C, but will carry full-load current even at higher temperatures because it is made to be insensitive to moderate temperature changes. Manufacturers of breakers will provide temperature data.

Designing short-circuit protection

Application of circuit overcurrent devices must carefully account for the ability of the devices to operate properly and safely on short-circuit faults—phase to ground faults and phase-to-phase faults in grounded wiring systems and on phase-to-phase faults in ungrounded wiring systems. In all cases, considerations should be made of the following points:

1. Under normal operation, a circuit draws current in proportion to the voltage applied and the impedance of the load. When a short circuit occurs, the source voltage no longer finds the normal opposition to current flow which the load presented. Instead, the voltage is applied across a load of much lower impedance, made up of the impedance of the conductors from the source of voltage to the point of short-circuit fault, the impedance of the transformer from which the circuit is derived and any other impedances due to equipment interposed in the circuit between the transformer and the point of fault.

2. Overcurrent protective devices in circuits at all voltage levels must be capable of interrupting the maximum possible short-circuit currents delivered by the system into a solid short on their load terminals, without destroying themselves in the operation. Fig. 113 shows a simple calculation of available short-circuit current, yielding symmetrical, single-phase, short-circuit current. The short-circuit protective device must be capable of safely interrupting this value of current and the asymmetrical current value which is obtained by using some multiplier (such as 1.25) times the symmetrical value. In a more rigorous analysis, this value would be reduced by all impedances in the circuit.

3. Coordinated selective protection for modern circuits provides fast, effective isolation of any faulted section of a system but does not interrupt service to any other section of the system. By careful study of time-current characteristics of protective devices, application can assure clearing of faults by the devices nearest to the faults on the supply side, as in Fig. 114.

4. "Let-through" current is another factor in effective application of protective devices for short circuits. A given protective device may be able to safely interrupt the maximum short-circuit current at its point of installation, but the time it takes to open the faulted circuit may be so long as to damage equipment or devices connected in series with the fault. Unless the device operates quickly enough, severe damage can be done due to the tremendous rupturing stresses created by short circuits. The system components must be related to the let-through current, which flows from the time the fault develops until the circuit is opened. Current-limiting fuses, for instance, open a short circuit in much less than a half cycle, thereby squelching let-through current.

Fig. 115 shows the two extreme conditions at which short circuits can start and continue to flow if they were not opened by fuses or breakers. In Fig. 115A, maximum asymmetry in the flow of short-circuit current is produced when the short circuit occurs at that point in the voltage wave for which the short-circuit current is exactly at its positive or negative peak value, as determined by the ratio of reactance to resistance in the short circuit—which establishes the phase angle difference between the voltage wave and the short-circuit current wave. In the case shown, when the short occurs at the given point on the voltage wave, the phase angle of the short circuit is such that the short-circuit current is exactly at its negative peak. Maximum asymmetry is thus pro-

FIG. 115—This is how short-circuit currents could flow if they were not opened by overcurrent protection

A—MAXIMUM ASYMMETRY

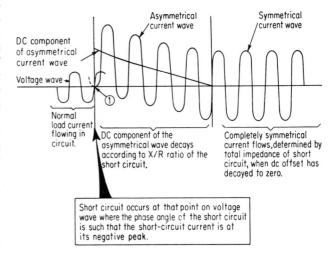

B—COMPLETE SYMMETRY

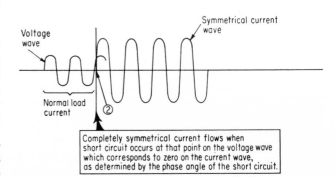

Ratings of Thermal-Magnetic CBs

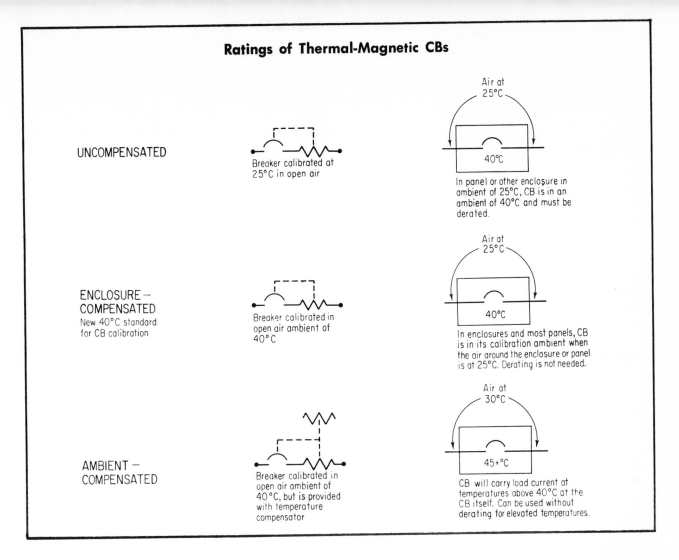

UNCOMPENSATED

Breaker calibrated at 25°C in open air

Air at 25°C

40°C

In panel or other enclosure in ambient of 25°C, CB is in an ambient of 40°C and must be derated.

ENCLOSURE — COMPENSATED
New 40°C standard for CB calibration

Breaker calibrated in open air ambient of 40°C

Air at 25°C

40°C

In enclosures and most panels, CB is in its calibration ambient when the air around the enclosure or panel is at 25°C. Derating is not needed.

AMBIENT — COMPENSATED

Breaker calibrated in open air ambient of 40°C, but is provided with temperature compensator

Air at 30°C

45+°C

CB will carry load current at temperatures above 40°C at the CB itself. Can be used without derating for elevated temperatures.

---

duced. The instantaneous change in phase relation between current and voltage produces an offset in the ac current wave which acts like a dc transient.

From the immediate condition of asymmetry, the dc component of the short-circuit current wave decays to zero at a rate determined by the ratio of reactance to resistance in the short circuit. For a purely resistive short circuit (zero ratio of reactance to resistance), a highly theoretical condition, the decay to zero of the dc component will be instantaneous. If the short circuit were purely reactive (infinite ratio of reactance to resistance), which is a practical impossibility, the dc component would never decay to zero, the current would remain offset, and the asymmetrical rms current would be equal to 1.73 × the symmetrical rms. Of course, actual circuits have ratios of reactance to resistance up to about 20, although the vast majority of cases have ratios less than 7 to 1. This means the dc decays to zero in several cycles.

In Fig. 115B, a short-circuit current wave of complete symmetry will flow when the short occurs at that point in the voltage wave for which the short-circuit current is at its zero value. Again the exact point in the voltage wave which will correspond in time to the zero value of the current wave is determined by the phase angle (or power factor, or ratio of reactance to resistance) of the short circuit.

Although short circuits can start at either of the two extremes shown in A and B, chances are infinitely greater that faults will occur at some intermediate degree of asymmetry. But because design must account for the worst possibility, short-circuit calculations should be made to determine the asymmetrical current which protective devices might be called upon to break.

From the character of asymmetry, it can be seen that the ratio of reactance to resistance is important in applying protective devices because it indicates how fast the dc will decay and how much current the device will be called upon to open if it attempts to open the circuit in the first half cycle, or in the second cycle, or the fourth, etc.—with the current being

FIG. 116—Fault current values in first half cycle

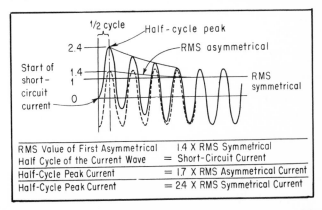

RMS Value of First Asymmetrical Half Cycle of the Current Wave	1.4 X RMS Symmetrical = Short-Circuit Current
Half-Cycle Peak Current	= 1.7 X RMS Asymmetrical Current
Half-Cycle Peak Current	= 2.4 X RMS Symmetrical Current

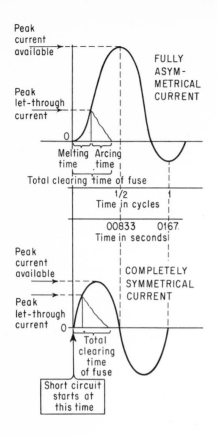

FIG. 117—Current-limiting effect of fuse

Peak current available

Peak let-through current

FULLY ASYMMETRICAL CURRENT

0

Melting time | Arcing time

Total clearing time of fuse

1/2 | 1
Time in cycles

00833 | 0167
Time in seconds

Peak current available

Peak let-through current

COMPLETELY SYMMETRICAL CURRENT

0

Total clearing time of fuse

Short circuit starts at this time

Comparison of fuse classes

(General-purpose cartridge type)

UL class	Range amps	Inter. cap. amps	Max. let-through	Time delay**	Dimensions
H	0–600	10K	None	No	Old NEC
J	0–600	100K or 200K	Yes*	No	Special†
K-1	0–600	10K, 25K 50K, 100K or 200K	Yes*	No	Old NEC
K-5	0–600	10K, 25K 50K, 100K or 200K	Yes*	Yes	Old NEC
K-9	0–600	10K, 25K, 50K, or 100K	Yes*	Yes	Old NEC
L	601–6000	100K or 200K	Yes*	No	Present NEMA Sizes

* UL standards state maximum peak let-through in amps and energy let-through (I²T) for each size and type of fuse. In 600A sizes, lowest let-through is Class J, increasing slightly through Classes K-1, K-5 and K-9.
** NEMA standards call for a minimum of 10 seconds delay at 500% of fuse rating. No UL standards adopted.
† Smaller than and noninterchangeable with NE Code size fuses.

less with each succeeding cycle. As a result, a fast-acting fuse, such as a current-limiting fuse, which will open the short circuit in the first half cycle will be breaking almost the maximum value of the asymmetrical wave and must be rated for that current value. On the other hand, a circuit breaker which will not act until the fourth cycle of the short-circuit current wave will only have to interrupt the level of current to which the asymmetrical wave has decayed.

On a fully asymmetrical short, maximum instantaneous current—the peak asymmetrical current—occurs at the end of the first half cycle of the current wave. Due to decay of the dc component, subsequent peaks are lower in value. Various values for this half-cycle asymmetrical current have been determined from study of actual circuits to be as in Fig. 116.

The foregoing explains the use of multipliers to determine the value of asymmetrical current from the calculated symmetrical value, such as that arrived at in Fig. 116. For fuses, which operate relatively fast, a multiplier of 1.4 is commonly used on the rms symmetrical short-circuit current value to get the rms asymmetrical value. For circuit breakers which operate almost as fast as some fuses, the same multiplier would be used in determining the possible current value of the asymmetrical wave when the breaker opens it. But for breakers which operate slower, say two or three cycles after the fault starts, a multiplier of only 1.25 or 1.1 will give the value to which the asymmetrical wave has decayed by that time.

The value of 1.4 as the multiplier for determining the first half-cycle value of rms asymmetrical current has been established for a ratio of reactance to resistance which is not exceeded in the majority of cases. Thus this multiplier yields the value to which

the asymmetrical current has decayed in the first half cycle. But, there are short circuits with higher-than-normal ratio of reactance to resistance so that the decay will not be as great in the first half cycle. A multiplier of, say, 1.5 or 1.6 would be required to get the possible value of first half-cycle rms asymmetrical current in such circuits. In all applications, when multipliers are used, the X/R ratio of the multiplier should be known as well as the X/R ratio of the circuit being protected.

Application of current-limiting fuses to quickly clear ground and short-circuit faults and to limit the energy let-through on circuits which could deliver fault currents over 100,000 or 200,000 amps is shown in Fig. 117. For a given short circuit, a current-limiting fuse may be called upon to interrupt either of the two extreme conditions shown here or some intermediate condition. For the fully asymmetrical case, the fuse would limit both rms value and peak available current if the melting time of the fuse were anything less than one-half cycle. But within its current-limiting range, a true current-limiting fuse must limit total clearing time to an interval not greater than the first symmetrical current loop and must limit the peak let-through current to a value less than the peak available current. Thus it is the action of a fuse in clearing a symmetrical short circuit that determines its current-limiting ability, as shown in the lower sketch. From the upper sketch, it can be seen that a fuse which had a melting time almost up to the peak of the asymmetrical first half cycle, would limit current let-through on an asymmetrical fault, but would not limit let-through if the short happened to occur as a completely symmetrical wave.

Comparison of Fuses by Operating Characteristics

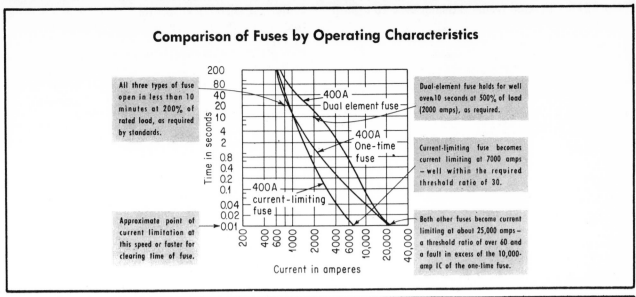

All three types of fuse open in less than 10 minutes at 200% of rated load, as required by standards.

Dual-element fuse holds for well over 10 seconds at 500% of load (2000 amps), as required.

Current-limiting fuse becomes current limiting at 7000 amps — well within the required threshold ratio of 30.

Approximate point of current limitation at this speed or faster for clearing time of fuse.

Both other fuses become current limiting at about 25,000 amps — a threshold ratio of over 60 and a fault in excess of the 10,000-amp IC of the one-time fuse.

Curves Explain Breaker Operation

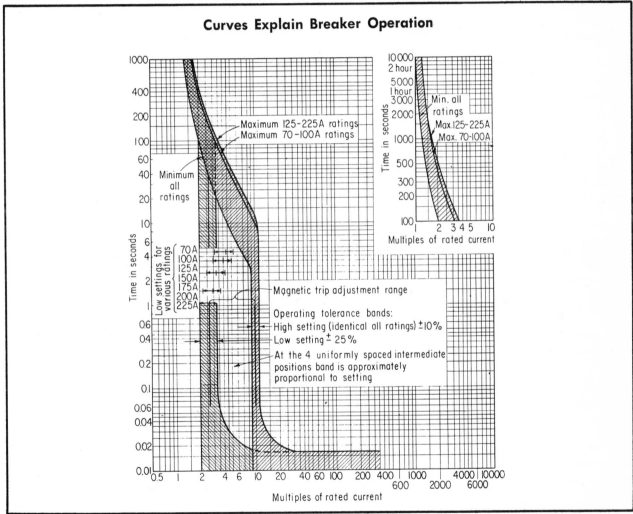

The rms value of the triangular wave shape of let-through current through the fuse is—

$$I_{LT} = I_p/1.7 \qquad \text{where,}$$
$$I_{LT} = \text{RMS let-through amps}$$
$$I_p = \text{Peak let-through amps}$$

Application of standard thermal-magnetic or fully-magnetic circuit breakers should be based on correlating their time-delay tripping curves and instantaneous trip settings to the requirements for overload protection, the current characteristics of the circuit being protected and the need for coordination in the operation of overcurrent devices connected in series (such as feeder device in series with subfeeder device in series with a branch-circuit device). Analysis of breaker operation in relation to a particular circuit is readily made by reference to the manufacturer's curves on the breaker.

FIG. 118—Making feeder taps not over 10 ft long

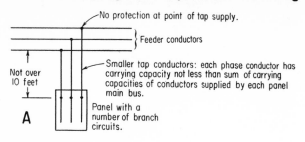

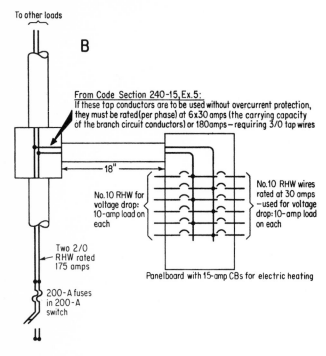

From Code Section 240-15, Ex.5:
If these tap conductors are to be used without overcurrent protection, they must be rated (per phase) at 6x30 amps (the carrying capacity of the branch circuit conductors) or 180 amps—requiring 3/0 tap wires

Feeder taps

Although basic code requirements dictate the use of an overcurrent device at the point at which a conductor receives its supply, exceptions to this rule are made in the case of taps to feeders. That is, to meet the practical demands of field application, certain lengths of unprotected conductors may be used to tap energy from protected feeder conductors.

Exceptions to the rule for protecting conductors at their points of supply are made in the case of 10-ft and 25-ft taps from a feeder, as described in Section 240-15, Exceptions No. 5 and No. 6. Application of the above tap exceptions should be made carefully, to effectively minimize any sacrifice in safety. The two tap exceptions are permitted as follows, without overcurrent protective devices at the point of supply:

TAPS NOT OVER 10 FT LONG (Fig. 118A) may be made from feeders provided—

1. The smaller conductors have a current rating not less than the sum of the allowable current-carrying capacities for the conductors of the one or more circuits or loads supplied by the tap.

2. The tap does not extend beyond the switchboard, panelboard or control devices which it supplies.

3. The tap conductors are enclosed in conduit, EMT or metal gutters when not a part of the switchboard or panelboard.

The wording of "1" above is taken from Section 240-15 and, if taken literally, can produce some in-

stallations with tap conductors larger than the feeder conductors from which they are tapped, as shown in Fig. 118B. Actually, the wording of the code section gives no clue as to what the code does want in the way of sizing the tap, unless it actually does intend what it says. A practical solution to the problem would be to select tap conductors with carrying capacity at least equal to the ampere rating of the panelboard busbars. This is especially consistent with new code rules which require that a lighting and appliance panel be protected against current in excess of the panel busbar ratings.

TAPS NOT OVER 25 FT LONG (Fig. 119) may be made from feeders provided—

1. The smaller conductors have a current rating at least one-third that of the conductors from which they are tapped.

2. The tap conductors are suitably protected from mechanical damage.

3. The tap is terminated in a single circuit breaker or set of fuses which will limit the load on the tap to its allowable current-carrying capacity.

Fig. 120 shows use of a 10-ft feeder tap to supply a single motor branch circuit. The conduit or busway feeder may be a horizontal run or may be a vertical run, such as a riser. If the tap conductors are of such size that they have a current rating at least one-third that of the feeder or busway conductors from which they are tapped, they could be run a distance of 25 ft without protection at the point of tap-off from the feeder or busway.

A common application of the 10-ft tap exception is the supply of panelboards from conduit feeders or busways, as shown in Fig. 121. The case shows an interesting requirement which arises from Section 384-16. This section requires that lighting and appliance panelboards must be protected on their supply side by overcurrent protection rated not more than the rating of the panelboard busbars. In the case here, this protection could not be placed at the point of tap on the busway because it would not be "readily accessible" as required by the code. But it could be a fused switch or circuit breaker main in the panelboard. Such protection could be rated up to the 100-amp main rating.

In Fig. 121, it would be better to use No. 2 TW or RHW to get tap capacity closer to the panel mains rating to permit load growth in panel. And if a 200-amp panel were used in such a layout, with a 200-amp main CB or fuses, the use of 200-amp rated tap conductors (e.g., 3/0 RHW) would give tap ca-

FIG. 119—Feeder taps not over 25 ft

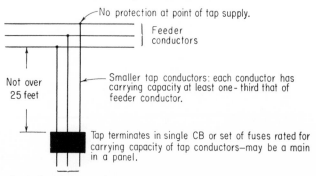

Conductors to a panel or a group of switches or CBs

FIG. 120—10-ft tap for motor circuit
(or could be 25 ft long)

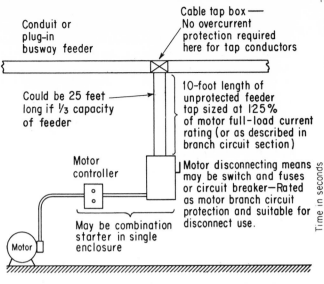

Conduit or plug-in busway feeder

Cable tap box — No overcurrent protection required here for tap conductors

Could be 25 feet long if 1/3 capacity of feeder

10-foot length of unprotected feeder tap sized at 125% of motor full-load current rating (or as described in branch circuit section)

Motor controller

Motor disconnecting means may be switch and fuses or circuit breaker—Rated as motor branch circuit protection and suitable for disconnect use.

May be combination starter in single enclosure

Motor

FIG. 121—10-ft busway tap to lighting panel
with unprotected conductors

Although not required for protection of the 10-foot tap, overcurrent protection is required for lighting and appliance panel to protect it in accordance with its main rating. Thus a 100-amp CB or 100-amp fuses must be installed AT THE PANEL. Such protection could not be installed at the point of tap-off because it would then not be readily accessible and would violate Section 240-16.

3-phase, 4-wire 600-amp busway

600-amp feeder protection

Minimum of four No. 6 RHW No. 4 TW

3-phase, 4-wire lighting and appliance panelboard with 12 single-pole, 15-amp circuits and 100-amp mains.

① Tap length not over 10 feet does not require overcurrent protection at point of supply to tap conductors.

② Tap conductors must have current rating not less than sum of current ratings of circuit conductors supplied, but may have higher rating.

③ For each phase of tap here, the conductor must be rated for 4 x 15 amps. (There are four single-pole circuits supplied by each phase.) Tap conductors must then be No. 6 RHW or No. 4 TW. Use of No. 2 TW or RHW might be better.

FIG. 122—Sizing tap conductors on
transformer primary and secondary
(200-amp busway switch is readily accessible)

600-amp busway 3-φ, 4-W, 480 volts

200-amp bus switch fused at 125 amps

3 No. 1/0 and 1 No. 2 in 2" C

3 No.6

Junction box

15-kva transformer

4 No.6

120/208-volt 3-φ panelboard

480-volt 3-φ panelboard

100-amp main CB in panel

Combining CB and Fuses

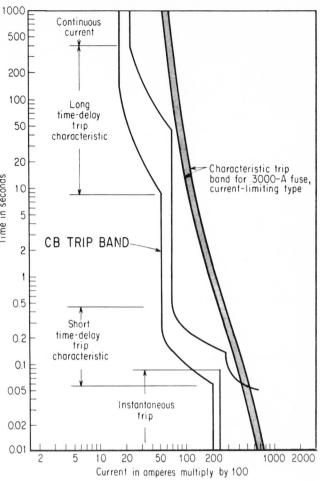

pacity of 1/3 feeder busway and the tap could then be run up to 25 ft without protection.

A somewhat involved, but not uncommon, case of unprotected feeder tap is shown in Fig. 122. This case cites the use of an unprotected feeder tap plus the need for main protection in a lighting panelboard.

The main CB in the 120-volt panel is required by Section 384-16 (a), because this is a lighting and appliance panelboard supplied by conductors having overcurrent protection in excess of the mains rating of the panelboard. The No. 6 conductors from the transformer to the panel, which are adequate for the load supplied by the panel, are protected by only the 125-amp fuses in the bus switch. Through the transformer this acts as protection rated at 290 amps. The 100-amp CB protects the panel at its rating. And, through the transformer, the 40-amp load on each phase of the secondary is a load of 17 amps on the 480-volt primary conductors. The primary conductors, therefore, could be No. 12s instead of No. 6s. The No. 6s were used for the primary because they were on hand for the secondary subfeed to the panel. The total tap—from JB to transformer, to panel—is not over 10 ft long.

Rated primary current of the 15-kva transformer is 18 amps; rated secondary current is 42 amps. As a result, No. 8 RHW secondary wires and No. 12 primary wires would not only have handled the load but would have also made available the full capacity of the transformer. But, it must be remembered, there was the requirement that the tap conductors

FIG. 123—Protecting busway subfeeders?

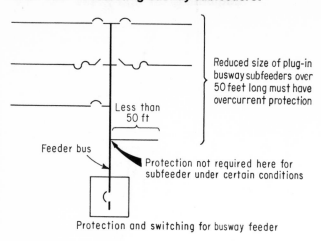

Reduced size of plug-in busway subfeeders over 50 feet long must have overcurrent protection

Less than 50 ft

Feeder bus

Protection not required here for subfeeder under certain conditions

Protection and switching for busway feeder

FIG. 124—No protection against the destruction of low-level arcing ground fault

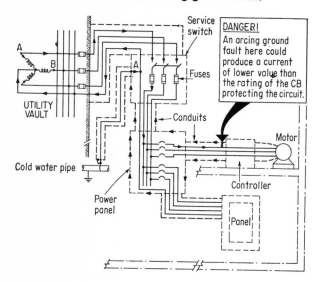

Service switch

DANGER! An arcing ground fault here could produce a current of lower value than the rating of the CB protecting the circuit.

Fuses

UTILITY VAULT

Motor

Cold water pipe

Conduits

Controller

Power panel

Panel

be rated for the sum of the branch-circuit conductor current ratings. The No. 6s are unprotected tap conductors. The CB also qualifies as overcurrent protection for the transformer, being rated not over 250% of transformer rated secondary current.

Overcurrent protection—either a fused-switch or circuit breaker—is usually required in each subfeeder tapping power from a busway feeder. This is necessary to protect the lower current-carrying capacity of the subfeeder and should be placed at the point at which the subfeeder connects into the feeder. However, the code provides that "Overcurrent protection may be omitted at points where busways are reduced in size, provided that the smaller busway does not extend more than 50 ft and has a current rating at least equal to one-third the rating or setting of the overcurrent device next back on the line . . ." See Fig. 123.

Protecting against ground faults

Fuses and circuit breakers, applied as described in the previous section on Overcurrent Protection, are sized to protect conductors in accordance with their

current-carrying capacities. The function of a fuse or CB is to open the circuit if current exceeds the rating of the protective device. This excessive current might be caused by operating overload, by a ground fault or by a short circuit. Thus, a 1000-amp fuse will blow if current in excess of that value flows over the circuit. It will blow early on heavy overcurrent and later on low overcurrents. But it will blow, and the circuit and equipment will be protected against the damage of the overcurrent. BUT, THERE IS ANOTHER TYPE OF FAULT CONDITION WHICH IS VERY COMMON IN GROUNDED SYSTEMS AND WILL NOT BE CLEARED BY CONVENTIONAL OVERCURRENT DEVICES. THAT IS THE PHASE-GROUND-FAULT (USUALLY ARCING) WHICH HAS A CURRENT VALUE LESS THAN THE RATING OF THE OVERCURRENT DEVICE.

The vast majority of modern grounded electrical systems, on which huge sums of money are expended for meticulously designed systems of conventional overcurrent protection, are completely unprotected against the most common type of electrical failure —low-current ground faults (from one phase-leg to grounded equipment enclosure). The fuses and/or CBs might be selected to have the highest interrupting capacities required by the available short-circuit currents of the system, and such factors as time-delay and current-limitation may be perfectly tailored to the needs of the particular system. But these vast sums of money are expended to provide protection for the very expensive electrical system (and protection for valuable industrial processes or commercial operations) against the type of electrical fault which almost never happens—the bolted 3-phase short circuit on the load terminals of any protective device in the system. At the same time, in spite of the expensive overcurrent provisions, the grounded system is totally unprotected against the fantastically destructive effects of the very common phase-to-ground fault. See Fig. 124.

On any high-capacity feeder, a line-to-ground fault (i. e., a fault from a phase conductor to a conduit, to a junction box or to some other metallic equipment enclosure) can and frequently does draw current of a value less than the rating or setting of the circuit protective device. For instance, a 500-amp ground fault on a 2000-amp protective device which has only a 1200-amp load will not be cleared by the device. If such a fault is a "bolted" line-to-ground fault, there will be a certain amount of heat generated by the I^2R effect of the current, but this will usually not be dangerous and such fault current will merely register as additional operating load, with wasted energy (wattage) in the system.

But, bolted phase-to-ground faults are very rare. The usual phase-to-ground fault exists as an arcing fault, and an arcing fault of the same current rating as the essentially harmless bolted fault can be fantastically destructive because of the unbelievably intense heat of the arc.

Of course, any ground fault current (bolted or arcing) above the rating or setting of the circuit protective device will normally be cleared by the device. In such cases, bolted-fault currents will be eliminated. But, even where the protective device eventually operates, in the case of a heavy ground fault current which adds to the normal circuit load current to produce a total current in excess of the rating of the normal circuit protective device (fuse or CB), the time-delay of the device may be hours or minutes —more than enough time for the arcing fault current to burn out conduit and enclosures, acting just like a torch, and even propagating flame to create a fire hazard.

In spite of the growth of effective and skilled application of conventional overcurrent protective devices, the problem of ground faults continues to exist and even grows with expanding electrical usage. In the interests of safety, definitive engineering design must account for protection against such faults. Phase overcurrent protective devices are normally limited in their effectiveness because (1) they must have a time delay and a setting somewhat higher than full load to ride through normal inrushes; and (2) they are unable to distinguish between normal currents and low magnitude fault currents which may be less than full-load currents.

Dangerous temperatures and magnetic forces are proportional to current for overloads and short circuits; therefore, overcurrent protective devices usually are adequate to protect against such faults. However, the temperatures of arcing faults are, generally, independent of current magnitude; and arcs of great and extensive destructive capability can be sustained by currents not exceeding the overcurrent device settings. Other means of protection are necessary therefore.

What is needed is a ground detection device which "sees" only ground fault current and which can be coupled to an automatic switch to open all three phases when a line-to-ground fault exists on the circuit.

With a ground-fault protection system as shown in Fig. 125, a ground fault anywhere in the system is immediately sensed in the ground-relay system, but its action to open the circuit is delayed to allow some normal overcurrent device near the point of fault to open if it can. As a practical procedure, such time delay is made from approximately two to four seconds, depending on the voltage of the circuit, the time-current characteristics of the overcurrent devices in the system, and the location of the ground-fault relay in the distribution system. Should any of the normal overcurrent protective devices fail to operate in the time predetermined to clear the circuit, and if the fault continues, the ground-fault protective relays will open the circuit. This provides added overcurrent protection not available by any other means.

As shown in Fig. 125, the ground-fault protective relays are located in the main switchboard and will thus detect any ground faults that may develop at any point in the wiring system—from the furthest point away—up to and including the switchboard. If desired, another set of ground-fault protective relays can be located at any point downstream from the service equipment.

Field experience has repeatedly shown that the ground-fault current values to be recognized should be set as low as practical so that virtually no ground-fault current will remain unrecognized, but by introducing a time-delay action this will permit the normal overcurrent protective device to operate. For a 4000-amp circuit, this value of relay setting is 810 amps. Ground-fault current in that range may never be

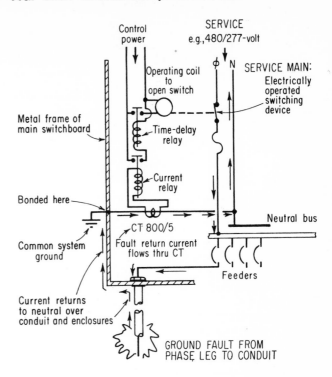

FIG. 125—Ground-fault protection at service

cleared by such sized overcurrent devices, but they will be cleared automatically by the ground-fault protective system. On the other hand, downstream overcurrent devices in the lower order of 200 amps and less will open by themselves at such low ground-fault values.

Ground-fault current values are highly unpredictable because of many variable factors. As such, the current values to be recognized and the time delay to be allowed are both a matter of judgment.

Another system of effective protection against ground-fault currents and their destructive capabilities makes use of a current-transformer and relay to operate electrically operated switching devices. This system provides more selective protection for individual circuits. Each branch circuit, each subfeeder, each feeder, each main can be equipped with its own separate detection and operation hookup to deenergize only the circuit with the ground fault— with adjustable time delay in each relay to coordinate its operation with other lineside relays to assure minimum outage on a ground fault. If the fault is on a branch circuit, the branch-circuit device will operate and not the subfeeder or other device supplying the branch circuit further upstream.

In this selective system with the zero-sequence relay, a single bushing CT is used, encircling all of the phase conductors and the neutral. When all unbalance of the phase legs, including third and ninth harmonics from magnetostrictive load devices like ballasts and other transformers, is returned over the system neutral conductor, the output of the zero-sequence CT encircling the conductors is zero. But when a fault to ground develops so that some phase current is not returning by the neutral but is returning along conduit or some other enclosure, the CT detects this ground leakage and produces a current

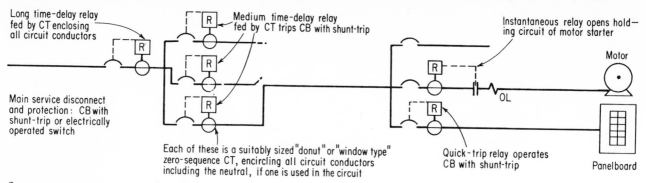

FIG. 126—Selective coordination scheme for protection against ground faults in grounded system

Long time-delay relay fed by CT enclosing all circuit conductors

Medium time-delay relay fed by CT trips CB with shunt-trip

Instantaneous relay opens hold-ing circuit of motor starter

Motor

Main service disconnect and protection: CB with shunt-trip or electrically operated switch

Each of these is a suitably sized "donut" or "window type" zero-sequence CT, encircling all circuit conductors including the neutral, if one is used in the circuit

Quick-trip relay operates CB with shunt-trip

Panelboard

*Note: All relays set to respond to 5 amps or more flowing in the ground-fault circuit

output to actuate a relay which trips the electrically operated switching device controlling the circuit.

A complete system of zero-sequence CTs and related relays with adjustable time delay is available for such protective application throughout a system.

Fig. 126 shows the idea behind the "total protection" scheme using a zero-sequence CT and associated relay on each circuit to be provided with protection against low-level ground faults. For any level of ground fault from 5 amps up, the CT-relay hookup will detect a ground fault on its load side and operate the shunt-trip of a circuit breaker or the coil of an electrically operated switch (such as by breaking the holding coil circuit of a contactor) to quickly clear the fault. This ground protection setup for each circuit is unaffected by operating overloads and short-circuit currents which cancel in the CT. The CT-relay control responds only to ground faults. The operating speed of circuit opening is very fast to minimize any damage due to ground faults and is limited only by the necessity for coordinating the operating speed of the relays to make sure that each ground fault will be cleared by the CT-relay nearest to the fault on the line side of the fault. But the protection is completed through the action of the fuses or CBs which provide for opening each circuit on an operating overload or short-circuit fault above the continuous rating of the devices.

System and equipment grounding

One of the most important, but least understood, considerations in design of electrical systems is that of grounding. The word "grounding" comes from the fact that the technique itself involves making a low-resistance connection to the earth or to ground.

For any given piece of equipment or circuit, this connection may be a direct wire connection to a grounding electrode which is buried in the earth; or it may be a connection to some other conductive metallic element (such as conduit or switchboard enclosure) which is connected to a grounding electrode.

The purpose of grounding is to provide protection of personnel, equipment and circuits by eliminating the possibility of dangerous or excessive voltages.

There are two distinct considerations in grounding for electrical systems: grounding of one of the conductors of the wiring system, and grounding of all metal enclosures which contain electrical wires or equipment when an insulation failure in such enclosures might place a potential on the enclosures and constitute a shock or fire hazard. The types of grounding are:

1. **WIRING SYSTEM GROUND.** This consists of grounding one of the wires of the electrical system to limit the voltage upon the circuit which might otherwise occur through exposure to lightning or other voltages higher than that for which the circuit is designed. Another purpose in grounding one of the wires of the system is to limit the maximum voltage to ground under normal operating conditions. Also, a system which operates with one of its conductors intentionally grounded will provide for automatic opening of the circuit if an accidental or fault ground occurs on one of its ungrounded conductors. See Fig. 127.

Selection of the wiring system conductor to be grounded depends upon the type of system. In 3-wire, single-phase systems, the midpoint of the transformer winding—the point from which the system neutral is derived—is grounded. For grounded 3-phase wiring systems, the neutral point of the wye-connected transformer(s) or generator is usually the point connected to ground. In delta-connected transformer hookups, grounding of the system can be effected by grounding one of the three phase legs, by grounding a center-tap point on one of the transformer windings (as in the 3-phase, 4-wire "red-leg" delta system) or by using a special grounding transformer which establishes a neutral point of a wye connection which is grounded.

According to the code, all interior alternating current wiring systems *must* be grounded if they can be so grounded that the maximum voltage to ground does not exceed 150 volts. This rule makes it *manda-*

FIG. 127—Operating a system with one circuit conductor grounded

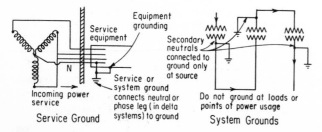

Service equipment

Equipment grounding

Secondary neutrals connected to ground only at source

Service or system ground connects neutral or phase leg (in delta systems) to ground

Incoming power service

Service Ground

Do not ground at loads or points of power usage

System Grounds

tory that the following systems or circuits operate with one conductor grounded:

1. 120-volt, 2-wire system or circuit must have one of its wires grounded.

2. 120/240-volt, 3-wire, single-phase systems or circuits must have their neutral conductor grounded.

3. 120/208-volt, 3-phase, 4-wire, wye-connected systems or circuits must operate with the neutral conductor grounded.

In all of the foregoing systems or circuits, the neutrals must be grounded because **"the maximum voltage to ground does not exceed 150 volts"** from any other conductor of the system when the neutral conductor is grounded. See Fig. 128.

Although the foregoing is the only mandatory rule of the code on grounding of wiring systems, the code does *recommend* that ac systems be grounded where the maximum voltage to ground would be above 150 volts but not over 300 volts. This recommendation says, in effect, that one of the system conductors *should* be grounded (but does not have to be grounded, as a code requirement) for the following systems:

1. 240-volt, 3-phase, 3-wire systems from delta-connected transformers.

2. 480-volt, 3-phase, 4-wire systems from wye-connected transformers—such as 480/277-volt (460/265-volt) systems.

However, if autotransformer type flourescent or mercury-vapor ballasts are to be supplied from 480/277-volt systems then the neutral conductor will usually have to be grounded at the voltage source to conform to Section 410-76. Of course, it should be noted that 480/277-volt systems are usually operated with

FIG. 129—Grounding equipment enclosures

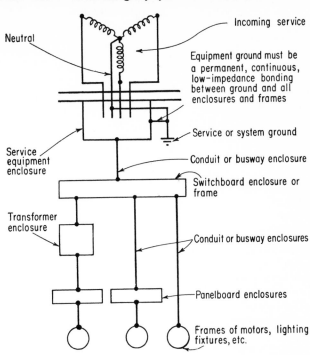

the neutral grounded as a matter of standard design.

For systems or circuits operating at voltages above 300 volts, the code simply says that such system or circuits *may* be grounded.

Direct-current systems—both 2-wire and 3-wire—must also be grounded if the voltage to ground will not exceed 300 volts. A 2-wire dc system, with no more than 300 volts between conductors, must be grounded unless it is used for supplying industrial equipment in limited areas and is equipped with a ground detector. In a 3-wire dc system, the neutral conductor must be grounded.

Grounded neutral systems are generally recommended for high-voltage (over 600) distribution. Although ungrounded systems do not undergo a power outage with only one-phase ground faults, the time and money spent in tracing faults indicated by ground detectors and other disadvantages of ungrounded systems have favored use of grounded neutral systems. Grounded systems are more economical in operation and maintenance. In such a system, if a fault occurs, it is isolated immediately and automatically.

Grounded neutral systems have many other advantages. The elimination of multiple faults caused by undetected restriking grounds greatly increases service reliability. The lower voltage to ground which results from grounding the neutral offers greater safety for personnel and requires lower equipment voltage ratings. And on high-voltage (above 600) systems, residual relays can be used to detect ground faults before they become phase-to-phase faults which have substantial destructive ability.

2. EQUIPMENT GROUND. This is a permanent and continuous bonding together (i.e., connecting together) of all noncurrent-carrying metal parts of equipment enclosures—conduit, boxes, cabinets, enclosures, housings, frame of motors and lighting fixtures—and connection of this interconnected system of enclosures to the system grounding electrode. See Fig. 129. The interconnection of all metal enclosures

FIG. 128—When to ground a system conductor

INTERIOR AC WIRING SYSTEMS

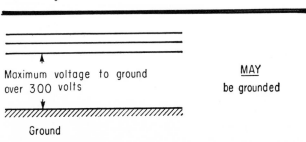

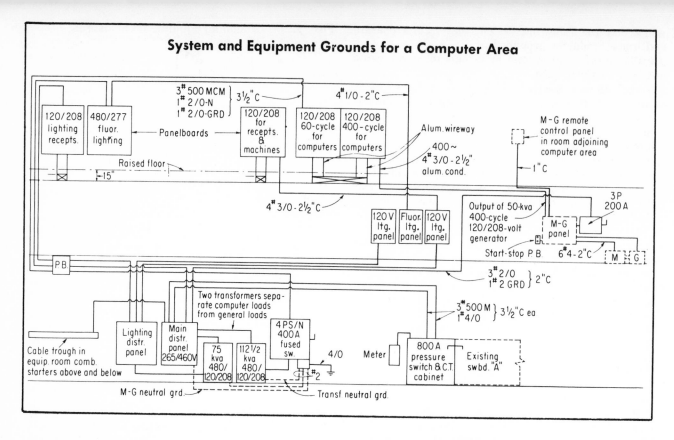

System and Equipment Grounds for a Computer Area

must be made to provide a low-impedance path for fault-current flow along the enclosures to assure operation of overcurrent devices which will open a circuit in the event of a fault. By opening a faulted circuit, the system prevents dangerous voltages from being present on equipment enclosures which could be touched by personnel, with consequent electric shock to such personnel.

Simply stated, grounding of all metal enclosures of electric wires and equipment prevents any potential-above-ground on the enclosures. Such bonding together and grounding of all metal enclosures are required for both grounded electrical systems (those systems in which one of the circuit conductors is intentionally grounded) and ungrounded electrical systems (systems with none of the circuit wires intentionally grounded).

FIG. 130—Characteristics of ungrounded systems

UNGROUNDED SYSTEMS

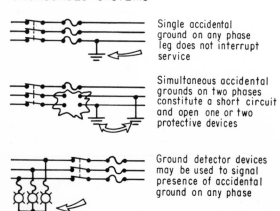

Single accidental ground on any phase leg does not interrupt service

Simultaneous accidental grounds on two phases constitute a short circuit and open one or two protective devices

Ground detector devices may be used to signal presence of accidental ground on any phase

But effective equipment grounding is extremely important for grounded electrical systems to provide the automatic fault clearing which is one of the important advantages of grounded electrical systems. A low-impedance path for fault current is necessary to permit enough current to flow to operate the fuses or circuit breaker protecting the circuit.

In a grounded electrical system with a high-impedance equipment ground return path, if one of the phase conductors of the system (i.e., one of the ungrounded conductors of the wiring system) should accidentally come in contact with one of the metal enclosures in which the wires are run, not enough fault current would flow to operate the overcurrent devices. In such a case, the faulted circuit would not automatically open and a dangerous voltage would be present on the conduit and other metal enclosures. This voltage presents a shock hazard and a fire hazard due to possible arcing or sparking from the energized conduit to some grounded pipe or other piece of grounded metal.

In a grounded system with a high-impedance equipment ground return system, a ground fault will not open the circuit, and a phase-to-phase fault must develop to operate the overcurrent device, with all of the attendant hazards of such conditions.

For effective protection against common ground faults, therefore, low impedance of the equipment bonding system is more important than low impedance of the earth ground itself. And in long runs of magnetic-material conductor enclosures, the ground circuit impedance should be taken as ten times the dc resistance to allow for the many variables.

Although the NE Code does not require grounding of electrical systems in which the voltage to ground would exceed 150 volts, it does recommend that ground-fault detectors be used with ungrounded systems supplying industrial equipment which operates at more than 150 volts and less than 600 volts. Such detectors indicate when an accidental ground fault develops on one of the phase legs of ungrounded systems. Then the indicated ground fault can be removed during downtime of the industrial operation—that is, when the production machinery is not running.

Many industrial plants prefer to use an ungrounded system with ground-fault detectors instead of a grounded system. With a grounded system, the occurrence of a ground fault is supposed to draw enough current to operate the overcurrent device protecting the circuit. But such fault-clearing opens the circuit —which may be a branch circuit supplying a motor or other power load or may be a feeder which supplies a number of power loads; and many industrial plants object to the loss of production caused by downtime. They would rather use the ungrounded system and have the system kept operative with a single ground fault and clear the fault when the production machinery is not in use. In some plants, the cost of downtime of production machines can run to thousands of dollars per minute. In other plants, interruption of critical process is extremely costly.

The difference between a grounded and ungrounded system is that a single ground fault will automatically cause opening of the circuit in a grounded system, but will not interrupt operations in an ungrounded system. However, the presence of a single ground fault on an ungrounded system exposes the system to the very destructive possibilities of a phase-to-phase short if another ground fault should simultaneously develop on a different phase leg of the system. See Fig. 130.

Making ground connections

When an electrical system is to be operated with one conductor grounded—either because it is required by the code (e.g., 120/240-volt, single phase) or because it is desired by the system designer (e.g., 240-volt, 3-phase, corner grounded)—a connection to the grounding electrode must be made at the service entrance. That is, the neutral conductor or other conductor to be grounded must be connected at the service equipment to a conductor which runs to a grounding electrode.

The code says that the connection of the grounding conductor to the system conductor which is to be grounded must be made "on the supply side of the service disconnecting means." This means that the grounding wire (which runs to the water pipe or driven ground rod) must be connected to the system neutral or other system wire to be grounded either in the enclosure for the service disconnect or in some enclosure on the supply side of the service disconnect. Such connection may be made, for instance, in the main service switch or circuit breaker or in a service panelboard or switchboard. Or, the grounding wire may be connected to the system grounded conductor in a gutter, CT cabinet or meter housing on the supply side of the service disconnect.

In addition to the grounding connection for the grounded system conductor at the point of service entrance to the premises, it is further required that another grounding connection be made to the same grounded conductor at the transformer which supplies the system. This means, for example, that a grounded

FIG. 131—Do not bond sub-panels because . . .
(arrows on lines indicate current flow)

1. THIS CONDITION WILL EXIST....AND...

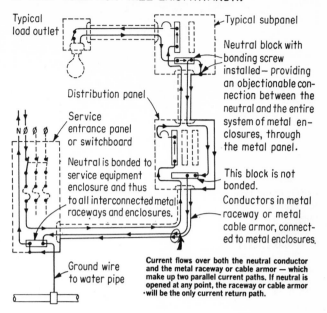

Typical load outlet

Typical subpanel

Neutral block with bonding screw installed—providing an objectionable connection between the neutral and the entire system of metal enclosures, through the metal panel.

Distribution panel

Service entrance panel or switchboard

Neutral is bonded to service equipment enclosure and thus to all interconnected metal raceways and enclosures.

This block is not bonded.

Conductors in metal raceway or metal cable armor, connected to metal enclosures.

Ground wire to water pipe

Current flows over both the neutral conductor and the metal raceway or cable armor — which make up two parallel current paths. If neutral is opened at any point, the raceway or cable armor will be the only current return path.

2. THIS HAZARD COULD DEVELOP

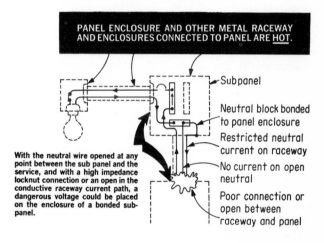

PANEL ENCLOSURE AND OTHER METAL RACEWAY AND ENCLOSURES CONNECTED TO PANEL ARE HOT.

Subpanel

Neutral block bonded to panel enclosure

Restricted neutral current on raceway

No current on open neutral

Poor connection or open between raceway and panel

With the neutral wire opened at any point between the sub panel and the service, and with a high impedance locknut connection or an open in the conductive raceway current path, a dangerous voltage could be placed on the enclosure of a bonded sub-panel.

service to a home must have the grounded neutral connected to a grounding electrode at the utility transformer on the pole, away from the house, as well as having the neutral grounded to a water pipe or other suitable electrode at the house. And in the case of a building served from an outdoor transformer pad or mat installation, the conductor which is grounded in the building must also be grounded at the transformer pad or mat, per NE Code Section 250-23(a).

One of the most important and widely discussed regulations of the entire code revolves around this matter of making a grounding connection to the system grounded neutral or grounded phase wire. The code says, "No connection to a grounding electrode shall be made to the grounded circuit conductor on the load side of the service disconnecting means, except as provided for in Section 250-24." This means that, aside from the conditions of Section 250-24, which covers a single service to two or more buildings, the neutral or other grounded system conductor

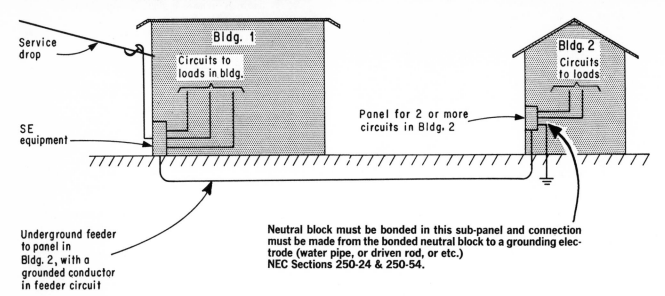

FIG. 132—This bonding of a sub-panel is required

Service drop

SE equipment

Bldg. 1
Circuits to loads in bldg.

Panel for 2 or more circuits in Bldg. 2

Bldg. 2
Circuits to loads

Underground feeder to panel in Bldg. 2, with a grounded conductor in feeder circuit

Neutral block must be bonded in this sub-panel and connection must be made from the bonded neutral block to a grounding electrode (water pipe, or driven rod, or etc.) NEC Sections 250-24 & 250-54.

must not be connected to any equipment enclosure which is grounded to a grounding electrode.

This latter rule in the code makes it a violation to bond the neutral block in a panelboard to the panel enclosure in other than a service panel. See Fig. 131. In a panelboard used as service equipment, the neutral block (terminal block) is invariably bonded to the panel cabinet by the bonding screw provided. And such bonding is required to tie the grounded conductor to the interconnected system of metal enclosures for the system (i.e., service equipment enclosures, conduits, busway, boxes, panel cabinets, etc.). It is this connection which provides for flow of fault current and operation of the overcurrent device (fuse or breaker) when a ground fault occurs. **But, there must not be** any connection between the grounded system conductor and the grounded metal enclosure system at any point on the load side of the service equipment, because such connection would constitute connection of the grounded system conductor to a grounding electrode (through the enclosure and raceway system to the water pipe or driven ground rod).

This rule on not connecting the grounded system wire to a grounding electrode on the load side of the service disconnect must not be confused with the rule of Section 250-60 which permits the grounded system conductor to be used for grounding the frames of electric ranges, wall ovens, counter-mounted cooking units and electric clothes dryers. The connection referred to in Section 250-60 is that of an ungrounded metal enclosure to the grounded conductor for the purpose of grounding the enclosure. The connection of the grounded system conductor to an enclosure which is already grounded is entirely different and is expressly prohibited.

As described previously, bonding of a panel neutral block to the enclosure is required in service equipment and in those cases where a panelboard is used to supply circuits in a building and the panel is fed from another building. This is covered in Section 250-24 which says, "Where more than one building is supplied by the same service, the grounded circuit conductor of the wiring system of any building utilizing one branch circuit supplied from such service may be connected to a grounding electrode at such building, and in the case of any building housing equipment required to be grounded or utilizing two or more branch circuits supplied from such service, and in the case of a building housing livestock, shall be so connected."

Fig. 132 illustrates the condition in which a sub-panel in a building must have its neutral block bonded and must have connection to a grounding electrode. The necessity for bonding the neutral block in such a sub-panel is based on Sections 250-24 and 250-54. The latter section says, "Where the alternating-current system is connected to a grounding electrode in or at a building as specified in Sections 250-23 and 250-24, the same electrode shall be used to ground conductor enclosures and equipment in or on that building." If the feeder circuit is in conduit, current flows on the conduit.

Design of motor feeders

Article 430 of the code covers general requirements for motor feeders. Basic sizing of feeder conductors involves the following procedures:

1. **The current-carrying capacity of feeder conductors supplying several motors must include capacity at least equal to 125% of the full-load current of the highest rated motor plus the sum of the** full-load currents of the other motors supplied by the feeder.

2. **The current-carrying capacity of feeder conductors supplying a single motor plus other loads must include capacity at least equal to 125% of the full-load current of the motor.**

3. **The current-carrying capacity of feeder con-**

FIG. 133—Table for calculating necessary capacitor kvar to improve load of desired power factor

Desired Power Factor in Percentage

Original Power Factor in Percentage

	80%	81	82	83	84	85	86	87	88	89	90	91	92	93	94	95	96	97	98	99	100
50%	.982	1.008	1.034	1.060	1.086	1.112	1.139	1.165	1.192	1.220	1.248	1.276	1.303	1.337	1.369	1.400	1.441	1.481	1.529	1.590	1.732
51	.936	.962	.988	1.014	1.040	1.066	1.093	1.119	1.146	1.174	1.202	1.230	1.257	1.291	1.323	1.357	1.395	1.435	1.483	1.544	1.686
52	.894	.920	.946	.972	.998	1.024	1.051	1.077	1.104	1.132	1.160	1.188	1.215	1.249	1.281	1.315	1.353	1.393	1.441	1.502	1.644
53	.850	.876	.902	.928	.954	.980	1.007	1.033	1.060	1.088	1.116	1.144	1.171	1.205	1.237	1.271	1.309	1.349	1.397	1.458	1.600
54	.809	.835	.861	.887	.913	.939	.966	.992	1.019	1.047	1.075	1.103	1.130	1.164	1.196	1.230	1.268	1.308	1.356	1.417	1.559
55	.769	.795	.821	.847	.873	.899	.926	.952	.979	1.007	1.035	1.063	1.090	1.124	1.156	1.190	1.228	1.268	1.316	1.377	1.519
56	.730	.756	.782	.808	.834	.860	.887	.913	.940	.968	.996	1.024	1.051	1.085	1.117	1.151	1.189	1.229	1.277	1.338	1.480
57	.692	.718	.744	.770	.796	.822	.849	.875	.902	.930	.958	.986	1.013	1.047	1.079	1.113	1.151	1.191	1.239	1.300	1.442
58	.655	.681	.707	.733	.759	.785	.812	.838	.865	.893	.921	.949	.976	1.010	1.042	1.076	1.114	1.154	1.202	1.263	1.405
59	.618	.644	.670	.696	.722	.748	.775	.801	.828	.856	.884	.912	.939	.973	1.005	1.039	1.077	1.117	1.165	1.226	1.368
60	.584	.610	.636	.662	.688	.714	.741	.767	.794	.822	.849	.878	.905	.939	.971	1.005	1.043	1.083	1.131	1.192	1.334
61	.549	.575	.601	.627	.653	.679	.706	.732	.759	.787	.815	.843	.870	.904	.936	.970	1.008	1.048	1.096	1.157	1.299
61	.515	.541	.567	.593	.619	.645	.672	.698	.725	.753	.781	.809	.836	.870	.902	.936	.974	1.014	1.062	1.123	1.265
63	.483	.509	.535	.561	.587	.613	.640	.666	.693	.721	.749	.777	.804	.838	.870	.904	.942	.982	1.030	1.091	1.233
64	.450	.476	.502	.528	.554	.580	.607	.633	.660	.688	.716	.744	.771	.805	.837	.871	.909	.949	.997	1.058	1.200
65	.419	.445	.471	.497	.523	.549	.576	.602	.629	.657	.685	.713	.740	.774	.806	.840	.878	.918	.966	1.027	1.169
66	.388	.414	.440	.466	.492	.518	.545	.571	.598	.626	.654	.682	.709	.743	.775	.809	.847	.887	.935	.996	1.138
67	.358	.384	.410	.436	.462	488	.515	.541	.568	.596	.624	.652	.679	.713	.745	.779	.817	.857	.905	.966	1.108
68	.329	.355	.381	.407	.433	.459	.486	.512	.539	.567	.595	.623	.650	.684	.716	.750	.788	.828	.876	.937	1.079
69	.209	.325	.351	.377	.403	.429	.456	.482	.509	.537	.565	.593	.620	.654	.686	.720	.758	.798	.840	.907	1.049
70	.270	.296	.322	.348	.374	.400	.427	.453	.480	.508	.536	.564	.591	.625	.657	.691	.729	.769	.811	.878	1.020
71	.242	.268	.294	.320	.346	.372	.399	.425	.452	.480	.508	.536	.563	.597	.629	.663	.701	.741	.783	.850	.992
72	.213	.239	.265	.291	.317	.343	.370	.396	.423	.451	.479	.507	.534	.568	.600	.634	.672	.712	.754	.821	.963
73	.186	.212	.238	.264	.290	.316	.343	.369	.396	.424	.452	.480	.507	.541	.573	.607	.645	.685	.727	.794	.936
74	.159	.185	.211	.237	.263	.289	.316	.342	.369	.397	.425	.453	.480	.514	.546	.580	.618	.658	.700	.767	.909
75	.132	.158	.184	.210	.236	.262	.289	.315	.342	.370	.398	.426	.453	.487	.519	.553	.591	.631	.673	.740	.882
76	.105	.131	.157	.183	.209	.235	.262	.288	.315	.343	.371	.399	.426	.460	.492	.526	.564	.604	.652	.713	.855
77	.079	.105	.131	.157	.183	.209	.236	.262	.289	.317	.345	.373	.400	.434	.466	.500	.538	.578	.620	.687	.829
78	.053	.079	.105	.131	.157	.183	.210	.236	.263	.291	.319	.347	.374	.408	.440	.474	.512	.552	.594	.661	.803
79	.026	.052	.078	.104	.130	.156	.183	.209	.236	.264	.292	.320	.347	.381	.413	.447	.485	.525	.567	.634	.776
80	.000	.026	.052	.078	.104	.130	.157	.183	.210	.238	.266	.294	.321	.355	.387	.421	.459	.499	.541	.608	.750
81	——	.000	.026	.052	.078	.104	.131	.157	.184	.212	.240	.268	.295	.329	.361	.395	.433	.473	.515	.582	.724
82	——	——	.000	.026	.052	.078	.105	.131	.158	.186	.214	.242	.269	.303	.335	.369	.407	.447	.489	.556	.698
83	——	——	——	.000	.026	.052	.079	.105	.132	.160	.188	.216	.243	.277	.309	.343	.381	.421	.463	.530	.672
84	——	——	——	——	.000	.026	.053	.079	.106	.134	.162	.190	.217	.251	.283	.317	.355	.395	.437	.504	.645
85	——	——	——	——	——	.000	.027	.053	.080	.108	.136	.164	.191	.225	.257	.291	.329	.369	.417	.478	.620

Example: Total kw input of load from wattmeter reading 100 kw at a power factor of 60%. The leading reactive kva necessary to raise the power factor to 90% is found by multiplying the 100 kw by the factor found in the table, which is .849. Then 100 kw × 0.849 = 84.9 kva. Use 85 kva.

ductors supplying a motor load and a lighting and/or appliance load must be sufficient to handle the lighting and/or appliance load as determined from the procedure for calculating size of lighting feeders, plus the motor load as determined from the previous paragraphs.

The code permits use of demand factors for motor feeders—based on reduced heating of conductors supplying motors operating intermittently or on duty-cycle or motors not operating together. Where necessary this should be checked to make sure that the authority enforcing the code deems the conditions and operating characteristics suitable for reduced capacity feeders.

Sizing conductors

The NE Code allows sizing of motor feeders (and mains supplying combination power and lighting

loads) on the basis of maximum demand running current, calculated as follows:

Running current = $(1.25 \times I_F) + (DF \times I_T)$
where, I_F = full-load current of largest motor

DF = demand factor

I_T = sum of full-load currents of all motors except largest.

But modern design dictates use of the maximum-demand starting current in sizing conductors for improved voltage stability on the feeder. This current is calculated as follows:

Starting current = $I_S + (DF \times I_T)$
where, I_S = average starting current of largest motor (use the percent of motor rated full-load current given for fuses in Tables 430-152 or 430-153).

Voltage drop

Voltage drop and I^2R loss must be carefully taken

DESIGN DATA

SINGLE-PHASE CIRCUITS
Amperes for One Kilowatt at Different Power Factors

Volts	POWER FACTOR IN PER CENT						
	100	95	90	85	80	75	70
100	10.0000	10.5263	11.1111	11.7647	12.5000	13.3333	14.2850
110	9.0909	9.5693	10.1010	10.9652	11.3636	12.1211	12.9870
115	8.6957	9.1533	9.6619	10.2302	10.8696	11.5942	12.4224
120	8.3333	8.7719	9.2592	9.8040	10.4166	11.1111	11.9049
125	8.0000	8.4211	8.8889	9.4118	10.0000	10.6667	11.4286
210	4.7619	5.0125	5.2910	5.6022	5.9524	6.3492	6.8027
220	4.5455	4.7847	5.0505	5.3476	5.6819	6.0606	6.4936
230	4.3479	4.5766	4.8309	5.1151	5.4349	5.7971	6.2113
440	2.2727	2.3923	2.5252	2.6738	2.8409	3.0303	3.2467
550	1.8182	1.9139	2.0202	2.1390	2.2728	2.4242	2.5974
1100	0.9091	0.9569	1.0101	0.0695	1.1364	1.2121	1.2987
2200	0.4545	0.4785	0.5050	0.5348	0.5682	0.6061	0.6494
2300	0.4348	0.4577	0.4831	0.5115	0.5435	0.5797	0.6211
2400	0.4167	0.4386	0.4630	0.4902	0.5208	0.5556	0.5952
2500	0.4000	0.4210	0.4444	0.4706	0.5000	0.5333	0.5714
6600	0.1515	0.1595	0.1684	0.1783	0.1894	0.2020	0.2165
11000	0.0909	0.0957	0.1010	0.1070	0.1136	0.1212	0.1299
13000	0.0769	0.0810	0.0855	0.0905	0.0962	0.1026	0.1099
25000	0.0400	0.0421	0.0444	0.0471	0.0500	0.0533	0.0571
45000	0.0222	0.0234	0.0247	0.0261	0.0278	0.0296	0.0317
60000	0.0167	0.0175	0.0185	0.0196	0.0208	0.0222	0.0238

THREE-PHASE CIRCUITS
Amperes per Wire for One Kilowatt at Different Power Factors

Volts	POWER FACTOR IN PER CENT						
	100	95	90	85	80	75	70
100	5.7735	6.0774	6.4150	6.7924	7.2169	7.6980	8.2479
110	5.2486	5.5249	5.8319	6.1749	6.5608	6.9982	7.4980
115	5.0204	5.2847	5.5783	5.9064	6.2756	6.6939	7.1721
120	4.8112	5.0645	5.3458	5.6603	6.0141	6.4150	6.8732
125	4.6188	4.8619	5.1320	5.4339	5.7735	6.1584	6.5983
210	2.7493	2.8940	3.0548	3.2345	3.4366	3.6657	3.9276
220	2.6243	2.7624	2.9159	3.0874	3.2804	3.4992	3.7490
225	2.5660	2.7010	2.8511	3.0188	3.2075	3.4213	3.6657
230	2.5102	2.6423	2.7891	2.9532	3.1378	3.3470	3.5860
240	2.4056	2.5322	2.6729	2.8301	3.0070	3.2075	3.4366
400	1.4434	1.5194	1.6038	1.6981	1.8042	1.9245	2.0620
440	1.3122	1.3812	1.4579	1.5437	1.6402	1.7495	1.8745
500	1.1547	1.2155	1.2830	1.3585	1.4434	1.5396	1.6496
550	1.0497	1.1050	1.1664	1.2350	1.3121	1.3996	1.4996
1100	.5249	.5525	.5832	.6175	.6561	.6998	.7498
2100	.2749	.2894	.3055	.3234	.3437	.3666	.3928
2200	.2624	.2762	.2916	.3087	.3280	.3499	.3749
2300	.2510	.2642	.2789	.2953	.3138	.3347	.3586
2400	.2406	.2532	.2673	.2830	.3007	.3208	.3437
2500	.2309	.2431	.2566	.2717	.2887	.3079	.3299
6600	.0875	.0921	.0972	.1029	.1093	.1167	.1249
11000	.0525	.0552	.0583	.0617	.0656	.0700	.0750
20000	.0289	.0304	.0321	.0340	.0361	.0385	.0412
25000	.0231	.0243	.0257	.0272	.0289	.0308	.0330
33000	.0175	.0184	.0194	.0206	.0219	.0233	.0250
50000	.0115	.0122	.0128	.0136	.0144	.0154	.0165
55000	.0105	.0111	.0117	.0124	.0131	.0140	.0150
60000	.0096	.0101	.0107	.0113	.0120	.0128	.0137

Design Data Used to Determine Capacitor PF Correction for Plug-In Busway to Motor Loads

Bus duct	Total hp	40% Demand	95% Eff.	Kw	Kva 80%	Kvar 80%	Kva 95%	Kvar 95%	Kvar diff.	Kvar use
! A	364	146	153	109	136	82	115	35	47	45
I B	374	150	157	117	142	85	124	38.4	46.6	45
I C	461	185	194	145	181	109	153	47	62	60
2 A	735	(30%) 220	230	172	215	130	181	56	74	75
2 B	1300	(30%) 390	410	306	382	230	322	100	130	135
3 A	729	291	307	229	286	172	241	75	97	105
3 B	275	110	116	87	109	65	92	29	36	45

FORMULAS: Power Factor $= \dfrac{KW}{KVA}$ KW output of motor = HP x .746 $\cos \phi_1 = .8$ $\cos \phi_2 = .95$

$KVA = \dfrac{1.73 \times E \times I}{1000}$ KW input to motor $= \dfrac{HP \times .746}{Efficiency}$ $\sin \phi_1 = .6$ $\sin \phi_2 = .312$

KVA input to induction motor $= \dfrac{HP \times .746}{P.F. \times Eff.}$ $KVA = \dfrac{KW}{\cos \phi}$ KVAR = KVA x $\sin \phi$

Power Factor $= \cos \phi$

into consideration when sizing motor feeders. The design percentage of tolerable voltage drop may vary with the particular operating conditions and layout of the motor loads served but should never exceed 3% drop from the service entrance to the point of origin of motor branch circuits. However, a maximum voltage drop of only 2% from the service to points of motor branch-circuit protection is widely used for motor feeder design.

Calculation of voltage drop should include consideration of reactance as well as resistance in the feeder conductors, as both contribute to the drop. Power factor must also be accounted for in these calculations. And voltage drop in a feeder must be analyzed in terms of the number of motors supplied, the size of each motor and the operating duty.

When a number of motors might be starting simultaneously or several motors driving sluggish loads might be started at or near the same time, the voltage drop in the feeder could be extreme unless its size accounted for the high load current. Of course, such conditions and analysis of them will often clearly indicate further subdivision or adjustment of feeder loads, selection of types of motors to use and selection of the best types of controllers to use. The initial value of starting current—the locked-rotor current—must be used in studying the effect of motor loads on voltage drop.

I²R losses in motor feeders—the watts lost in the conductors due to heat developed by current flow through the conductors—equal the square of the total current drawn through the conductors times the total resistance of the conductors. This loss may frequently be substantial even when the voltage drop in the feeder is within recommended limits. All voltage drop studies and calculations should include consideration of further increasing conductor size—over that necessary to limit voltage drop—in order to limit I²R loss and the kwhr energy costs of such useless power loss.

Power factor

Improvement in the power factor of a motor feeder by placing the proper kvar rating of capacitor at the supply end of the feeder reduces the amount of current flow to a given kw load and reduces voltage drop, by eliminating the reactive current from the feeder conductors.

The power factor of a circuit supplying several motors is determined as follows:

1. For each motor, multiply its horsepower by its power factor at 75% of rated load.

2. Add up these products for all of the motors.

3. The sum obtained in "2" divided by the total horsepower connected to the circuit will give the approximate (but accurate enough for most calculations) power factor of the circuit. Correction of the circuit to raise the power factor to a desired level can then be made by selecting capacitor kvar rating for the given load based on calculations contained in the literature of capacitor manufacturers.

Fig. 133 is a type of handy table commonly used for computing the required kvar (reactive kva) of capacitor equipment to raise power factor from one value to another for a given kw load.

Protection of motor feeders

Overcurrent protection for a feeder to several motors must have a rating or setting not greater than the largest rating or setting of branch-circuit protective device for any motor of the group plus the sum of the full-load currents of the other motors supplied by the feeder. This is shown in Fig. 134, covering basic calculations.

If two or more motors of equal horsepower rating are the largest in the group, one of these should be considered as the largest for the calculation of feeder overcurrent protection. **It should be noted that according to Section 430-62 (b), in large capacity installations where extra feeder capacity is provided for load growth or future changes, the feeder overcurrent protection may be calculated on the basis of the rated current-carrying capacity of the feeder conductors.**

In some cases, such as where two or more motors on a feeder may be started simultaneously, feeder conductors may have to be larger than usually required for feeders to several motors. In such cases, correspondingly larger ratings or settings of feeder overcurrent protection may be used.

FIG. 134—Calculating a motor feeder

Typical calculation of conductor size and overcurrent protection for a feeder serving a group of motors is shown here:

A feeder supplies four 3-phase motors as follows:
1—50-hp squirrel cage induction motor (full-voltage starting)
1—30-hp wound-rotor induction motor
2—10-hp squirrel-cage induction motors (full-voltage starting)
The feeder is a 3-phase, 440-volt, 60-cycle supply.

Step 1. From Table 430-150, the motors have full-load current ratings as follows:
50-hp motor = 63 amps—which requires No. 3 TW or No. 4 RHW branch-circuit conductors.
30-hp motor = 39 amps—which requires No. 6 TW or No. 6 RHW branch-circuit conductors.
10-hp motor = 14 amps—which requires No. 12 TW or No. 12 RHW branch-circuit conductors.

Step 2. The feeder conductors must have a carrying capacity as follows:
$1.25 \times 63 = 79$ amps $+ 39$ amps $+ (2 \times 14$ amps$) = 146$ amps.
The feeder conductors must then be No. 3/0 TW or No. 1/0 RHW.

Step 3. Overcurrent protection (From Table 410-146)
1. The 50-hp motor must be protected at not more than 200 amps (fuse) for branch-circuit protection.
2. The 30-hp motor must be protected at not more than 60 amps (fuse) for branch-circuit protection.
3. Each 10-hp motor must be protected at not more than 45 amps (fuse) for branch-circuit protection.

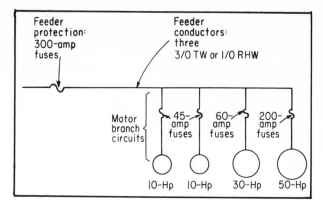

Step 4. Feeder overcurrent protection
The maximum rating or setting for the overcurrent device protecting such a feeder must not be greater than the largest rating or setting of branch-circuit protective device for one of the motors of the group plus the sum of the full-load currents of the other motors. From the above, then, the maximum allowable size of feeder fuses is—
$200 + 39 + 14 + 14 = 267$ amps, or 300-amp fuses.
NOTE: The values obtained by these calculations are minimum basic sizes and ratings required for the given load. Use of circuit-breaker protection would involve other calculations. And voltage drop and line losses would also have to be considered. Overall layout, and choice of equipment could also affect ultimate sizings.

FIG. 135—Feeder calculations for a combination load

The following is a calculation procedure, based on the NE Code, for sizing circuit elements to supply a load of—

A. Four 3-phase, 220-volt, squirrel-cage induction motors, designed for 40C temperature rise, marked Code letter H, started across the line and rated:
one—10-hp motor,
one—7½-hp motor and
two—1½-hp motors; plus

B. A 20-kw, single-phase 115-volt lighting load.

Step 1—Average full load currents (Table 430–150)
10 hp—27 amps
7½ hp—22
1½ hp— 5

Step 2—Main feeder for motors (Section 430–24)
10: 1.25 x 27 or 33.75 amps
7½: 22
1½: 2 x 5   10
                ———
Total   65.75 amps
3 No. 6 RHW in 1-in. conduit.

Step 3—Individual branch circuits for each motor (Section 430–22)
10: 1.25 x 27 or 33.75 amps
3 No. 8 TW or RHW in ¾-in. conduit
7½: 1.25 x 22 or 27.5 amps
3 No. 10 TW or RHW in ¾-in.
1½: 1.25 x 5 or 6¼ amps
3 No. 14 TW or RHW in ½-in.

Step 4—Motor overcurrent protection (running protection usually thermal relays, heaters, etc. in controller, Section 430–32). Since the same 125% factor applies for this as it does for the individual branch-circuit size calculation, the maximum rated thermal elements, etc., shall be for each
10 hp: 33.75 amps
7½ hp: 27.5
1½ hp: 6.25

Step 5—Maximum rating of branch-circuit overcurrent protection. Table 430–152 (also see Section 430–52) shows for

these motors and Code letter H a maximum of 300% for fuse rating, therefore for
10 hp: 27 x 3 or 81 amps—use 100-amp block with three 90-amp fuses
7½: 22 x 3 or 66 amps—use 100-amp block with three 70-amp fuses
1½: 5 x 3 or 15 amps—use 30-amp block with three 15-amp fuses

Step 6—Main motor feeder protection (Section 430–62)
10 hp: 27 x 3 or 81 (or 90) amps
7½: 22
1½: 2 x 5 or 10
            ———
        113 (or 122) amps
Use 200-amp switch with three 125-amp fuses.

Step 7—The following pertains to the lighting load. Assume this to be 115/230 single phase. Full-load current would be
$$\frac{20 \times 1000}{230}$$ or 87 amps

Use 100-amp switch with two 90-amp fuses. [If 87-amp load is continuous, a fused switch must be selected so that load is not over 80% of the fuse rating. This means minimum fuse size would be 87 x 1.25 = 108.75, or a 110-amp fuse for each phase, in a 200-amp switch. (Per NEMA standards)]

Use three No. 3 RHW in 1¼-in. conduit (or three No. 2 RHW).

Step 8—If these two loads will be fed from separate services then the above calculations are complete. If a combination service is to be used, then we can serve this customer with a 4-wire, 240-volt, delta service. The lighting load is thus fed only from two of the three phases.

Step 9—Motor feeder   113 amps (starting demand)
Lighting (2 phases) 87
                    ———
                    200 amps

The main switch would be a 200-amp size with two 200-amp fuses in two phases and one 125-amp fuse in the third phase.
Two main service lines would be 2/0 RHW, one would be No. 6 RHW and the neutral would be No. 3 RHW. These, of course, are minimum sizes based only on NE code rules of safe application.

In selecting the size of a feeder overcurrent protective device, it should be noted that the NE Code calculation is concerned with establishing a maximum value for the fuse or CB. If a lower value of protection is suitable, it may be used.

Protection for a feeder to both motor loads and a lighting and/or appliance load must be rated on the basis of both of these loads. The rating or setting of the overcurrent device must be sufficient to carry the lighting and/or appliance load plus the rating or setting of the motor branch-circuit protective device if only one motor is supplied, or plus the highest rating or setting of branch-circuit protective device for any one motor plus the sum of the full-load currents of the other motors, if more than one motor is supplied.

Fig. 135 presents basic NE Code calculations for arriving at minimum requirements on wire sizes and overcurrent protection for a combination power and lighting load. Such considerations as voltage drop, I^2R loss, spare capacity, lamp dimming on motor starting, etc., would have to be made to arrive at actual sizes to use for the job. But, the circuiting as shown would be safe—although maybe not efficient or effective for the particular job requirements.

Wiring methods for distribution

Once the voltage and current ratings and other electrical characteristics of feeder circuits have been established, design is completed by selecting the actual physical makeup of the circuits. This means selection of either a raceway system or a cable system.

Although busway and interlocked armor cable have been constantly gaining popularity in distribution systems, wire in rigid conduit or electrical metallic tubing are still the most used methods. For underground applications, a number of metallic-jacketed cables and nonmetallic-jacketed cables have proved extremely reliable for direct earth burial. And for in-building feeders, Type MI cable, Type ALS cable and Type MC offer advantages in some hazardous locations. Cable assemblies—like aluminum sheathed cable, corrugated-metal-jacketed cables and prewired plastic conduit—also offer advantages in many different types of installations.

For outdoor distribution, choice has to be made between overhead or underground circuits. Primary and secondary distribution between buildings can usually be served best by underground installations for a number of reasons:

1. Accident hazards are minimized and isolated.

2. Ambient temperature is lowest and cable capacities are highest.

3. Cables are not in the way as obstructions to expansion of buildings or as interference to work.

4. Appearance of installations is neater, and architectural and landscape design is not marred by unsightly poles.

The cost of underground installation is not always justified under these conditions:

1. Where chemical ingredients in the soil constitute a serious corrosion threat to directly buried metal conduits (galvanized steel or aluminum).

2. Where extensive changes or expansions of buildings or plants would require removal or alteration of underground feeders.

3. Where proper installation of underground circuits is complicated by conditions of the ground such as excessive rock.

Cable selection

Selection of feeder conductors for all types of primary and secondary voltage circuits should be made

FIG. 136—Aluminum conductors for large feeders

Equivalent aluminum and copper conductors based on voltage drop on three single conductors enclosed in a magnetic conduit, 80% power factor, 75°C insulation. Wire temperature and corresponding current-carrying capacities at 30°C ambient.

Copper conductors		Aluminum conductors			
Size	Voltage drop phase to phase per amp per 1000 ft	Amps	Size	Voltage drop phase to phase per amp per 100 ft	Amps
1/0	.232	150	3/0	.228	155
2/0	.193	175	4/0	.190	180
3/0	.163	200	250MCM	.169	205
4/0	.138	230	350MCM	.134	250
250MCM	.126	255	400MCM	.124	270
350MCM	.104	310	500MCM	.108	310
400MCM	.097	335	600MCM	.098	340
500MCM	.088	380	750MCM	.089	385

Conduit sizes for three conductors of equivalent current-carrying capacities (New Work)

Copper		Aluminum	
3—No. 1/0	2″	3—No. 3/0	2″
3—No. 2/0	2″	3—No. 4/0	2½″
3—No. 3/0	2″	3—No. 250MCM	2½″
3—No. 4/0	2½″	3—No. 350MCM	3″
3—No. 250MCM	2½″	3—No. 400MCM	3″
3—No. 350MCM	3″	3—No. 500MCM	3″

FIG. 137—Aluminum conductors in NM cable

60°C Insulated aluminum conductors used in nonmetallic sheathed cable		
Circuit wires AWG	Ampacity	AL Grounding wire (in cable) AWG
No. 12	15	No. 14
No. 10	25	No. 12
No. 8*	30	No. 12
No. 6*	40	No. 10*
* Stranded		

FIG. 138—Code rules on installing UF cable

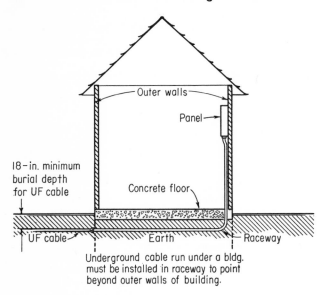

Underground cable run under a bldg. must be installed in raceway to point beyond outer walls of building.

on the basis of careful consideration of the many factors involved, including:

CONDUCTOR SIZE is determined according to—
   A. load current to be supplied,
   B. voltage drop and regulation,
   C. temperature rise within the limitations of the insulation,
   D. reasonable energy losses,
   E. ability to withstand short-circuit heating, and
   F. spare capacity for load growth.

Although copper has been the long-time standard for electric conductor material, there has been steady and sometimes rapid growth in the use of aluminum conductors. Often, the material-cost savings with aluminum conductors can be very substantial. And the light weight of such conductors can be very substantial. And the light weight of such conductors provides reductions in cost of installation labor. Suitable lugs and connectors for aluminum conductors are widely available.

Fig. 136 presents data on the use of aluminum conductors for large-size feeders in all types of commercial, institutional and industrial buildings. Allowable current-carrying capacities for aluminum conductors in raceway or cable, in direct burial and in free air are given in Tables 310-14 and 310-15 of the NE Code. Although comparison between cop-

per and aluminum conductors is usually made on the basis of current rating alone, comparison on the basis of voltage drop is better because practical equivalents are thereby indicated. Of course, aluminum conductors of the same current rating or voltage drop rating as copper conductors will be larger and may require a larger conduit. This must be considered in economic analysis of aluminum conductor application. These considerations are represented in Fig. 136.

Nonmetallic sheathed cable with aluminum conductors and aluminum grounding wire is available for use as feeders (and branch circuits) in all types of 600-volt building systems. Fig. 137 shows current ratings and makeups for such cables. The conductors of such NM feeders should only be used with switches, overcurrent devices, panels and neutral blocks equipped with terminals suitable for aluminum conductors.

INSULATION must be selected according to—
   For voltage up to 600:
   A. cost,
   B. temperature rise, including both ambient temperature and temperature due to heating effect of load,
   C. ease of installation, and
   D. environment in application, such as moisture, fumes, chemicals, petroleum products, acids, alkalies, etc.
   For high voltage (over 600 volts):
   A. tested and proved physical and electrical characteristics.

PROTECTIVE COVERING must be selected according to—
   A. excellence of protection for the insulation against environment (moisture, chemicals, acids, etc.),
   B. excellence of protection against physical damage, such as abrasion, impact, cutting, etc., and
   C. ability of any metallic coverings to withstand corrosion and electrolysis.

A very important consideration, indicated above, is the provision of conductor size to meet the potential heating load of short-circuit currents in cables. With expanded use of circuit-breaker overcurrent protection, coordination of protection from loads back to the source has introduced time delays in operation of overcurrent devices. Cables in such systems must be able to withstand any impressed short-circuit currents for the durations of overcurrent delay. For example, a motor circuit to a 100-hp motor might be required to carry as much as 15,000 amps for a number of seconds. To limit damage to the cable due to heating effect, a much larger size conductor than necessary for the load current alone may be required.

A wealth of data on selection and installation of conductors and cables is given in "Chapter 3—Wiring Methods and Materials" of the NE Code. Fig. 138, for instance, shows some requirements of the code for Type UF underground feeder cable.

Section 300-7 contains a second paragraph, which reads: "Underground cable run under a building shall be in a raceway that is extended beyond the outer wall of the building." The rule does not recognize the past practice of burying Type UF cables in the ground beneath a building and using short conduit stubs where such cables emerge through the floor to boxes or panels.

Types of raceways

Feeder conduit may be rigid metal conduit or electrical metallic tubing for 4-in. or smaller size conduit. Rigid metal conduit of steel or aluminum provides excellent mechanical protection for the conductors, encloses possible faults and is a low-resistance path to ground to assure quick operation of circuit protective devices in the event of fault currents. EMT offers light weight, with ease of handling, cutting and bending.

A big advantage in the use of conduit for feeders is that a conduit installation reduces the distance to which short-circuit problems extend into a building from the service. Breaking the load into the smaller feeders inherent in a conduit-and-cable distribution system introduces more impedance between distribution point and final branch-circuit overcurrent protective devices, thereby reducing the size of the short circuits which these final overcurrent protective devices must handle, while total impedance and consequent distribution system losses introduced by breakup into small feeders are not appreciably increased for the overall project. And in a conduit installation, electrical faults are localized to relatively small portions of the distribution system: repairs can be made quickly, with little interruption of service.

The lower reactance of circuits in aluminum conduit can produce important reduction in voltage drop. In the initial design of an office building, sizing of feeders for the given loads was based on the voltage drop characteristics of circuits in steel conduit. For the original plan, available kva at each lighting panel conformed to anticipated initial and future demands of tenants. When, however, a decision was made to install the feeders in aluminum conduit, available tenant kva capacity had to be recalculated on the basis of lower reactance—and, consequently, voltage drop—of circuits in nonmagnetic enclosures. As a result, it was found that load could be increased from 10-15% without exceeding conductor current rating or the required limit of 2% voltage drop in each feeder.

Section 348-5 of the code permits EMT sizes up to 4 in. The new EMT sizes of 2½ in. and larger have the *same outside diameter* as rigid metal conduits of corresponding sizes. This provides availability of fittings for the new EMT sizes. Accordingly, the interior cross-sectional areas (sq in.) are proportionally larger, and this provides more wiring space for greater ease of installation of conductors in these new sizes of EMT. Fig. 139 illustrates some approximate dimensional comparisons between the new EMT sizes and those for existing heavy-wall rigid metal conduit in corresponding sizes. It is significant that with increased internal diameters for respective sizes of EMT, the sq in. cross-sectional areas are from 16% to 22% more. To prevent any misunderstanding, it should be stressed that the greater cross-sectional area of the inside of these new EMT sizes, compared with rigid, *does not offer* the chance to fill such EMT runs with more conductors than could be used in corresponding sizes of rigid conduit. Number of conductors permitted in "conduit or tubing" is the same for rigid or EMT, from Tables 1 through 8 of NE Code, Chapter 9.

The NE Code regulates use of rigid metal conduit

FIG. 139—EMT vs. rigid in 2½, 3 and 4 in.

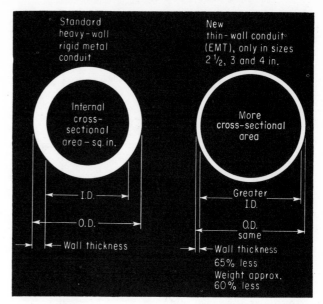

Trade size rigid and EMT	Inches outer dia. (O.D.) EMT and rigid	Wall thickness in.		Inside cross-sectional area sq. in.		More C.S.A. % for EMT
		Rigid	EMT	Rigid	EMT	
2½	2.875	0.203	0.072	4.79	5.85	22%
3	3.500	0.216	0.072	7.38	8.84	19%
4	4.500	0.237	0.083	12.72	14.75	16%

and EMT when either is used in corrosive locations. A new code rule says: "Unless made of a material judged suitable for the condition, or unless corrosion protection approved for the condition is provided, ferrous or nonferrous metallic conduit, elbows, couplings and fittings shall not be installed in concrete or in direct contact with the earth, or in areas subject to severe corrosive influences." Note that this covers both rigid steel and aluminum conduits, but does leave finite interpretation of the meaning of the rule up to the local inspector. This rule also permits the development of products, tests and standards to provide suitable materials for highly corrosive conditions such as found in certain soils or poured concrete that may contain soluble chlorides.

Other types of conduit and raceways also find regular application in modern electrical design:

Cable troughs and cable racks are widely used for supporting and routing feeders in many types of industrial buildings. Troughs of metal mesh construction provide a sturdy, flexible system for supporting feeder cables, particularly where routing of the runs is devious or where provision for change or modification in circuiting is important. Cable racks are used for supporting interlocked armor cable feeders in many installations. They have also been used to support secondary feeders of neoprene-jacketed cables. Article 318 of the code covers design and installation of cable tray and rack systems. Fig. 140 shows code details.

Asbestos-cement and other composition ducts with feeder conductors are also used, offering minimum

FIG. 140—Using cable trays and racks
(NE Code Article 318)

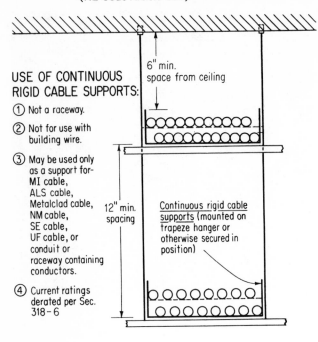

USE OF CONTINUOUS
RIGID CABLE SUPPORTS:

① Not a raceway.

② Not for use with
building wire.

③ May be used only
as a support for:
MI cable,
ALS cable,
Metalclad cable,
NM cable,
SE cable,
UF cable, or
conduit or
raceway containing
conductors.

④ Current ratings
derated per Sec.
318-6

6" min.
space from ceiling

12" min.
spacing

Continuous rigid cable
supports (mounted on
trapeze hanger or
otherwise secured in
position)

FIG. 141—Thinwall conductors for rewiring benefit

75°C NO. 12 WIRES IN ½-IN. CONDUIT

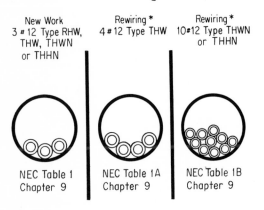

New Work
3 #12 Type RHW,
THW, THWN
or THHN

Rewiring *
4 #12 Type THW

Rewiring *
10 #12 Type THWN
or THHN

NEC Table 1
Chapter 9

NEC Table 1A
Chapter 9

NEC Table 1B
Chapter 9

REDUCED CONDUIT FOR SAME WIRES

New Work
3 - ⅟₀ RHW, THW
THWN, THHN in
2" conduit

Rewiring*
3 - ⅟₀ TW, THW
in 1½" conduit

Rewiring*
3 - ⅟₀ THWN, THHN
in 1¼" conduit

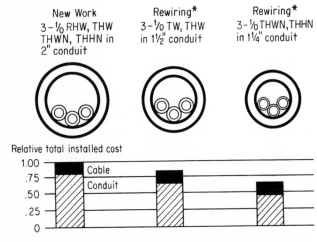

Relative total installed cost

1.00
.75   Cable
.50   Conduit
.25
0

* Based upon 40% maximum fill. Where code limitations·do not
apply, these represent practical arrangements for New Work.

voltage drop due to greatly reduced conductor reactance, because of the absence of the core effect of magnetic conduit, which increases inductive reactance.

Still another type of conduit used in modern distribution is rigid plastic conduit. Article 347 of the code covers "Rigid Nonmetallic Conduit," including: fiber, asbestos cement, soapstone, high density polyethylene and rigid polyvinyl chloride for underground use and rigid polyvinyl chloride, alone, for use above ground. Such conduits are accepted for use underground at any voltage. They may be encased in at least 2 in. of concrete or directly buried at not less than 24 in. below grade, for circuits up to 600 volts. At higher voltage, they must be encased in at least 2 in. of concrete. Other uses recognized by the code include:

1. In concrete walls, floors and ceilings.
2. In places with corrosive atmospheres, with the conduit exposed.
3. In cinder fill.
4. In wet locations.
5. In dry and damp locations not prohibited by Section 347-3.

Rigid nonmetallic conduit may not generally be used: 1. less than 8 ft above ground outdoors unless protected against physical damage; 2. in hazardous locations; 3. in the concealed spaces of combustible construction; 4. for the support of fixtures or other equipment; 5. where subject to mechanical damage; 6. where subject to excessive temperature; and 7. in sunlight unless approved for the purpose.

When rigid plastic conduit is used, it will generally be necessary to carry an equipment grounding conductor with the circuit conductors to provide connection to ground for all equipment with non-current-carrying metallic parts where they might be a shock or fire hazard—as required in Article 250 on grounding. In one particular job, over 38,000 ft of bare copper conductors from Nos. 4 to 14 were used for grounding of metal outlet boxes, panel enclosures, etc. And the material and labor costs of the grounding conductors have to be added to the job, along with the possibility in many cases that a larger size of conduit will have to be used to accommodate the extra wire for grounding in addition to the regular circuit wires. **Section 347-11 requires that such an equipment grounding wire be installed in the nonmetallic conduit.**

Raceway conductor fill

The number of conductors permitted in a particular size of conduit or tubing is covered in Chapter 9 of the code, in Tables 1, 1A, 1B and 2 for conductors all of the same size used for new work and rewiring. Tables 3 to 7 cover combinations of conductors of different sizes when used for new work or rewiring. For nonlead-covered conductors, three or more to a conduit, the sum of the cross-sectional areas of the individual conductors must not exceed 40% of the interior cross-section·area of the conduit or tubing for new work or for rewiring existing conduit or tubing.

THWN and THHN are the smallest diameter building wires. Fig. 141 shows how the greatly reduced insulation wall on Type THWN or THHN

FIG. 142—Counting the neutral for conductor derating

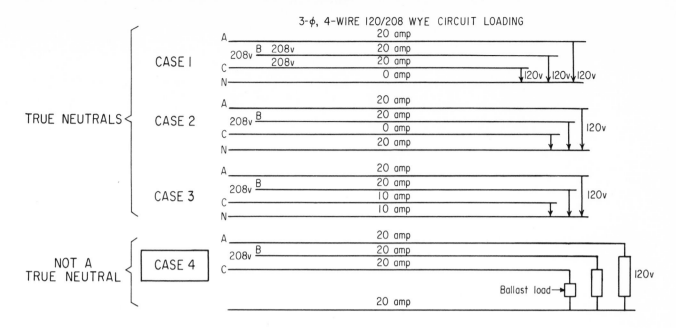

affects conduit fill for rewiring existing conduits. Although THWN and THHN offer no advantage in conduit occupancy for new work (Table 1, Chapter 9, NE Code, applies to all wires), these smaller wires appreciably reduce installation labor due to the reduced conduit fill. And the nylon jacket on THWN and THHN has an extremely low coefficient of friction. THWN is a 75° rated wire for general circuit use in dry or wet locations. THHN is a 90°C rated wire for dry locations only.

To fill conduit to the code allowance is a minimum practice and frequently difficult or impossible from the mechanical standpoint of pulling the conductors into the conduit, due to twisting and bending of the conductors within the conduit. Bigger-than-minimum conduit should generally be used to provide some measure of spare capacity for load growth, and in many cases, the conduit to be used should be upsized considerably to allow future installation of some larger, anticipated size of conductors.

When sizing feeder conductors on the basis of the loads to be served, the voltage drop to be expected and the computed amount of spare capacity, the derating factors applicable to conductors in conduit must be applied:

According to Note 8 for Tables 310-12 through 310-15: Tables 310-12 and 310-14 give the allowable current-carrying capacities for not more than three conductors in a raceway or cable. Where the number of conductors in a raceway or cable exceeds three, the allowable current-carrying capacity of each conductor shall be reduced as shown in the following table:

Number of conductors	Per Cent of Values in Tables 310-12 and 310-14
4 to 6	80
7 to 24	70
25 to 42	60
43 and above	50

The code does not require application of derating requirements in the case of Wireways (Article 362), Auxiliary Gutters (Article 374) and Low-Energy Power, Low-Voltage and Signal Circuits (Article 725). But the conductor fill requirements must be observed for wireways, auxiliary gutters, surface metal raceway, underfloor raceways, etc.

When selecting the size of conduit, neutral conductors are included in the total number of conductors because they occupy space as well as phase conductors. A completely separate consideration, however, is the relation of neutral conductors to the number of conductors which determines whether a derating factor must be applied to conductors in a conduit.

It should be noted that neutral conductors which carry only unbalanced current from phase conductors (as in the case of normally balanced 3-wire, single-phase or 4-wire, 3-phase circuits) are not counted when determining the current derating of conductors on the basis of the number in a conduit, as just described. Of course, a neutral conductor used with 2-phase legs of a 4-wire, 3-phase system to make up a 3-wire feeder is not a true neutral in the sense of carrying only current unbalance. Such a neutral carries the same current as the other two conductors under balanced load conditions and must be counted as a phase conductor when derating more than three conductors in conduit.

Because the neutral of a 3-phase, 4-wire wye feeder to a load of fluorescent or mercury ballasts will carry current even under balanced loading on the phases, such a neutral is not a true noncurrent-carrying conductor and should be counted as a phase wire when determining the number of conductors to arrive at a derating factor for more than three conductors in a conduit. As a result, all of the conductors of a 3-phase, 4-wire feeder to a fluorescent load would be derated to 80% of their nominal allowable current-carrying capacities from Tables 310-12 or 310-14. And because this is a derating of the conductor current capacity, the conductors must be protected in accordance with their new derated capacity.

Complete Busway Distribution for a Laboratory Building

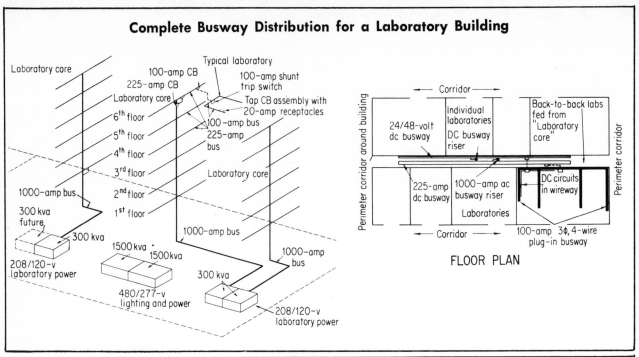

Busway Application

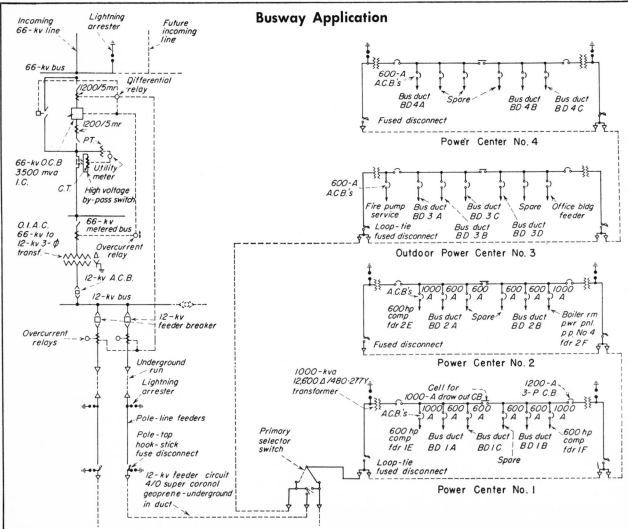

Fig. 142 shows four basic conditions of neutral loading and the need for counting the neutral conductor when derating a circuit to fluorescent or mercury ballasts, as follows:

CASE 1—With balanced loads of equal power fac-

tor, there is no neutral current, and consequently no heating due to neutral. For purposes of heat derating according to the code, this circuit produces the heating effect of three conductors.

CASE 2—With two phases loaded and the third

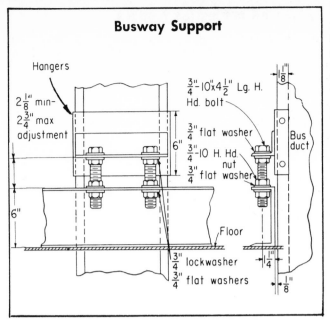

Busway Support

Hangers

$2\frac{1}{8}''$ min- $2\frac{3}{4}''$ max adjustment

$\frac{3}{4}''$-10x$4\frac{1}{2}''$ Lg. H. Hd. bolt

$\frac{3}{4}''$ flat washer

$\frac{3}{4}''$-10 H. Hd. nut

$\frac{3}{4}''$ flat washer

Bus duct

6"

6"

Floor

$\frac{3}{4}''$ lockwasher

$\frac{3}{4}''$ flat washers

$\frac{1}{8}''$

$\frac{1}{4}''$

$\frac{1}{8}''$

Busway has proved a versatile, flexible and economical method of electrical distribution. Offering safety, reliability, ease of layout and efficient operation, busway systems require only basic engineering in their design. And they are capable of carrying large and small blocks of power from main switchboards to loadcenters to loads. For point-to-point power distribution, the overall economy of busway—labor and material costs—makes it particularly effective for heavy loads.

Busways are designed specifically to minimize voltage drop or reactance, to serve high-amperage intermittent loads such as those created by resistance welders, or to carry high-cycle current for special lighting, laboratory or induction heating purposes. They also are available as slotted assemblies to accommodate moving trolleys.

Construction variety is similarly broad, inasmuch as conductors may be of copper or aluminum, hollow or solid, rectangular, oval or beam-shaped. Conductors also may be insulated or bare, with phase bars grouped or interleaved, and with silver plating applied either for entire lengths or only at connection joints and power tap points.

Insulators have comparable variety in composition, contours and spacing arrangements, and variations in busway casings require corresponding assortments of supporting brackets, clamps and hangers for hanging busway.

Although busways have broad application potential, they are limited. The NE Code rules that "busways may be used only for exposed work." Some exception, however, has been made to this rule in cases where concealment is not permanent—such as above certain types of suspended ceilings. Some opinion rules that as long as it can be reached without removing any permanent part of the building construction, the busway is really exposed.

unloaded, the neutral carries the same as the phases, but there is still the heating effect of only three conductors.

CASE 3—With two phases fully loaded and the third phase partially loaded, the neutral carries the difference in current between the full phase value and the partial phase value, so that again there is the heating effect of only three full-load phases.

CASE 4—With a balanced load of fluorescent ballasts, third harmonic generation causes a neutral current approximating phase current and there will be heating effect of four conductors. Such a neutral conductor should be counted with the phase conductors when determining conductor derating due to conduit occupancy.

Wireways or auxiliary gutters may contain up to 30 conductors at any cross section (excluding signal circuits and control conductors used for starting duty only between a motor and its starter). The total cross sectional area of the group of conductors must not be greater than 20% of the interior cross-sectional area of the wireway or gutter. And derating factors for more than three conductors do not apply to wireway the way they do to wires in conduit.

Busways

One of the most popular applications in modern electrical design is the busway system. Although use of busway for feeders, plug-in subfeeders and branch-circuit systems has been a continuing industrial system development for many years, the use of feeder and plug-in busway in large commercial and institutional buildings has come into widespread acceptance over recent years, stimulated by developments in busway construction.

FIG. 143—Modern busway circuits

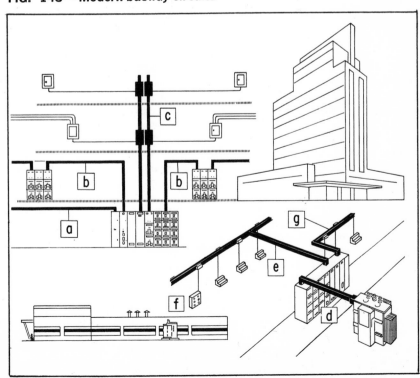

Made up of copper or aluminum busbars supported by insulators within a metal housing, busways are factory-assembled and supplied in standard 10-ft sections.

Low-reactance feeder busway provides low voltage-drop characteristics due to close spacing and special construction of the busbars which minimize reactance. This type of busway is used for all types of high-capacity feeders and risers. Because of its low reactance, it has also found application in high-frequency distribution systems.

Typical ratings on feeder busway range from 600 amps to 6000 amps, for single-phase (2 or 3 poles) or 3-phase (3 or 4 poles), for 120/240-volt single-phase systems, for 120/208-volt or 480/277-volt 3-phase, 4-wire systems or for 3-phase, 3-wire systems, all up to 600 volts. Feeder busways are also available in weatherproof type. And busways are available with an extra busbar to provide equipment grounding throughout a system.

Plug-in distribution busway, with easily accessible plug-in openings for tapping to loads directly or through switch and protective devices, is available in ratings from 225 amps to 1500 amps.

Fig. 143 shows how busway applications are advantageous in many types of structures. For example, upper sketch shows low-impedance feeder busways used to bring power from outside source to main interior switchgear of tall commercial building (a), then carrying power to upper-floor control centers (b and c). Lower sketch shows use of weatherproof feeder busway connecting outdoor transformer with interior switchgear of industrial plant (d), feeder busway then connecting with center-tap of plug-in system (e), while plug-in busways carry power to various equipment. (f and g).

Armored cables for feeders

Armored cable has been in use in electrical work for many years and still finds widespread application. Article 334 of the code, now entitled "Metalclad Cable," identifies so-called "interlocked armor" cable as Type MC and distinguishes its construction, application and installation from standard "armored cable" which is designated Type AC (AC, ACT & ACL).

Interlocked armored cable is available for use at 600 volts, 5000 volts and 15,000 volts. The high-voltage types of IA cable offer very effective use for primary feeders in loadcenter distribution systems. The 600-volt class of IA cable is rapidly gaining in popularity for feeder applications in commercial and industrial systems.

Interlocked armor cable for secondary feeders is a completely flexible and protected cable assembly, available in sizes from No. 6 to 750 MCM, with three or four conductors. IA cable consists of a galvanized steel, interlocked and spiralled armor wrap around the insulated assembly of individually insulated conductors. The conductors are stranded and may be copper or aluminum. The armor may also be of aluminum or bronze.

There are some general criteria for choosing between IA cable and busway. Where the routing is devious and there are many obstructions, IA cable often can be used to advantage. For straight runs, particularly long runs of high current capacity, busway is usually better. Above 1000-amp capacity, busway for a feeder generally costs less. Below 500 amps, a feeder may more economically be interlocked armor cable. However, where the advantages of busway are required, cost of material and installation is not primarily important.

Feeder distribution centers

In modern buildings, feeder distribution centers provide for protection and control of feeders to various loads. In 3-phase, 4-wire systems, both lighting and power feeders may originate from a single distribution center. In those systems using separate power and light services, a separate distribution center is generally used with each type of feeder.

Modern distribution centers for lighting and appliance feeders include dead-front panelboards and dead-front switchboards. Feeders are tapped through fused switches or circuit breakers from the buses in such distribution centers.

Distribution centers frequently are supplied by the service conductors to buildings and contain the main service switches. This is the most common arrangement in commercial and institutional buildings; although subfeeder distribution centers are supplied by feeders from the main distribution center (the service panel or switchboard). In many industrial buildings, feeder distribution centers may be supplied from transformers which step high-voltage distribution to utilization levels.

Selection of suitable panelboards and/or switchboards for feeder distribution is based on many factors:

For larger distribution panelboards, it is often advantageous to select free-standing panels, which can be mounted directly on the floor. This reduces labor costs and speeds up the installation. For mounting in or on walls, flush- or surface-mounted panelboards are available. Combination meter and distribution panelboards are available for installations requiring separate utility meters for each tenant within the same building. Such equipment contains two or more meter stab assemblies, factory-bussed line and load connections to meters, and panel-base assemblies. The panel-base assembly on the load side of each meter receives a plug-in feeder overcurrent device to which an individual tenant's feeder is connected.

Special panelboards and switchboards can be obtained, which contain relays and contactors for applications requiring remote-control operation of various circuits. For use in wet, corrosive or hazardous locations, panelboards of approved types are available for such environmental conditions.

Switching devices

In selecting the size of each feeder disconnecting means in switchboards or panelboards, care must be taken that the ampere rating of the switch or circuit breaker is adequate for the load, for the switching duty to which it will be subjected and for any load growth to be designed into the system. A first step in such sizing of the switch or circuit breaker is as follows (see Fig. 144):

MOTOR LOAD ONLY IN POWER PANEL. The switch must have an ampere rating at least equal to the required current rating of the feeder conductors. This current rating is equal to 125% of the full-load current of the largest motor plus the sum of the full-load currents of the other motors fed from the panel. But a switch must accommodate the fuses which protect the feeder and these may have a maximum rating equal to the largest rating or setting of branch-circuit protective device in the power panel plus the sum of the motor currents of the other motors fed from the panel. Or a CB may have a higher trip setting. This may require a larger device. And if two or more motors fed from the panel must be started simultaneously, the starting current drain may be so heavy as to require increased size of feeder conductors and disconnect.

MOTOR AND LIGHTING LOAD IN POWER PANEL. The switch must have an ampere rating at least equal to that required for the motor load (as described above) plus the amperes for the lighting and appliance load on the panel.

When fused switches are used, heat load on the fuses should be considered in sizing the assembly. Because fuses are rated according to their ability to carry current continuously when placed in open air, on a bench, in a horizontal position, consideration must be made of the effect on fuses of heat accumulation due to their enclosed mountings in safety switches. To assure continuous operation of loads—minimizing the chance of nuisance fuse blowing—fusible switches must be rated to accommodate fuses which are at least 25% higher in rating than load currents which will be flowing for several hours or longer. Another way of stating this application requirement is that the load current must not exceed 80% of the fuse rating, as in Fig. 145. This is not an NE Code requirement. It is in NEMA and UL standards on switch design.

In selecting feeder disconnect and protection equipment, consideration should be given to spare capacity in this equipment. Depending upon the anticipated future requirements and the manner in which extra capacity was included in the feeders, space should be provided in switchboards and/or feeder panelboards for additional switches or circuit breakers or for future installation of larger switching and protection units. And design of the distribution system must integrate all provisions for future expansion of feeder capacities. This includes the routing of spare feeder conduit, accessibility to feeder raceway in which capacity has been allowed for increase in feeder conductors, and ease of connections in the switching and protection assemblies.

Construction of modern switchboards and feeder panelboards will accommodate all of these design provisions of load growth. Care in the selection of the proper type of switching and protection assem-

FIG. 144—Selecting size of feeder disconnect switch

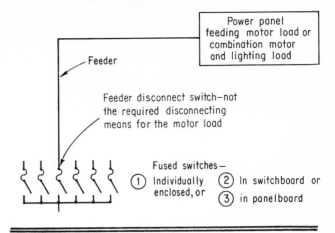

FIG. 145—Limit continuous load to 80% of fuse rating in switch

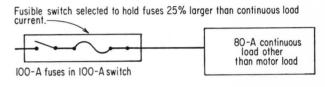

FIG. 146—Fuse speed coordinates with switch IC

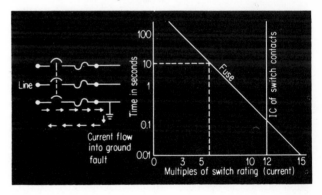

blies—with buses of substantial capacity for future expansion of the system—is essential to economy of distribution design.

An important consideration in selection of fusible switches is coordination between the electrical characteristics of the switch and the particular type of fuses used in the switch. With very high short circuits available in the large feeders of modern distribution systems, fused switches used in panels, switchboards or in individual enclosures must be carefully rated for the following two conditions:

1. FAULT INTERRUPTION SERVICE—In addition to being fully rated to make and break load currents up to its full current rating, every switch must have ability to interrupt ground-fault or short-circuit currents which it might be called upon to break. This is shown in Fig. 146 and works as follows—

The contact mechanism has a repetitive load-break capability up to 12 times the continuous current rating of the contact assembly. This means that

FIG. 147—Heavy-duty switch with effective IC

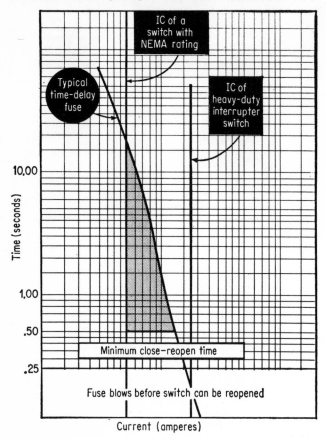

IC of a switch with NEMA rating

Typical time-delay fuse

IC of heavy-duty interrupter switch

10.00

Time (seconds)

1.00

.50

.25

Minimum close–reopen time

Fuse blows before switch can be reopened

Current (amperes)

particular fuses used in it. When a switch and its fuses are properly coordinated, the fuses will always operate fast enough to break any current which the switch could not safely open, before any person could operate the switch.

2. SHORT-CIRCUIT WITHSTANDABILITY — Every switch must be capable of safely withstanding the amount of energy which passes through it from the time a short-circuit fault develops until the fuses in the switch open the fault. Every switch—fusible and nonfusible—must be able to take the thermal and magnetic forces produced by "let-through" fault current. This ability of a switch is a function of the construction of the switch and the operating speed of the fuses used in it. To be properly applied, a switch must remain operable after any fault that is cleared by the fuses in the switch.

Fig. 147 shows the coordination between a typical time-delay fuse and a heavy-duty interrupter switch. The melting-time vs current curve is compared with two different switch interruption ratings—taking ¼ to ½ second as the fastest possible time for closing and reopening the switch. Note that NEMA switch IC could pose a hazard.

From the above, the factors to consider in selecting a fused switch are as follows:

1. The required fuse interrupting capacity is determined by the short-circuit current available from the system at the point of application.

2. The minimum switch withstandability is determined by the i^2t of fuse let-through current (from the fuse manufacturer).

3. Minimum switch IC is based on fuse speed and switch operating time.

It can be seen that switches with high withstandability and high IC can be used with slower operating fuses which have longer melting times and higher let-through currents. But switches with lower withstand and IC ratings must be protected by fuses with lower let-through and faster opening characteristics. The heavy-duty switches, for instance, could be used with K-5 and K-9 fuses in high-capacity circuits; whereas, lighter-duty switches would require use of K-1 or Class J fuses to be used in the same circuits.

Selection of switchgear will depend upon voltage rating, ampere rating, number of phases and short-circuit rating. Circuit breaker switchgear may be of the stationary type, in which the breakers are bolted to the bus and frame, or of the draw-out type, in which the breakers are mounted on a slide-out mechanism for easy removal and maintenance, disconnecting the breaker from the bus. Switchboards may be equipped with provisions for instrument transformers and metering. Feeders from the switchboard may be carried directly to lighting or power branch-circuit panelboards, to subfeeder distribution switchboards or panelboards, to motor control centers or to individual motor loads.

Motor centers

A power panelboard is a fused-switch, circuit breaker or fuse panelboard from which motor branch circuits originate. It may provide only protection for the branch-circuit conductors; but in most cases, the power panel also provides disconnect for each motor.

the breaker mechanism can safely break any overload up to that value. But the opening time-current line for the fuses shows that at 12 times the contact current rating, the fuse will open in 0.1 second—which is so short a time that the operator could not possibly open the breaker-switch while the fault current is flowing. For values of fault current lower than 12 times breaker rating, it would be possible to open the breaker before the fuse operates. But in such cases, the breaker contacts are operating within their rated load-break range. For values of fault current higher than 12 times breaker rating, the fuse will always operate to open the circuit before anyone could possibly open the breaker contact mechanism. This is effective coordination between switch interrupting capacity and speed of fuse operation.

An example of dangerous application would be use of the fuses in a switch which had an interrupting capacity of, say, two times the contact continuous rating. As shown, a fault current of better than five times the contact rating would take 10 seconds to operate the fuse. If someone opened the switch during that 10 seconds (which is possible), the switch contacts would be breaking a current higher than that for which they are safely rated—with hazard to life and property as well as to the switch itself. Switches are coordinated with their current-limiting fuses to assure safe operation. Closing and quickly reopening a switch (without intentional delay) before the fuse clears the fault is called "fuse racing." Coordination between a switch and fuses depends upon the construction and operating characteristics of the switch and the time-current characteristics of the

A motor control center is a dead-front assembly of cubicles, each of which contains branch-circuit overcurrent protection, motor disconnect means, motor controller and motor running overcurrent protection. It is a type of switchboard which contains all the protective and control means for the motors supplied from it. Selection and application of power panels and motor control centers should be related to future requirements. Such units must have necessary spare capacity in their buses and must be adapted to whatever change or expansion is anticipated. Layout of power panels and motor control centers should be related to voltage drop and the lengths of feeders.

A. Miscellaneous motor loads in the majority of commercial and institutional buildings and in many industrial buildings are usually circuited from power panels to which feeders deliver power. This type of distribution is a standard method of motor circuiting, generally limited to handling a number of motors of small integral horsepower or fractional horsepower sizes, located in a relatively small area such as a fan room or pump room.

B. In industrial buildings, where a large number of motors are used over a large area, distribution of power to the individual motor loads generally follows the method of tapping motor branch circuits from the feeder. As was indicated in the discussion of branch circuits, tapping a feeder to motor branch circuits may be done in several ways, by providing various combinations of branch-circuit overcurrent protection and motor control disconnect means. The feeder-tap method of supplying motor branch circuits is, of course, the basis for plug-in busway distribution.

Generally, layout of motor feeders should be as direct as possible to minimize voltage drop and power losses due to I^2R losses in the conductors. Inductive reactance drop should also be checked in large size feeder conductors.

480Y/277-volt systems

The growth of electrical loads in commercial buildings was responsible for the development of the 480Y/277-volt, 3-phase, 4-wire, grounded system which has many characteristics similar to industrial type systems. Air conditioning loads and business and other machine loads increased the ratio of power to lighting loads, calling for the type of circuit treatments and layouts which industrial plants use to economically and efficiently serve heavy motor loads.

Higher-voltage feeders to motor loads and to step-down transformers for lighting and receptacle circuits proved the ideal solution. Less wire is needed to distribute the heavy power requirements, and voltage drop and other losses are effectively minimized. And the availability of extensive lines of lighting equipment which operates on 277-volt circuits has contributed greatly to the widespread success of this system.

From studies made, it has been found that a typical 480Y system can provide savings of more than $25 per kva demand over a 120/208-volt system to handle the same load. Many installations over the years—in schools, office buildings, industrial plants, shopping centers and sports arenas—have convincingly proved the economic and operating advantages of the 480/277-volt system.

System application

The 480Y system was developed to meet the requirements of prevailing commercial building load conditions.

Usually, most general lighting is fluorescent and can be served by 277-volt circuits. Motors for air conditioning compressors, circulating fans, elevators and pumps make up an average load of about 4 volt-amps per square foot. These motors can be more efficiently and economically supplied at 480 than at lower voltages, and they are less expensive than lower-voltage motors of the same hp ratings. The combined power and general lighting loads average between 5 and 15 watts per sq ft. Receptacle and miscellaneous loads—desk lamps, local lights, business machines, appliances, water coolers, etc.—average only about ½ to 2 watts per sq ft.

As can be seen from the above, about 80% of a building load may be served directly by 480/277-volt feeders. Provision of 120-volt circuits may be made either by using separate 120/208-volt substations or by using dry-type transformers (480 to 120/240 or 480, 3-phase, to 120/208) installed locally at the center of each concentration of 120-volt loads. The latter method offers greater economy, even when the amount of 120-volt loading is as high as 5 watts per sq ft. Fig. 148 sets down the approach to calculations for sizing a transformer subfeed.

Transformer grounding

With the growing popularity of distribution systems using transformer loadcenters, particularly the 480/277-volt system, effective grounding of transformer secondaries is an important consideration. The elements of this design matter are as follows:

1. Any system which operates at not more than 150 volts to ground must be grounded.

2. This requires the grounding of secondaries of dry-type transformers serving 120/208-volt, 3-phase or 120/240-volt, single-phase circuits for lighting and appliance outlets and receptacles, at loadcenters throughout a building, as shown in Fig. 149.

3. All code rules applying to both system and equipment grounding must be satisfied in such installations.

4. Grounding of the secondary neutral may be made to the nearest water pipe anywhere in the

Neutral Grounding of Transformers

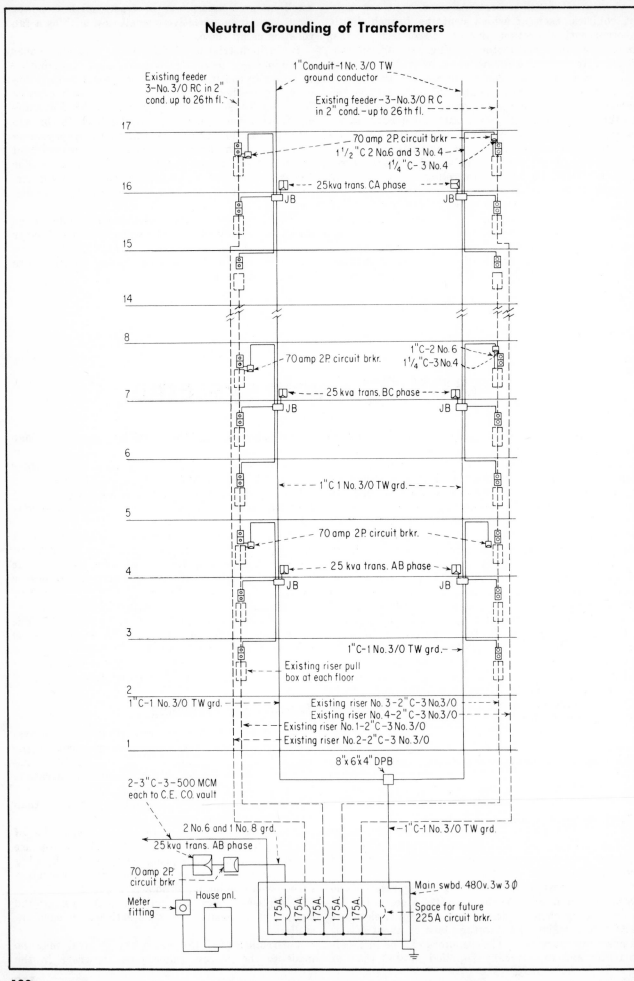

FIG. 148—Step-by-step sizing of feeders and transformers

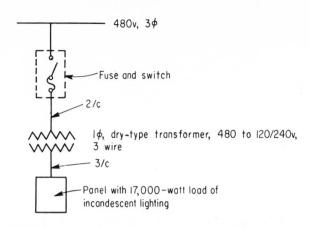

480v, 3φ

Fuse and switch

2/c

1φ, dry-type transformer, 480 to 120/240v, 3 wire

3/c

Panel with 17,000-watt load of incandescent lighting

Step 1. On the basis of 15-amp branch circuits, and for continuous operation of the load, we can have as much as 0.8 x 15 x 120 x 1440 watts per circuit. The panel will have to contain at least 17,000/1440 or 12 circuits.

Step 2. For the 17,000-watt connected load operating at 100% demand, the minimum capacity of secondary conductors will have to be 17,000/240 or 70 amps. Three No. 4 Type R, TW, RHW of THWN in 1¼-in. conduit are required.

STEP 3. The main buses of the lighting panelboard must have at least 70-amp capacity.

Step 4. The smallest standard size transformer to be used here is 25 kva. Under some conditions, it might be possible to use a 15-kva transformer operated overloaded during peak hours.

STEP 5. On the basis of the 17,000-watt load, the primary current would be 17,000/480 or 35 amps. Two No. 8 Type R, TW, RHW, or THWN in ¾-in. conduit.

Step 6. The transformer overcurrent protective device could be rated as high as 250% of the rated primary current. The rated primary current for this transformer is 25,000/480 or 52 amps. The transformer then can be protected by any protective device set or rated for not more than 2.5 x 52 or 130 amps. But, if this protective device is to protect the panel, which must have main or line-side protection at not more than the amp rating of its mains, it must be rated not more than 35 amps if the panel mains are rated at 70 amps. Or it could be rated 50 amps if the panel mains are rated at 100 amps. Note the 2-to-1 stepdown in amps from secondary to primary of the transformer.

Step 7. But the protection used ahead of the transformer must also protect the primary circuit conductors to the transformer and the secondary conductors to the panel. Maximum protection for the No. 8s must be set at no more than 40 or 50 amps, depending upon type of insulation. But a primary fuse set at more than 35 amps would not protect the secondary No. 4s with Type R or TW insulation. Type RHW or THWN No. 4s, however, rated at 85 amps would be protected by primary fuses rated up to 40 amps.

FIG. 149—What must be grounded at dry-type transformer?

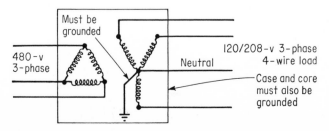

Must be grounded

480-v 3-phase

Neutral

120/208-v 3-phase 4-wire load

Case and core must also be grounded

FIG. 150—Bonding rules pose problem with water-pipe ground

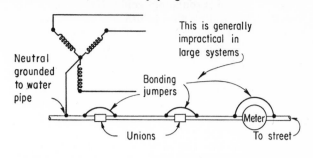

Neutral grounded to water pipe

This is generally impractical in large systems

Bonding jumpers

Unions

Meter

To street

FIG. 151—Single conductor must be used to ground frame and neutral

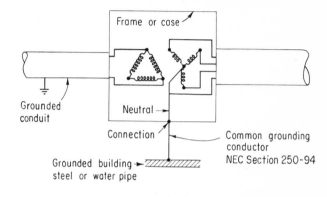

Frame or case

Grounded conduit

Neutral

Connection

Common grounding conductor NEC Section 250-94

Grounded building steel or water pipe

FIG. 152—Using primary conduit to ground neutral and frame
(Where inspection authority permits)

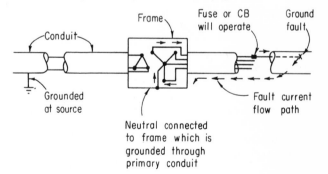

Conduit

Frame

Fuse or CB will operate

Ground fault

Grounded at source

Fault current flow path

Neutral connected to frame which is grounded through primary conduit

building, provided bonding jumpers are used to assure continuity of the ground path wherever the piping may contain insulating sections or is liable to become disconnected, as at meters, valves and service unions, as shown in Fig. 150. See NE Code Section 250-112 (a).

5. According to Section 250-54, when a system (in this case, the electrically isolated circuits from the transformer secondary) is grounded to an electrode in a building, the same electrode must be used at the same point to provide ground connection for wire enclosures and other housings, frame, enclosures, etc., even though the equipment may be grounded already through the conduit system supplying the transformer. And the conductor which is used to connect the system neutral to the grounding electrode must also be used to ground equipment, conduit and other raceways and enclosures, per Section 250-53. These rules have the effect of requiring the bonding

together of the transformer secondary neutral and the transformer frame at the transformer, with a single common grounding conductor running to a water pipe, building steel or other electrode, as shown in Fig. 151. By connecting the system neutral and the transformer frame together, the ground return path for fault currents on the secondary circuits is kept short to have low enough impedance and sufficient current-carrying capacity to handle any fault currents and to assure operation of the overcurrent devices protecting the circuits, as required by Section 250-51.

6. Common practice with dry-type local transformers in many installations is to merely connect the secondary neutral point to the transformer frame, leaving the supply conduit to the transformer to provide the path to ground back to the main service ground, but depending upon the connection between neutral and frame to provide effective return for clearing faults, as shown in Fig. 152. It should be noted, however, that some inspection agencies do insist that the transformer frame and the neutral point be connected to a suitable grounding electrode, such as a cold water pipe or building steel. The common conductor used for this grounding run is sized like a service ground wire.

Grounding of transformer housings must be made by connection to grounded cable armor or metal raceway (see Fig. 153) or by use of a grounding conductor run with circuit conductors (either a bare conductor or a conductor with green colored covering) or by a separate grounding conductor installed the same as a grounding conductor for equipment, Section 250-92 (b).

Fig. 154 shows an important detail for effective grounding of a transformer case and secondary neutral. A common technique for protecting bare or insulated system grounding conductors (one which grounds the wiring system and equipment cases) and for protecting equipment-only grounding conductors makes use of a metal conduit sleeve, run open or installed in concrete. In all such cases, the code says that "Metallic enclosures for grounding conductors shall be electrically continuous from the point of attachment to cabinets or equipment to the grounding electrode, and shall be securely fastened to the ground clamp or fitting." This means that

FIG. 153—Grounding of transformer housing

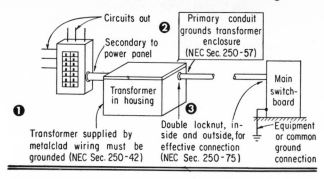

FIG. 155—Bond a grounding conductor to both ends of conduit sleeve

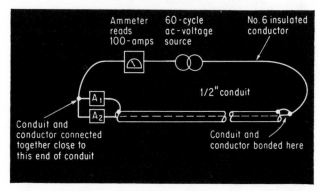

Ammeter A₁ (indicates amount of current in conduit) = 97 amps

Ammeter A₂ (indicates amount of current in conductor) = 3 amps

The presence of the steel conduit acts as an iron core to greatly increase the inductive reactance of the conductor. This choke action raises the impedance of the conductor to such a level that only 3 amps flow through the conductor and the balance of 97 amps flows through the conduit. This division of current between the conduit and the conductor points up the importance of assuring tight couplings and connectors throughout every conduit system and for every metal raceway system and metal cable jacketing. In particular, this stresses the need for bonding both ends of any raceway used to protect a grounding conductor run to a water pipe or other grounding electrode. Such conduit protection must be securely connected to the ground electrode and to the equipment enclosure in which the grounding conductor originates. If such conduit is left open, lightning and other electric discharges to earth through the grounding conductor will find a high-impedance path. The importance of high conductivity in the conduit system is also important for effective equipment grounding, even when a specific equipment grounding conductor is used in the conduit.

FIG. 154—Protective steel conduit on grounding conductor must always be electrically in parallel with conductor

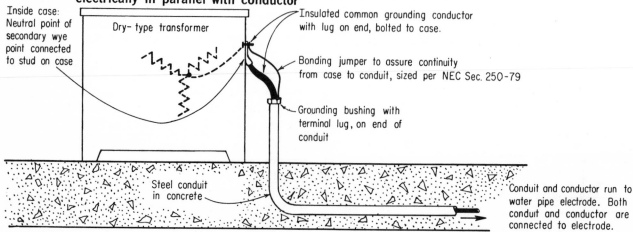

the grounding conductor must be connected to its protective conduit at both ends so that any current which might flow over the conductor will also have the conduit as a parallel path.

The necessity for making a grounding conductor electrically parallel with its protective conduit applies to any grounding conductor. If the protective conduit in any such case was arranged so that the conductor and conduit were not acting as parallel conductors—such as the conduit would be in Fig. 154 if there were no bonding jumper from the conduit bushing to the conductor lug—the presence of magnetic metal conduit (steel) would serve to greatly increase the inductive reactance of the grounding conductor to limit any flow of current to ground. The steel conduit would act as the core of a "choke" to restrict current flow. Fig. 155 shows the "skin effect" of current flow over a conduit in parallel with a conductor run through it. This clearly shows the conduit itself to be a more important conductor than the actual conductor. Of course, nonmagnetic conduit—such as aluminum—would have a different effect, but it should also be in parallel.

Isolating transformer

Fig. 156 shows the application of a completely packaged transformer loadcenter to provide power for the ungrounded, isolated circuits required in hospital operating suites. Factors involved in such installations are as follows:

1. Any electrical circuit within or partially within an anesthetizing location must be supplied from an ungrounded distribution system. An anesthetizing location is any area in a hospital in which flammable anesthetics are or may be administered to patients —operating rooms, delivery rooms, anesthesia rooms and any corridors, utility rooms or other areas used for administering anesthetics.

2. Any transformer used to obtain the ungrounded

FIG. 156—Transformer for ungrounded circuits in hospital operating rooms

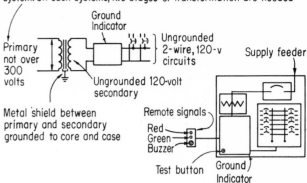

Supply cannot be made directly from two phase legs of 480/277-v system. On such systems, two stages of transformation are needed

COMPLETE PACKAGED UNGROUNDED DISTRIBUTION CENTER FOR HOSPITAL OPERATING ROOM: Main CB, isolating transformer, ground indicator and CB panel for ungrounded circuits. For in-wall or floor mounting close to operating suite.

circuits must have its primary rated for not more than 300 volts between conductors and must have proper overcurrent protection. The ungrounded secondary system must be equipped with an approved ground contact indicator—to give a visual and audible warning if a ground fault develops anywhere in the ungrounded system.

3. Isolating transformers must be installed out of the hazardous area. The ground indicator and its signals must also be installed out of the hazardous area. In an anesthetizing location, the hazardous area extends to a height of 5 ft above the floor.

4. Fixed lighting fixtures above the hazardous area in an anesthetizing location, other than the surgical luminaire, and certain X-ray equipment may be supplied by conventional grounded branch circuits. See NE Code Section 517-6 (e).

High-voltage systems

Depending upon the conditions and requirements in any particular case, design of a distribution system may incorporate modern methods such as loadcenter distribution from unit substations, high-voltage distribution to substations and alternative supply lines to each substation. The loadcenter substation is the key to this modern distribution.

In the layout of loadcenter distribution, loadcenter unit substations are located in the approximate center of the area occupied by the load devices supplied from the substation. Of course, the exact location of a substation with respect to the equipment it supplies depends upon the number and relative sizes of the load devices and the construction characteristics of the building. The number of unit substations required in any installation will depend upon the total load to be served and the capacities of the individual unit substations.

Each unit substation is fed by high-voltage (2400 volts to 13,800 volts) incoming power lines, trans-

forms the power down to low voltage (under 600 volts) and supplies feeders to motors and other power loads and feeders to lighting loads, either directly— for 277-volt lighting—or indirectly through stepdown transformers for 120-volt circuits.

The use of loadcenter substations allows efficient and economical distribution of large bulks of power throughout a building. Distributing power at high voltages requires much lower feeder current-carrying capacities than would be required to distribute the same amount of power at low voltage. As a result, the primary feeders are relatively small in size and not subject to the severe voltage-drop conditions which result from the use of long, low-voltage-but-high-current feeders to load concentrations. And the locations of the unit substations, in the center of each load concentration, permit the use of very short secondary feeders or branch circuits to loads, again minimizing voltage drop and I^2R loss.

Many advantages may be realized through the use

FIG. 157—Basic and modified forms of radial system

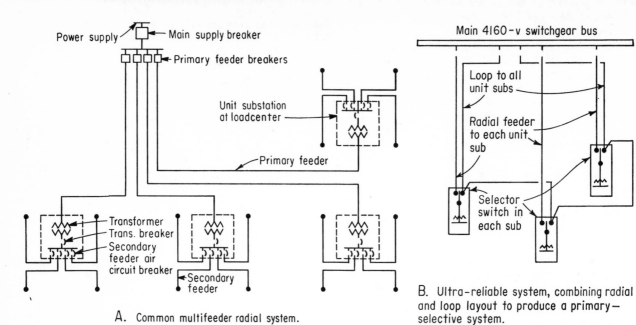

A. Common multifeeder radial system.

B. Ultra-reliable system, combining radial and loop layout to produce a primary—selective system.

of loadcenter distribution in industrial plants. It has been estimated that the savings in feeder sizes alone may run as high as 20%. And other substantial savings are effected through elimination of much heavy-capacity secondary switchgear.

Design procedure

Design of a loadcenter distribution system for any building begins with analysis and breakdown of the total load within the building.

In general, the total load in the plant is broken into blocks and apportioned among a number of unit substations. The number of unit subs selected for any installation must take into account certain facts of economy involved in equipment application:

a. Generally, the smaller the unit sub, the more expensive it is per kva.

b. The greater the number of unit subs, the greater the amount of primary cables.

c. But the use of a large number of unit subs, each covering only a small area of load accumulation, reduces the lengths of secondary feeders.

d. The use of a small number of very large subs, however, requires less primary conductors but more secondary conductors.

From investigation of standard kva ratings of unit subs and system costs per kva, it has been found that economy usually dictates the use of unit subs rated from 500 to 1500 kva. Maximum economies can be realized from the use of substations rated from 750 to 1000 kva.

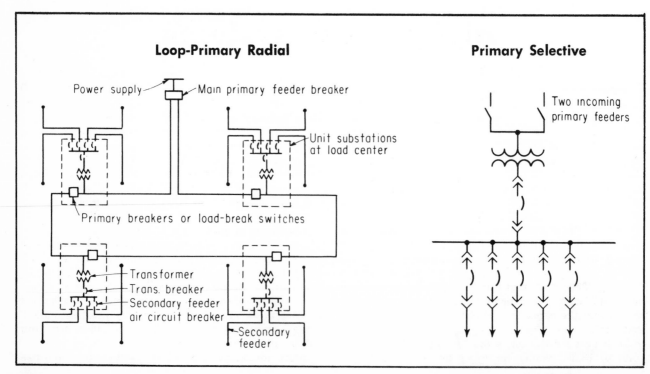

Loop-Primary Radial

Primary Selective

FIG. 158—Two types of network distribution systems

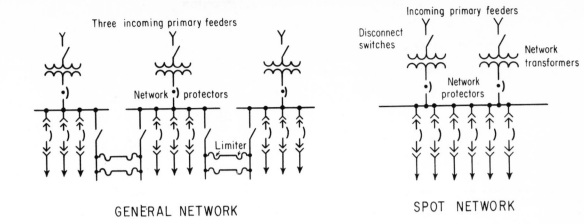

GENERAL NETWORK

SPOT NETWORK

A typical loadcenter substation contains high-voltage switchgear or just terminals in an incoming section, a transformer section in which the power is stepped to low voltage and a section containing switching and protection for the outgoing secondary feeders. High-voltage switchgear may utilize circuit breakers, air- or oil-break interrupting switches (with or without power fuses) or oil-filled cutouts.

The most common arrangement for the incoming line section of modern loadcenter substations consists of a high-voltage load interrupter switch, with suitable power fuses for protection of the substation. In a typical case, the primary feeder to the substation might originate in a metalclad CB switchgear center. In some cases, where the primary feeder switchgear is located near the unit sub and no other sub is fed by the feeder, additional protection and switching are not required in the incoming line section of the substation and an air-filled terminal chamber can satisfy incoming line requirements. Where fuses cannot be coordinated for primary transformer protection, a power circuit breaker will be required.

Oil-filled or dry-type transformers are used in unit subs, offering advantages for indoor and outdoor applications. Secondary switching and protection usually consists of completely enclosed assemblies of drawout-type circuit breakers or molded-case circuit breakers.

Layout of substations

Of the loadcenter distribution systems in use today, the majority follow a simple radial pattern. The simple radial system offers a high order of reliability and service continuity and is safe, flexible, stable and easy to operate and maintian.

A widely used form of the basic radial system, Fig. 157, has individual primary feeders to unit subs for a flexible system.

Where more flexibility is required, use of two unit subs with a normally open secondary tie breaker between them forms a secondary-selective system. A double-ended substation, with primary supply to each

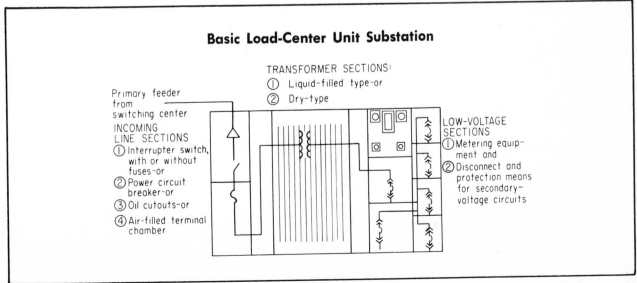

Typical Shielded Cable Construction

Outer jacketing of tough plastic (such as polychloroprene or polyethylene) resists oils, chemicals, weather, flame, corrosive fumes, abrasion, moisture. For use in air, in conduit, in underground duct or direct burial.

Metallic shielding encloses entire length of conductor to confine dielectric stresses

Rubber-type insulation

Stranded copper or aluminum conductor

Semi-conducting tape

Protective tape over shield

Grounding at Stress Cones on Shielded Cables

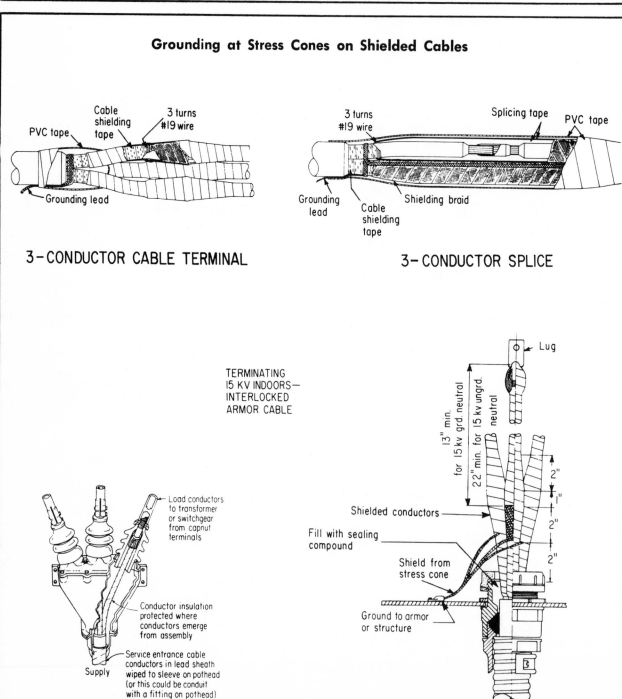

PVC tape

Cable shielding tape

3 turns #19 wire

Grounding lead

3-CONDUCTOR CABLE TERMINAL

3 turns #19 wire

Splicing tape

PVC tape

Grounding lead

Cable shielding tape

Shielding braid

3-CONDUCTOR SPLICE

TERMINATING
15 KV INDOORS—
INTERLOCKED
ARMOR CABLE

Load conductors to transformer or switchgear from capnut terminals

Conductor insulation protected where conductors emerge from assembly

Service entrance cable conductors in lead sheath wiped to sleeve on pothead (or this could be conduit with a fitting on pothead)

Supply

Lug

13" min. for 15 kv grd. neutral

22" min. for 15 kv ungrd. neutral

Shielded conductors

Fill with sealing compound

Shield from stress cone

Ground to armor or structure

2"

1"

2"

2"

Shielding of Rubber-Insulated Conductors

Code Table 710-5

Method of Installation	Neutral Grounded		Neutral Ungrounded	
	Fibrous Covered	Ozone-Resistant Jacket Covering	Fibrous Covered	Ozone-Resistant Jacket Covering
In metallic conduit or trough above grade located indoors and in dry locations				
Single conductor	2	5*	2	3
Multi-conductor	2	5	2	5
Underground ducts and conduits and other wet locations				
Single conductor	2	3**	2	3
Multi-conductor	2	5	2	5
On insulators—				
Only multi-conductor	Not required under 5 kv		3	5
Directly in soil—				
Single conductor	——	3	——	3
Multi-conductor	——	5	——	5

Voltage in KV (L-L) Above which Shielding is Required

* It is presumed that installation conditions will be such as to maintain a high level of jacket surface resistivity and so minimize the possibility of destructive discharge. Pulling dry or the use of insulating type pulling lubricants will help attain these conditions. Where surface contamination cannot be prevented and high surface resistivity cannot be maintained, metallic shielding shall be used at over 3 kv.

Note: Metallic sheathed single or 3-conductor cables require no metallic shielding for voltages 5 kv and less. In the case of portable equipment cables it is good practice to specify shielding for all voltages above 2 kv.

** For three single conductor cables, cabled together without outer covering, the value is 5 kv.

end and a normally open secondary tie within the assembly, invariably is used to form a secondary-selective system. In operation, each substation or each end of a double-ended sub operates as a straight radial system. If one primary feeder or transformer should fail or be taken out of service, the load normally carried on that substation or that end of a double-ended substation is automatically transferred to the still-operating substation.

The secondary-selective system represents a cost increase of only 5% to 15% over a simple radial system.

Similar to the basic system, the loop system has the primary feeder looped back on itself at the point of power supply to increase system reliability, at slight cost increase over a basic system which might use a single primary feeder to a number of unit subs. By the use of main primary feeder breakers at the source point and automatic sectionalizing breakers at the points of tap to the loadcenter subs, the occurrence of primary feeder faults will not interrupt service to any loads. By opening one of the sectionalizing breakers in the loop, the system may be operated as two simple radial systems.

A primary-selective radial system provides choice of primary feeder for improved service reliability in the event of primary feeder fault. Transfer means is provided to assure rapid reconnection from one primary to the other.

Two network layouts of unit subs are shown in Fig. 158. In the spot network, two or three transformers in one location or "spot" are connected to a common secondary bus and divide the load. Upon pri-

mary or transformer fault, the secondary is isolated from the faulted section by automatic operation of the network protector, providing a high order of supply continuity in the event of faults. The general form of the network system is similar except that widely separated individual substations are used with associated network protectors and tie circuits run between the secondary bus sections. System provides for interchange of power to accommodate unequal loading on the transformers. Limiters protect the ties.

Primary voltage

Selection of the primary voltage to be used with loadcenter distribution depends upon the available utility lines, the total load to be supplied and the number of unit subs to be used. Consultation with the local utility is essential to selection of the best primary voltage.

FIG. 159—Primary wiring methods

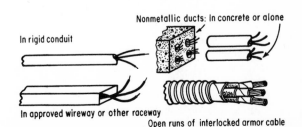

In rigid conduit

Nonmetallic ducts: In concrete or alone

In approved wireway or other raceway

Open runs of interlocked armor cable

Average Sound Levels (Decibels) For Various Occupancies

Occupancy	Decibel Range
Apartments and hotels	35–45
Average factory	70–75
Classrooms and lecture rooms	35–40
Hospitals, auditoriums, churches	35–40
Private offices, conference rooms	40–45
Offices—small	53
—medium (3 to 10 desks)	58
—large	64
—factory	61
Stores—average	45–55
—large (5 or more clerks)	61
Residence—without radio	53
—with radio, conversation	60
Radio, recording, television	25–30
Theaters, music rooms	30–35
Street—average	80

Note: Manufacturers now sound rate dry-type transformers to meet or exceed NEMA Audible Sound Level standards. Select a transformer with a decibel rating lower than the ambient sound level of the area in which it is to be installed.

Primary distribution at 13.8 kv usually offers the best loadcenter design at lowest cost for very large industrial plants with demand load above 20,000 kva. Between 10,000 kva and 20,000 kva, plant load may be economically served by either 13.8-kv or 4160-volt primaries. For plants with demands below 10,000 kva, primary distribution at 4160 volts is generally recommended.

Conductors

Article 710 of the NE Code covers general requirements on all circuits and equipment operated with more than 600 volts between conductors. Specific requirements on high-voltage application are covered within the articles on services, motors and controllers, transformers, capacitors, outside wiring.

1. Where rubber-insulated conductors for permanent installations operate at voltages higher than those in NE Code Table 710-5, they must be of a type having metallic shielding for confining their dielectric field.

2. The metallic shielding or any other static voltage shields on shielded cable must be stripped back to a safe distance according to the circuit voltage—at all terminations of the shielding, as in potheads and joints. At such points, stress reduction must be provided by such methods as the use of potheads, terminators, stress cones or similar devices. And the metallic shielding tape must be grounded.

3. Circuit conductors must be suitable for the voltage and conditions under which they are installed. See Fig. 159. They must be installed:

A. In rigid conduit, or

B. In raceways or ducts, or

C. As open runs of metal armored cable suitable for purpose.

D. Where accessible to qualified persons only, open runs of nonmetallic sheathed cable or bare conductors may also be used.

4. Grounding of systems and equipment must conform with Article 250.

5. Where necessary, a pothead or other approved means must be used to protect the insulation of conductors against moisture or mechanical injury where such conductors emerge from a metal sheath.

An important phase of high-voltage electrical design is selection and specification of cable termination techniques. Some facts on this subject are as follows:

1. Paper-insulated cable must be terminated in potheads. A pothead is a type of cable terminal which provides sealing to the sheath of the cable for making a moistureproof connection between the wires within the cable and those outside. This requirement also extends to such cable operated under 600 volts.

2. Varnished-cambric cables should be terminated in potheads, but may be terminated with taped connections in dry locations (or under 600 volts).

3. Rubber-insulated cables are commonly terminated in potheads, but may be terminated without potheads in accordance with manufacturer's instructions.

4. Although many modern high-voltage cables can be terminated without potheads, many engineers consider potheads the best termination for any high-voltage cable.

5. The use of potheads for cable connections to equipment offers a number of advantages—

A. Seals cable ends against moisture which would damage the insulation.

B. Provides a compartment for surrounding the termination with insulating compounds to increase strength of electrical insulation.

C. Seals cable ends against loss of insulating oils.

D. Provides engineered support and connection.

6. Stress relief cones provide protection against insulation failure at the terminals of shielded high-voltage cables. Manufacturers of cable and cable ter-

minators provide special kits for preparing stress relief cones for cables operating at high voltages.

Article 230 covers extensive detail on high-voltage service to buildings. One basic rule is that conductors must enter either a metalclad switchgear or a transformer vault when the voltage between conductors exceeds 15 kv.

Control and protection

Modern high-voltage distribution, in the range from 2300 volts up to 15,000 volts, makes use of three principal devices for load switching and short-circuit protection of circuits. These are:

1. Metalclad oilless (air-break) circuit breaker switchgear.

2. Enclosed load-interrupter switchgear furnished with power fuses.

3. Oil-fuse cutouts.

High-voltage power circuit breakers provide load switching, short-circuit protection, electrical operation, adjustable time delays of trip characteristics for selectively coordinated protection schemes, quick reclosing after tripping and various relay protective hookups, such as differential relay protection of transformers. There are both oil-type and oilless (or air-type) CBs, although the oilless type is the common type for indoor applications in systems up to 15 kv and higher. Oil CBs are generally used for outdoor applications above about 15 kv. Power CBs are made available in completely packaged assemblies for ready connection into the system.

Fused load-interrupter switchgear, typically rated up to 1200 amps, can match the ratings and required performance capabilities of power circuit breakers for a large percentage of applications in which either might be used. The load-interrupter switchgear does not provide as quick reclosing after fault opening as a CB because fuses have to be replaced. And it does not offer differential-relay protection of transformers against internal faults. Both of these shortcomings, however, are not generally sufficiently important in most industrial and commercial systems to warrant the substantially higher cost of CB equipment and its installation.

NEMA AUDIBLE SOUND LEVELS
For dry-type general-purpose specialty transformers
600-volt or less, single or 3-phase

TRANSFORMER RATING (KVA)	AVERAGE SOUND LEVEL (DECIBELS)
0-9	40
10-50	45
51-150	50
151-300	55
301-500	60

NEMA AUDIBLE SOUND LEVELS
Oil-immersed and dry-type self-cooled transformers
15,000-volt insulation class and below

KVA	OIL IMMERSED (DECIBELS)	DRY TYPE (DECIBELS)	
		Ventilated	Sealed
0-300	55 DB	58 DB	57 DB
301-500	56 DB	60 DB	59 DB
501-700	57 DB	62 DB	61 DB
701-1000	58 DB	64 DB	63 DB
1001-1500	60 DB	65 DB	64 DB
1501-2000	61 DB	66 DB	65 DB
2001-3000	63 DB	68 DB	66 DB

FIG. 160—Simple operation of transformer on fault

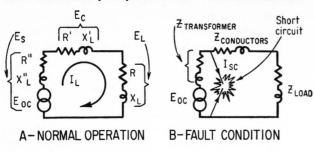

A—NORMAL OPERATION   B—FAULT CONDITION

FIG. 161—Askarel transformers indoors

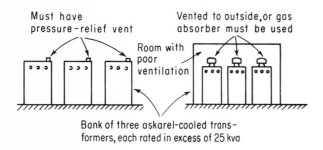

Must have pressure-relief vent

Vented to outside, or gas absorber must be used

Room with poor ventilation

Bank of three askarel-cooled transformers, each rated in excess of 25 kva

UNITS RATED OVER 35,000 VOLTS MUST BE USED IN A VAULT

FIG. 162—Installing oil-filled transformers

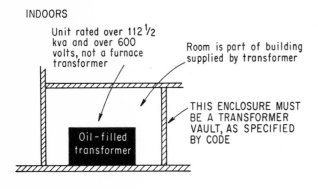

INDOORS

Unit rated over 112½ kva and over 600 volts, not a furnace transformer

Room is part of building supplied by transformer

THIS ENCLOSURE MUST BE A TRANSFORMER VAULT, AS SPECIFIED BY CODE

Oil-filled transformer

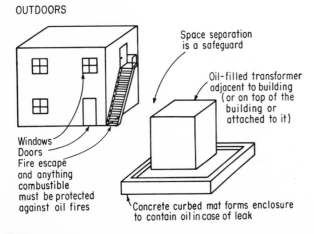

OUTDOORS

Space separation is a safeguard

Oil-filled transformer adjacent to building (or on top of the building or attached to it)

Windows Doors Fire escape and anything combustible must be protected against oil fires

Concrete curbed mat forms enclosure to contain oil in case of leak

Power fuses used in load-interrupter switches are available in current-limiting and noncurrent-limiting types. The current-limiting type is constructed with a silver-sand internal element, similar to 600-volt current-limiting fuses; and such fuses have generally higher interrupting ratings at some voltages but their continuous current-carrying ratings are limited. They do offer reduction of thermal and magnetic stresses on fault by reducing the energy let-through.

Oil-filled cutouts are also finding wide use as low-cost switching and protective mechanisms for primary electrical systems. The oil-filled cutout is a completely enclosed, single-pole assembly with a fusible element immersed in the oil-filled housing and two terminals on the outside. The circuit is broken safely and rapidly by an internal mechanism made up of the fuse in its carrier and two contacts which the carrier bridges in the closed position. Operation is controlled at the end of the mechanism's shaft which comes out of the top of the unit.

Transformers

In selecting a transformer, consideration of the "impedance" of the unit is involved in evaluating the ability of the transformer to supply short-circuit currents into faults on the load side of the transformer. The impedance of a transformer is the opposition which the transformer presents to the flow of short-circuit current through it. This is shown basically in Fig. 160. Under normal conditions of operation (A), a transformer winding can be considered to be a source of voltage, E_s. This source is made up of a generator-producing open-circuit voltage, E_{oc}, and having internal resistance, R'', and inductive reactance X_L''. Under normal conditions, load current I_L flows, determined by the transformer impedance, the impedance of the circuit conductors and the impedance of the load. When a short occurs (B) the transformer open-circuit voltage, E_{oc}, is connected across a total load made up only of the transformer impedance and whatever part of the circuit conductor impedance that is in the short circuit. Assuming the supply to the transformer primary can deliver the necessary primary current, the secondary short-circuit current is equal to E/Z. Thus the transformer impedance is the limiting factor for short-circuit current.

All transformers have impedance and it generally is expressed as a voltage percentage. It is the percentage of normal rated primary voltage which must be applied to the transformer to cause full-load-rated current to flow in the short-circuited secondary. For instance, if a 480-volt to 120-volt transformer has an impedance of 5%, this means that 5% of 480, or 24 volts, applied to the primary will cause rated load current to flow in the secondary. If 5% of primary voltage will cause such current, then 100% of primary voltage will cause 100/5 (or 20) times full-load rated secondary current to flow through a solid short circuit on the secondary terminals.

The NE Code presents detailed rules on installation of dry-type and liquid-filled transformers in Article 450. Some of these are as follows:

Dry-type transformers installed indoors must conform to the following:

A. Units rated 112½ kva or less must be mounted at least 12 in. from combustible material unless a fire-resistant, heat-insulating barrier is used between the transformer and the combustible material or unless the unit is rated not over 600 volts and is completely enclosed except for ventilating openings.

B. Units rated over 112½ kva must be installed in a transformer room of fire-resistant construction unless they are Class B or Class H insulated and are separated from combustible material by 6 ft horizontally and 12 ft vertically or are separated by a fire-resistant, heat-insulating barrier.

C. Transformers rated over 35 kv must be installed in a code-constructed vault.

Askarel-insulated transformers installed indoors must conform to the code (see Fig. 161):

Regulations on installing oil-filled transformers are shown in Fig. 162.

The code requires overcurrent protection for each transformer or bank of transformers operating as a unit. Protection shall be provided as follows:

1. An overcurrent protective device—rated or set at not more than 250% of the rated primary current —must be placed in the primary connection of each transformer. Such protection, however, is not required if the overcurrent device protecting the primary circuit is rated or set at not more than 250% of the rated primary current.

2. A transformer is not required to have an individual overcurrent device in the primary connection if it has an overcurrent device—rated or set at not more than 250% of the rated secondary current—in the secondary connection, or if it is equipped with an integral thermal overload protector. In such a case, the primary feeder overcurrent device must have a rating or setting at not more than six times the rated current of the transformer for transformers having not more than 6% impedance, and not more than four times the rated current of the transformer for transformers having more than six but not more than 10% impedance.

Service-entrance layout

For any building, the service consists of the conductors and equipment used to deliver electric energy from the utility supply lines to the interior distribution system. Service may be made to a building either overhead or underground, from a utility pole line or from an underground transformer vault.

Article 230 of the code covers services:

1. Although the code states that "a building shall be supplied through only one set of service conductors," there are exceptions made. If more than one service drop is made to a building, more than one set of service conductors may be used to supply the building. In the case of apartment houses, shopping centers and other multiple-occupancy buildings, which do not have individual occupancy above the second floor, two or more sets of service entrance conductors may be tapped from a single set of service drop conductors or two or more subsets of service entrance conductors may be tapped from a single set of main service-entrance conductors. Cases of separate light and power services to a single building and separate services to water heaters for purposes of different rate schedules are exceptions to the general rule of single service.

2. Only one service drop may be used to supply a building from a single transformer or from a single secondary utility distribution system. Exceptions to this rule are made under several conditions. If a separate service is necessary for fire pumps or for emergency lighting, or if the size and layout of the building and its load cannot be handled by a single service, or if the building has multiple-occupancy without space for service equipment accessible to all occupants, or if an additional service of different voltage or other characteristics is needed for special classes of use, more than one drop may be used.

Current rating of service feeders

Sizing of service-entrance conductors involves the same type of step-by-step procedure as set forth for sizing feeders in the Distribution section of this manual. A set of service-entrance conductors is sized just as if it were a feeder. In general, the service-entrance conductors must have a minimum current-carrying capacity sufficient to handle the total lighting and power load served. Where the code gives demand factors to use or allows the use of acceptable demand factors based on sound engineering determination of less than 100% demand requirement, the lighting and power loads may be modified.

From the analysis and calculations given in the Distribution section, a total power and lighting load can be developed to use in sizing service-entrance conductors. Of course, where separate power and lighting services are used, the sizing procedure should be divided into two separate procedures.

When a total load—initial and future—has been established for the service-entrance conductors, the required current-carrying capacity is easily determined by dividing the total load in kva (or kw with proper correction for power factor of the load) by the voltage of the service.

From the required current rating of conductors, the required size of conductors is determined. Sizing of the service neutral is the same as for feeders.

An extremely important element of service design is that of fault consideration. Service busway and other service conductor arrangements must be sized and designed to assure safe application with the service disconnect and protection. That is, service conductors must be capable of withstanding the let-through thermal and magnetic stresses on a fault.

Service disconnect

Service-entrance conductors must be equipped with a readily accessible means of disconnecting the conductors from their source of supply:

A. Section 230-70 (d) says: "The disconnecting means for ungrounded conductors shall consist of either: 1. A manually operable switch or circuit breaker equipped with a handle or other suitable operating means positively identified and marked for mechanical operation by hand. 2. An electrically operated switch or circuit breaker provided the switch or circuit breaker can be opened by hand in event of failure of the power supply and the open and closed positions are clearly indicated to the operator."

The code further states that, "Large circuit breakers which are to be closed and opened by electrical, pneumatic or other power shall be capable of being closed by hand for maintenance purposes and shall also be capable of being tripped by hand under load without the use of power." See Sec. 240-25 (a).

Thus any circuit breaker used for service disconnecting means must comply with both Section 240-25 (a) and Section 230-70 (d); it must be capable of being both closed and opened by hand. But an electrically operated switch only has to comply with Section 230-70 (d). It has to be capable of being opened by hand when power is lost, but does not have to provide manual closing.

Electrical operation can be adapted to remote pushbutton control to provide for opening the service when fire or other conditions make the mechanical handle of the disconnect means inaccessible. Remote electrical operation is required by some local codes.

B. The disconnect may consist of not more than six switches or six circuit breakers, in a common enclosure or individual enclosures, located either inside or outside the building wall as close as possible to the point at which the conductors enter the building. See Figs. 163 and 164.

For other than residential application, a power panel containing up to six switches or circuit breakers may be used as service disconnect even in cases where the fuses in the switches or the circuit breakers are rated 15 or 20 amps. As explained in the Distribution section, a lighting and appliance panel used as service equipment in individual residential occupancies may have up to six main breakers or fused switches provided none is rated 20 amps or less. However, a lighting and appliance panel used as service equipment for commercial or industrial buildings (i.e., any nonresidential use), must have not more than two main devices—with the sum of their ratings not greater than the panel bus rating.

Single-pole switches or circuit breakers equipped with handle-ties may be used in groups as single disconnects for multiwire circuits, simultaneously providing overcurrent protection for the service. Multipole switches and circuit breakers may also be used as single disconnects. The requirements of the code are satisfied if all of the service-entrance conductors can be disconnected with no more than six operations of the hand—regardless of whether each hand motion operates a single-pole unit, a multipole unit or a group of single-pole units controlled by a single hand motion. Of course, a single main device for service disconnect and overcurrent protection—such as a main CB or fused switch—gives better protection to the service conductors.

C. Multiple-occupancy buildings having individual occupancy above the second floor shall have service equipment grouped in a common accessible place, the disconnecting means consisting of not more than six switches (or six CBs), as in Fig. 165.

Multiple-occupancy buildings that do not have individual occupancy above the second floor may have

FIG. 163—Three ways to set up service

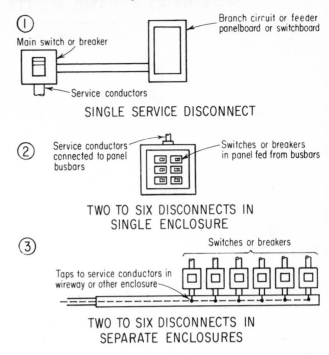

SINGLE SERVICE DISCONNECT

TWO TO SIX DISCONNECTS IN SINGLE ENCLOSURE

TWO TO SIX DISCONNECTS IN SEPARATE ENCLOSURES

FIG. 164—Location of service disconnect

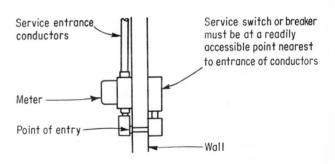

service conductors run to each occupancy. The service disconnecting means in each occupancy may then consist of not more than six switches (or six CBs). See Fig. 166.

D. For a group of buildings under single management, disconnect means must be provided for each building, as in Fig. 167. NE Code Section 230-76 requires that the conductors supplying each building in the group be provided with a "readily accessible means, within or adjacent to the building, of disconnecting all ungrounded conductors" from the supply.

The meaning of the word "adjacent" in the rule has often caused confusion in applying the rule. Some authorities permit the use of the feeder switch in the main building as the only disconnect for each feeder to the outlying buildings, providing the switches in the main building are accessible to the occupants of the outlying buildings. There is no definite distance which can be applied to the word "adjacent." Other inspection and engineering authorities prefer a readily accessible feeder disconnect within each outlying building, as shown regardless of distance from

SERVICE ARRANGEMENTS FOR SHOPPING CENTERS

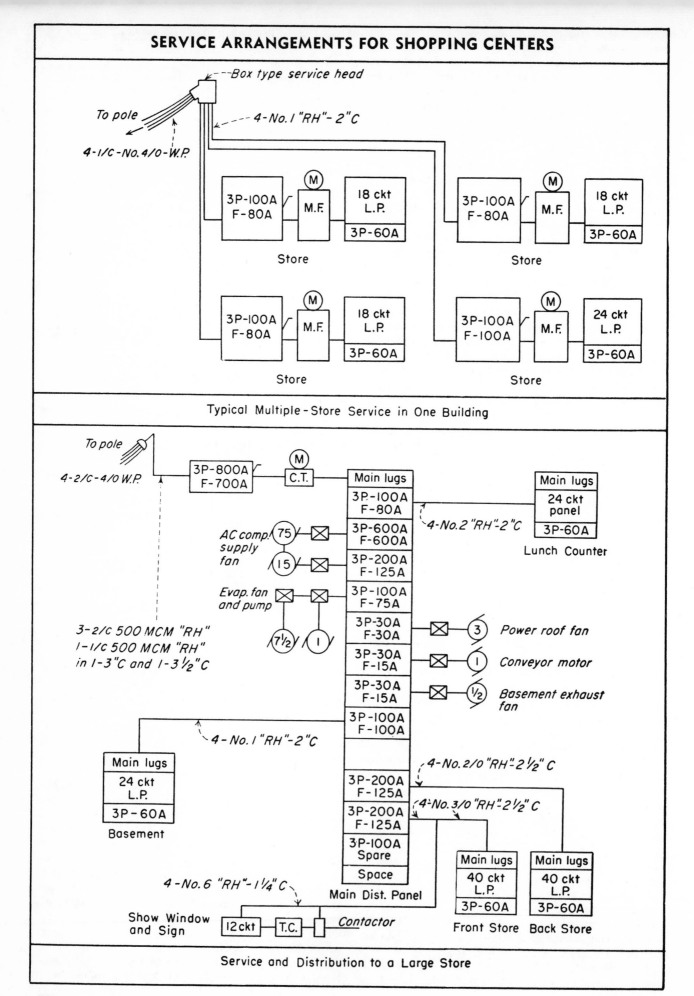

Box type service head

To pole

4-1/C-No.4/0-W.P.

4-No.1 "RH"- 2"C

| 3P-100A F-80A | M M.F. | 18 ckt L.P. |
| 3P-60A |

| 3P-100A F-80A | M M.F. | 18 ckt L.P. |
| 3P-60A |

Store

Store

| 3P-100A F-80A | M M.F. | 18 ckt L.P. |
| 3P-60A |

| 3P-100A F-100A | M M.F. | 24 ckt L.P. |
| 3P-60A |

Store

Store

Typical Multiple - Store Service in One Building

To pole

4-2/c-4/0 W.P.

3P-800A F-700A | M C.T. | Main lugs

Main lugs
24 ckt panel
3P-60A

Lunch Counter

3P-100A F-80A

4-No.2 "RH"-2"C

AC comp. supply fan

75

15

3P-600A F-600A

3P-200A F-125A

Evap. fan and pump

3P-100A F-75A

3P-30A F-30A

3 Power roof fan

7½

1

3P-30A F-15A

1 Conveyor motor

3P-30A F-15A

½ Basement exhaust fan

3-2/c 500 MCM "RH"
1-1/c 500 MCM "RH"
in 1-3"C and 1-3½"C

3P-100A F-100A

4-No.1 "RH"-2"C

Main lugs
24 ckt L.P.
3P-60A

Basement

3P-200A F-125A

4-No.2/0 "RH"-2½" C

3P-200A F-125A

4-No.3/0 "RH"-2½" C

3P-100A Spare

Space

Main lugs
40 ckt L.P.
3P-60A

Main lugs
40 ckt L.P.
3P-60A

Main Dist. Panel

4-No.6 "RH"-1¼" C

Show Window and Sign

12 ckt | T.C. | Contactor

Front Store   Back Store

Service and Distribution to a Large Store

FIG. 165—Multiple-occupancy building with individual occupancy above the second floor

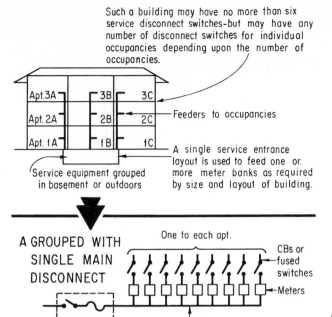

Such a building may have no more than six service disconnect switches—but may have any number of disconnect switches for individual occupancies depending upon the number of occupancies.

Apt.3A 3B 3C
Apt.2A 2B 2C
Apt.1A 1B 1C

Feeders to occupancies

A single service entrance layout is used to feed one or more meter banks as required by size and layout of building.

Service equipment grouped in basement or outdoors

A GROUPED WITH SINGLE MAIN DISCONNECT

One to each apt.

CBs or fused switches

Meters

One service switch or CB

Meter bank of nine meters and apartment disconnects

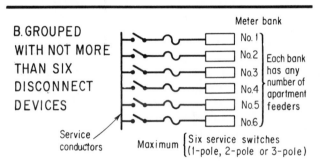

B. GROUPED WITH NOT MORE THAN SIX DISCONNECT DEVICES

Meter bank
No.1
No.2
No.3
No.4
No.5
No.6

Each bank has any number of apartment feeders

Service conductors

Maximum { Six service switches (1-pole, 2-pole or 3-pole)

FIG. 166—Service to buildings without individual occupancy above second floor

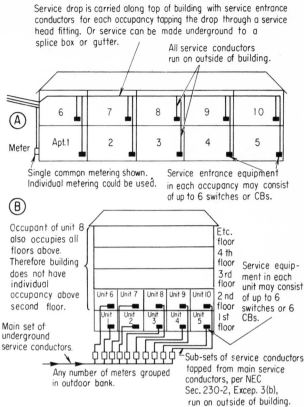

Service drop is carried along top of building with service entrance conductors for each occupancy tapping the drop through a service head fitting. Or service can be made underground to a splice box or gutter.

All service conductors run on outside of building.

Ⓐ
6 7 8 9 10
Apt.1 2 3 4 5

Meter

Single common metering shown. Individual metering could be used.

Service entrance equipment in each occupancy may consist of up to 6 switches or CBs.

Ⓑ
Occupant of unit 8 also occupies all floors above. Therefore building does not have individual occupancy above second floor.

Etc. floor
4th floor
3rd floor
2nd floor
1st floor

Unit 6 Unit 7 Unit 8 Unit 9 Unit 10
Unit 1 Unit 2 Unit 3 Unit 4 Unit 5

Service equipment in each unit may consist of up to 6 switches or 6 CBs.

Main set of underground service conductors.

Any number of meters grouped in outdoor bank.

Sub-sets of service conductors tapped from main service conductors, per NEC Sec. 230-2, Excep. 3(b), run on outside of building.

FIG. 167—Disconnect for multibuilding layout

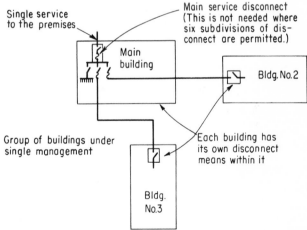

Single service to the premises

Main service disconnect (This is not needed where six subdivisions of disconnect are permitted.)

Main building

Bldg. No.2

Group of buildings under single management

Each building has its own disconnect means within it

Bldg. No.3

main building. The same reasoning applies to the overcurrent protection for each building.

E. If an emergency power supply is provided to feed the conductors controlled by the service disconnecting means, the disconnector must be of such design that the regular supply is disconnected before the emergency supply is connected—unless special provisions are made for parallel operation and suitable control.

F. Service fuses, meters, high-impedance shunt circuits (such as meter potential coils), supply-conductors for time switches, surge protective capacitors, instrument transformers, lightning arresters and circuits for emergency systems, fire pump equipment and fire alarms may be connected on the supply side of the disconnecting means.

The continuous current rating of a disconnect must be sufficient for full-load current, and its momentary current rating must be such that the device can withstand possible short-circuit currents for the length of time it takes for the circuit to be cleared. Interrupting capacity of a disconnect must be sufficient for any possible conditions of operation. Requirements for interruption of loads and overloads must be related to time-current characteristics of service protection de-

vices. On primary circuits, disconnect should usually be able to break full-load current up to its own rating. On secondary circuits, a switch may need interrupting ability anywhere from its own current rating up to more than ten times its current rating.

Overcurrent protection

Each ungrounded service-entrance conductor must be protected by an overcurrent device in series with the conductor. The overcurrent device must have a rating or setting not higher than the allowable current capacity of the conductor, except as follows:

135

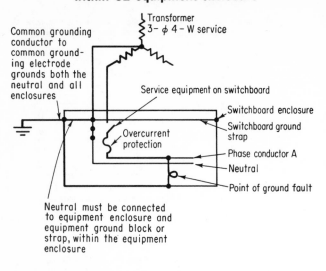

FIG. 168—Bond neutral to equipment within SE equipment enclosure

Transformer
3–φ 4–W service

Common grounding conductor to common grounding electrode grounds both the neutral and all enclosures

Service equipment on switchboard

Switchboard enclosure

Switchboard ground strap

Overcurrent protection

Phase conductor A

Neutral

Point of ground fault

Neutral must be connected to equipment enclosure and equipment ground block or strap, within the equipment enclosure

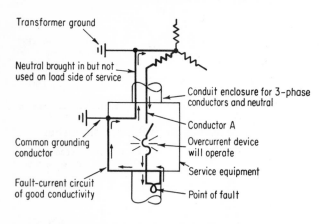

FIG. 169—Bond neutral to service enclosure even when neutral is not used in system

Transformer ground

Neutral brought in but not used on load side of service

Common grounding conductor

Fault-current circuit of good conductivity

Conduit enclosure for 3-phase conductors and neutral

Conductor A

Overcurrent device will operate

Service equipment

Point of fault

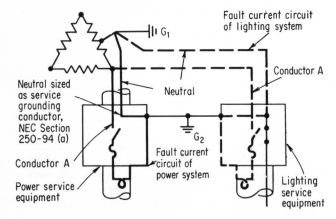

FIG. 170—Neutral must be brought in to each service equipment

Fault current circuit of lighting system

G₁

Conductor A

Neutral sized as service grounding conductor, NEC Section 250-94 (a)

Neutral

G₂

Conductor A

Fault current circuit of power system

Conductor A

Power service equipment

Lighting service equipment

1. If the service supplies motor loads, the overcurrent device may be rated or set in accordance with the required protection for a feeder supplying a motor load or for a feeder supplying a power and lighting load.

2. Not more than six circuit breakers or six sets of

fuses may serve as overcurrent protection for the service-entrance conductors. The grouping of single-pole CBs as multipole devices, as permitted for disconnect means, may also apply to overcurrent protection. And a set of fuses is all of the fuses required to protect the ungrounded conductors of a circuit.

Grounding

The service ground and the equipment ground must have their common point of connection within the service equipment enclosure whether a separate service equipment is used or the service equipment is on the switchboard. A common grounding conductor shall be run from the common point so obtained to the grounding electrode as required by Sections 250-53 and 250-54. Connection of the system neutral to the switchboard frame within the switchboard provides the lowest impedance for the equipment ground return to the neutral. If a grounding conductor was used to ground the neutral to the water pipe or other grounding electrode and a separate grounding conductor was used to ground the switchboard frame and housing to the water pipe or other electrode, without the neutral and the frame being connected together in the switchboard, the length and impedance of the ground path would be increased. The proven hazard is that the impedance of the fault current path can limit fault current to a level too low to operate the overcurrent devices "protecting" the faulted circuit. Fig. 168 shows the right way.

Whenever a service is derived from a grounded neutral system, the grounded neutral conductor must be brought into the service-entrance equipment, even if the grounded conductor is not needed for the load supplied by the service. This is required to provide a low-impedance ground-fault current return path to the neutral to assure operation of the overcurrent device, for safety to personnel and property. See Fig. 169.

The same requirements apply to installations of separate power and light services derived from a common 3-phase, 4-wire, grounded, "red-leg" delta system. **The neutral from the center-tapped transformer winding must be brought into the 3-phase power service equipment as well as into the lighting service, even though the neutral will not be used for power loads.** This is shown in Fig. 170, and is now required by Section 250-23(b).

Emergency power

In occupancies where interruption of electrical power supply to the building would result in panic, hazard to life or property or major production loss, provision should be made for emergency supply of power in the event of failure of the regular supply. Such provision may be made by designing an emergency system supplied by—

1. Storage batteries,
2. Emergency-generator set,
3. Separate emergency service, or
4. Subservice tapped ahead of disconnect means for the normal service conductors.

Detailed requirements and recommendations for emergency electrical systems are given in Article 700 of the NE Code.

Emergency Power

TYPICAL UNIT EMERGENCY LIGHT
FOR USE ON BRANCH CIRCUITS

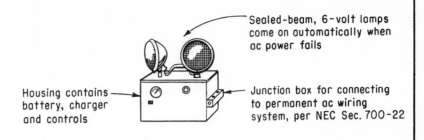

Sealed-beam, 6-volt lamps
come on automatically when
ac power fails

Housing contains
battery, charger
and controls

Junction box for connecting
to permanent ac wiring
system, per NEC Sec. 700-22

BASIC LAYOUT OF FULL-SYSTEM
DC EMERGENCY LIGHTING

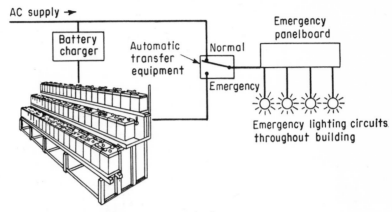

AC supply →

Battery
charger

Automatic
transfer
equipment

Normal

Emergency

Emergency
panelboard

Emergency lighting circuits
throughout building

115-volt or 230-volt battery bank

EMERGENCY SYSTEM

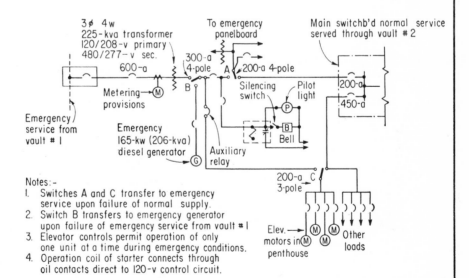

3∅ 4w
225-kva transformer
120/208-v primary
480/277-v sec.

600-a

Metering
provisions

300-a
4-pole

Emergency
service from
vault # 1

Emergency
165-kw (206-kva)
diesel generator

To emergency
panelboard

A   200-a 4-pole

Silencing
switch

Pilot
light

Bell

Auxiliary
relay

Main switchb'd normal service
served through vault # 2

200-a

450-a

200-a C
3-pole

Elev.
motors in
penthouse

Other
loads

Notes:-
1. Switches A and C transfer to emergency
service upon failure of normal supply.
2. Switch B transfers to emergency generator
upon failure of emergency service from vault # 1
3. Elevator controls permit operation of only
one unit at a time during emergency conditions.
4. Operation coil of starter connects through
oil contacts direct to 120-v control circuit.

DIESEL GENERATOR
AUXILIARY EQUIPMENT

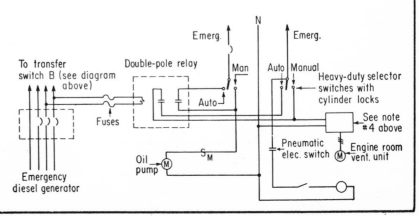

To transfer
switch B (see diagram
above)

Double-pole relay

Fuses

Auto

Emerg.

Man

N

Auto Manual

Emerg.

Heavy-duty selector
switches with
cylinder locks

See note
#4 above

Emergency
diesel generator

Oil
pump

S M

Pneumatic
elec. switch

Engine room
vent. unit

Conditions of Emergency Supply

A
FOR
INTERNAL
FAILURES
ONLY

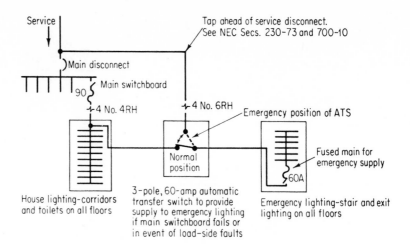

Service

Tap ahead of service disconnect.
See NEC Secs. 230-73 and 700-10

Main disconnect

Main switchboard

90

4 No. 4RH

4 No. 6RH

Emergency position of ATS

Normal position

Fused main for emergency supply

60A

House lighting-corridors and toilets on all floors

3-pole, 60-amp automatic transfer switch to provide supply to emergency lighting if main switchboard fails or in event of load-side faults

Emergency lighting-stair and exit lighting on all floors

B
FOR
EXTERNAL
FAILURES
ONLY

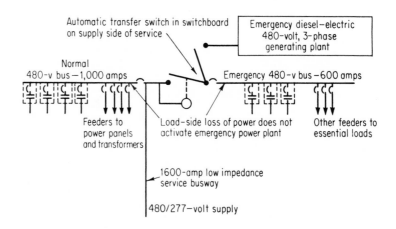

Automatic transfer switch in switchboard on supply side of service

Emergency diesel-electric 480-volt, 3-phase generating plant

Normal
480-v bus—1,000 amps

Emergency 480-v bus—600 amps

Feeders to power panels and transformers

Load-side loss of power does not activate emergency power plant

Other feeders to essential loads

1600-amp low impedance service busway

480/277-volt supply

C
FOR
INTERNAL
AND
EXTERNAL
FAILURES

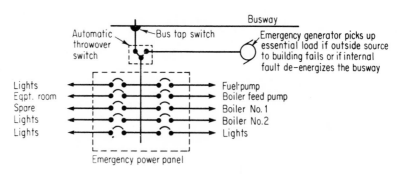

Busway

Automatic throwover switch

Bus tap switch

Emergency generator picks up essential load if outside source to building fails or if internal fault de-energizes the busway

Lights
Eqpt. room
Spare
Lights
Lights

Fuel pump
Boiler feed pump
Boiler No. 1
Boiler No. 2
Lights

Emergency power panel

Separate Emergency Service

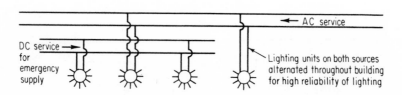

AC service

DC service for emergency supply

Lighting units on both sources alternated throughout building for high reliability of lighting

Service Calculations for Motor and Lighting Load

(Basic NE Code Method)

1. Size of motor branch circuit conductors: 125% x 28 amps equals 35 amps. This requires No. 8's.

2. Size of motor branch circuit fuses: 300% x 28 amps equals 84 amps. This requires maximum fuse size of 90 amps or 100 amps. Smaller fuses, such as time-delay type, may be used.

3. Size of service entrance conductors: 125% x 28 amps plus 80 amps (lighting load) equals 115 amps.

4. Size of main fuses: 90 amps (from 2 above) plus 80 amps equals 170 amps. This requires maximum fuse size of 200 amps. Again, smaller fuses may and should be used where possible to improve the overload protection on the circuit conductors.

NOTE: Values given here may vary with characteristics of motor.

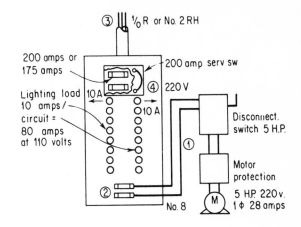

Service Overcurrent Protection

Each ungrounded service entrance conductor must be protected by an overcurrent device in series with the conductor. The overcurrent device must have a rating or setting not higher than the allowable current-carrying capacity of the conductor, except as follows:

1. If the service supplies motor loads, the overcurrent device may be rated or set in accordance with the required protection for a feeder supplying several motors or for a feeder supplying a power and lighting load. If only a single motor is supplied, the overcurrent protection should include a value of rating or setting equal to that used to protect the motor branch circuit.

2. Not more than six circuit breakers or six sets of fuses may serve as overcurrent protection for the service entrance conductors. The accompanying diagrams indicate the application and protective limitations of this six subdivision method.

In this case, service conductors could be overloaded (up to 240 amps, if CB's here are 2-pole). If main overcurrent protection, rated at 125 amps, were installed at point "A", service conductors would be protected against any load in excess of the calculated demand

CASE 1

No. 2 RH
115 amps
115/230 v

Meter

"Point 'A'"

60) 60) 30) 30) 30) 30)

Current-carrying capacity of service entrance conductors determined by demand load, calculated as described in this section.

This may be
① Group of six single-pole CB's or switches, or
② Group of six multi-pole CB's or switches, or
③ Group of more than six single-pole CB's or switches serving multi-wire circuits and arranged as multi-pole devices by "handle ties" or other means to provide disconnect of all ungrounded conductors with no more than six operations of the hand

Code permits use of up to six circuit breakers or fused switches as service disconnect means and service overcurrent protection Or one unfused main switch at point "A" and six sets of fuses (for multi-wire circuits) may also satisfy code requirements on disconnect and protection.

CASE 2

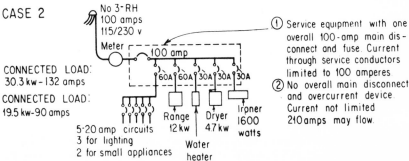

No 3-RH
100 amps
115/230 v

Meter

100 amp

CONNECTED LOAD:
30.3 kw – 132 amps

CONNECTED LOAD:
19.5 kw – 90 amps

60A 60A 30A 30A 30A

5-20 amp circuits
3 for lighting
2 for small appliances

Range
12 kw

Dryer
4.7 kw

Ironer
1600
watts

Water
heater
4.5 kw

① Service equipment with one overall 100-amp main disconnect and fuse. Current through service conductors limited to 100 amperes.
② No overall main disconnect and overcurrent device. Current not limited 210 amps may flow.

Sizing Service Entrance For A Modern Home

1. Calculate the load of general lighting and general-purpose receptacle outlets—to be served by 120-VOLT GENERAL PURPOSE circuits. For each 500 sq ft of floor area in the house (excluding porches, garages, unused spaces and unfinished areas, etc.), allow one such circuit. Allow an extra circuit for any part of 500 sq ft left over. Multiply the required number of circuits by 2000 to get the total load in watts. (It should be noted that the same figure could be arrived at by multiplying the total square feet of floor area by 4 watts per-sq-ft.)

2. Add the total circuit capacity—in watts—allowed for the appliance load in the kitchen, dining room, pantry, laundry and utility area, to be served by 120-VOLT APPLIANCE circuits. This watts total can be obtained by multiplying the number of such circuits laid out in branch circuit design by 2000. Or an assumed load of 4000 watts (two appliance circuits) can be used when the exact number of such circuits is not known.

3. Take 3000 watts of the sum of Steps 1 and 2 at 100% demand.

4. Add to this figure 35% (demand) of the remainder from the first three steps.

5. The sum of Steps 3 and 4 is the amount of capacity which must be provided in the service entrance conductors to supply the general lighting and general-purpose receptacle loads.

6. Add 8000 watts for an electric range (not over 12-kw rating). If the electric cooking appliances consist of a built-in oven and range top(s), the code must be consulted to get the proper demand load.

7. Add together the rated watts of all fixed appliances to be served by individual circuits not previously accounted for in the calculation. If both electric heating and air conditioning are to be used in the house, the rating in watts of only the larger of the two loads need be used in this total. This is due to non-simultaneous use of the two facilities.

8. Get the total of: the general lighting and general-purpose receptacle load (from Step 5); the electric range demand load (from Step 6); and 100% of the sum of fixed appliance loads (from Step 7).

9. Divide this grand total of watts by 240 (for 120/240-volt, 3-wire, single-phase service) to get the required ampere rating of the service conductors.

Common Demand Factors for Sizing Service and Main Feeders

Power Load Devices	Range of Common Demand Factors
Motors for pumps, compressors, elevators, machine tools, blowers, etc.	20 to 60%
Motors for semi-continuous operations in various mills and process plants	50 to 80%
Motors for continuous operations—as in textile mills	70 to 100%
Arc furnaces	80 to 100%
Induction furnaces	80 to 100%
Arc Welders	30 to 60%
Resistance welders	10 to 40%
Resistance heaters, ovens and furnaces	80 to 100%

Modern Design Elements of Secondary Voltage Services

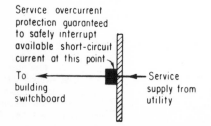

Service overcurrent protection guaranteed to safely interrupt available short-circuit current at this point

To building switchboard

Service supply from utility

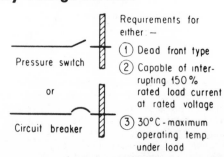

Pressure switch

or

Circuit breaker

Requirements for either :—
1. Dead front type
2. Capable of interrupting 150% rated load current at rated voltage
3. 30°C - maximum operating temp. under load

MAXIMUM PROTECTION for service installation is assured by mounting service protective devices of adequate interrupting capacity for the short-circuit duty as close as possible to the service terminals at the building wall.

EFFECTIVE DISCONNECT means should be a pressure-contact switch or a circuit breaker, of suitable design for service application with ability to withstand possible short-circuit stresses at the point of its application.

Service Calculation for Residence

Code section 220–7 sets forth an optional method of calculating service demand load for a residence. This method may be used instead of the standard method under the following conditions:

(1) Only for a one-family residence,

(2) served by a 115/230-volt, 3-wire, 100-amp or larger service, and

(3) where the total load is supplied by one set of service entrance conductors.

This new method was added to recognize the greater diversity attainable in large capacity installations. It therefore permits a smaller size of service entrance for such installations than could be permitted by using the load calculations of section 220–4.

Table 220-7
Optional Calculation for One-Family Residence

LOAD (in kw or kva)	Per Cent of Load
Air conditioning and cooling including heat pump compressors [see Section 220-4(k)]	100%
Central electrical space heating [see Section 220-4(k)]	100%
Less than four separately controlled electrical space heating units [see Section 220-4(k)]	100%
First 10 kw of all other load	100%
Remainder of other load	40%

All other load shall include 1500 watts for each 20 ampere appliance outlet circuit [Section 220-3(b)]; lighting and portable appliances at 3 watts per square foot; all fixed appliances (including electric space heating when there are four or more separately controlled units [see Section 220-4(k)], ranges, wall-mounted ovens and counter-mounted cooking units) at nameplate rated load (kva for motors and other low power-factor loads).

TYPICAL CALCULATION

Given: 1500-sq ft house with all electric utilization.

1500 watts for each of two (minimum of two required) kitchen appliance circuits	3,000 watts
1500 sq ft @ 3 watts per sq ft for general lighting and receptacles	4,500 watts
14 kw of electric space heating from more than four separately controlled units	14,000 watts
12-kw electric range	12,000 watts
3-kw water heater	3,000 watts
5-kw clothes dryer	5,000 watts
3-kw load of unit air conditioners—because this load is less than the space heating load and will not be operated simultaneously with it, no load need be added.	
	41,500 watts

First 10 kw @ 100% = 10,000 watts
Remainder @ 40%
31,500 x 0.4   = 12,600 watts
22,600 watts demand load

Size of service 22,600 ÷ 230 = 98 amperes = 100-amp Service

Under certain load conditions, this calculation may arrive at a required service capacity substantially less than 100 amps. In such cases, however, 100 amps is the minimum size service which can be used. When using the alternative calculation method of Section 220–4, it should be noted that a calculated demand load of 10 kw or more requires that the minimum size service be 100 amps, 3-wire.

Electric comfort heating

Fundamental to the design of any electric comfort heating installation is the determination of heating capacity which must be provided. This involves calculating the "heat loss" of the structure at the lowest sustained outdoor temperatures at which comfort is expected to be maintained. The amount of heat lost through a building's walls, floor and ceiling is proportional to the difference in temperature, the area involved, and the conductivity of the building materials used. Heat must be provided to replace this transmitted loss and to raise the temperature of any cold air which is introduced for ventilating purposes or by natural infiltration.

The procedures outlined here for residences are representative of those used for any structure. The simplified tables of heat-loss factors given are sufficiently accurate where currently recommended thermal insulating techniques are used, since the thermal resistance of most commonly used building materials becomes relatively insignificant compared with that of the insulation.

Calculating heat loss

Heat loss is expressed either in *Btu per hr* (abbreviated *Btuh*) or *watts*. Both are measures of the *rate* of heat transfer and may be converted one to the other:

$$\text{watts} = \frac{\text{Btuh}}{3.413} = \text{Btuh} \times 0.293$$

$$\text{Btuh} = \text{watts} \times 3.413.$$

Watts are more commonly used by the electrical man, since electric heating equipment is rated in watts.

In general, the calculating procedure involves determining the wall, floor and ceiling area (from plans or by actual measurement); locating the *heat-loss factors* of these buildings elements (see Tables 1 through 8); and finding the temperature differences involved. These values are then substituted in one or more of the four formulas A, B, C or D given on the following pages. Additional considerations will be discussed as they arise in connection with the hypothetical residential floor plan which follows.

Formula A is used for all building sections (walls, ceilings, floors, windows, doors) exposed to the outside air. Since the earth beneath concrete floor is not as cold as the outside air, heat loss through slab floors is not proportional to the design temperature difference. At or near grade level, the heat loss from a slab has been found to be roughly proportional to the linear feet of slab edge, or perimeter. Formula B is used for such floors. Basement floors, on the other hand, are usually far enough below grade to be influenced more by the ground-water temperature than by the outside air temperature. Formula C will give results sufficiently accurate for most purposes where the basement is to be heated. The ground-water temperature (usually between 40 and 60F) may be found for the locality by contacting the closest weather bureau office.

Heat loss through basement walls may be calculated using Formula A and the last column of Table 2. However, the temperature difference for the below-grade portion of the wall should be taken as the difference between the inside temperature (normally 70F) and the average of the outside design temperature and the ground-water temperature. The full design temperature difference should be applied to that portion of the wall above grade level.

Attics or attic spaces above ceilings should be well ventilated, hence outdoor temperatures are assumed to exist above the ceiling under such conditions.

Formula A is also used where a heated space adjoins an unheated space, such as a storeroom or an unheated basement. Judgment is required in choosing the temperature difference to use. An unheated basement primarily below grade is assumed to be 30 or 35 degrees cooler than the space above if the floor between is insulated. Crawl spaces beneath the floor are normally well ventilated and so are assumed to be at outdoor temperature.

Where an outside door opens into a vestibule, foyer, or long hall, such a space is usually calculated as a room in itself, and heat is provided. Otherwise, hall losses may be added to those of adjacent rooms in sizing the capacity of these rooms, and no heater is

Example: Residential heat-loss calculations

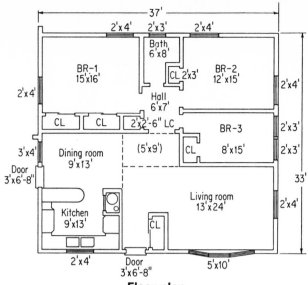

Floor plan

Inside design temperature 70F
Outside design temperature 0F
Design temperature difference 70F
Ground-water temperature 50F
Ceiling height . . . . 8 ft

Annual Degree-Days: 5000
Electric Heating Rate: 1.5 cents per kwhr

Wall areas (sq ft)

Room	Calculations	Glass wall area	Window area	Door area	Net Wall area
BR-1	$(15 + 16) \times 8$	248	16	0	232
BR-2	$(12 + 15) \times 8$	216	16	0	200
BR-3	8×8	64	12	0	52
LR	$(13 + 24) \times 8$	296	78	20	198
DR	9×8	72	12	20	40
K	$(9 + 13) \times 8$	176	8	0	168
BATH	6×8	48	6	0	42

Note: Length of outside wall is multiplied by ceiling height to get gross wall area; net wall area is obtained by subtracting the window and door areas from the gross wall area.

Heat-loss factors

Building section	Applicable table	Factor (watts/ sq ft per deg TD)	Heat loss at 70 deg TD (watts/ sq ft)
Walls: Wood siding & sheathing; gypsum board inside; R-11 insulation; 8-ft ceiling height.	2	.025	1.75
Ceiling: Gypsum board; ventilated attic above; R-19 insulation.	1	.018	1.26
Floor: Hardwood floor on subfloor; ventilated crawl space below; R-13 insulation.	3	.019	1.33
Windows: Tightly fitted storm sash.	5	.132	9.24
Doors: 1½″ solid wood with storm door.	6	.094	6.58
Infiltration: (¾ air change per hr)	9	.00396*	0.28**

* watts/cu ft per deg TD   ** watts/cu ft

Floor and ceiling areas; volume

Room	Calculations	Area (sq ft)	Volume (cu ft)
BR-1	240 — 5 (Linen Closet) + 17 Hall & LC)	252	2016
BR-2	180 + 6 (Closet) + 15 (Hall & LC)	201	1608
BR-3	120 + 15 (Hall & LC)	135	1080
LR	312 + 25 (Dotted area)	337	2696
DR	117 + 20 (Dotted area)	137	1096
K		117	936
BATH	48 — 6 (Closet)	42	336
	Total	1221	9768

Notes: Hall & linen closet areas were divided among bedrooms. Dotted area (5′ × 9′) was divided between living room and dining room.
Room volume is obtained by multiplying the floor area by the ceiling height.

Calculating procedure

A For walls, ceilings, doors, windows; and for floors over an unheated basement or crawl space:

Heat loss (watts) = W × A × TD

W = heat-loss factor (watts/ sq ft per deg TD) from Tables 1 through 6.
A = area (sq ft).
TD = design temperature difference (deg F).

B For concrete floors laid at or near grade level:

Heat loss (watts) = W × L

W = heat-loss factor (watts/ft of exposed edge) from Table 5.
L = total length of slab edge exposed to the outdoors at the foundation (ft).

Formulas (A), (B), (C) and (D) are applied in turn to each room of the structure to be heated, since heating equipment must be furnished to satisfy the heat-loss requirements of each room. Note that heat loss occurs only through building sections exposed to the outdoors or to a space at a temperature lower than that maintained indoors (usually 70F).

The sum of the transmission losses and infiltration losses for each room will give the total rating in watts of the heaters required.

The accompanying example will serve to demonstrate the general procedure for calculating residential heat loss.

C For concrete basement floors below grade level:

Heat loss (watts) = .0293 × TD × A

TD = difference between inside design temperature and ground-water temperature (deg F)
A = floor area (sq ft)

D For infiltrating air.

Infiltration loss (watts) = W × V

W = heat-loss factor (watts/cu ft per deg TD) from Table 4 (usual practice is to assume ¾ air change per hr).
V = volume of space to be heated (cu ft).

Table 1.—Heat loss through residential ceilings (Assuming space above insulation is ventilated, and wood framing covers 15% of ceiling area)

Installed resistance of insulation R	Heat-loss factor (watts/sq ft per deg TD)	
	Ceilings using plaster or gypsum board products	Ceilings using acoustical tile or insulating board products
15	.022	.020
16	.021	.019
17	.020	.018
18	.019	.017
19–20	.018	.016
21–22	.016	.015
23–24	.015	.014
25	.014	.013
30	.011	.010
35	.009	.009
40	.008	.008
45	.007	.007
50	.006	.006

Table 2.—Heat loss through frame walls (Assuming wood framing covers 20% of wall area)

Installed resistance of insulation R	Heat-loss factor (watts/sq ft per deg TD)		
	Masonry walls of low-density concrete 80 lb/cu ft or less	Frame walls using insulating board and insulating lath products	Frame walls using wood or metal lath and wood sheathing or masonry walls of stone, concrete block, or high-density concrete
5	.021	.030	.037
6	.020	.028	.034
7	.019	.027	.031
8	.018	.025	.029
9	.017	.024	.027
10	.016	.022	.026
11–12	.015	.021	.025
13–14	.014	.019	.022
15*	.013	.017	.019
20–21*	.012	.014	.016
22–23*	.011	.013	.015

* Using 2- by 6-in. studs.

Table 3.—Heat loss through wood floors
(Assuming wood framing covers 15% of floor area.) Floor consists of wood subfloor on joists and hardwood floor or tile or linoleum on suitable base.

Installed resistance of insulation R	Heat-loss factor (watts/sq ft per deg TD)
5	.035
6	.031
7	.028
8	.026
9	.024
10	.022
11	.021
12	.020
13	.019
14	.018
15	.017
20	.014
25	.012
30	.010
35	.009
40	.008

Table 4.—Heat loss due to infiltration
(Watts per cu ft per deg TD)

No. of air changes per hr	Heat-loss factor
1/10	.00053
1/8	.00066
1/4	.00132
1/2	.00264
3/4	.00396
1	.00527
1½	.00791

Table 5.—Heat loss through concrete slab on grade
(Watts/ft of exposed edge)

Outdoor design temp. (deg. F)	Unheated slab				Heated slab			
	R=6 to 7	R=5.0	R=3.33	R=2.50	R=6 to 7	R=5.0	R=3.33	R=2.50
−30 and colder	7.5	10.0	14.9	19.6	10.1	13.5	20.2	27.0
−25 to −29	7.0	9.4	14.0	18.8	9.7	12.9	19.3	25.8
−20 to −24	6.6	8.8	13.1	17.6	8.9	12.0	17.8	24.0
−15 to −19	6.3	8.2	12.6	16.7	8.1	11.4	17.3	22.8
−10 to −14	5.9	7.9	11.7	15.8	7.6	10.8	16.1	21.7
− 5 to − 9	5.6	7.3	11.1	14.9	7.0	10.2	15.2	20.5
0 to − 4	5.3	7.0	10.5	14.1	7.0	9.4	14.0	18.8
+ 5 to + 1	4.9	6.5	9.7	12.9	6.6	8.8	13.1	17.6
+10 to + 6*	4.6	6.2	9.1	12.3	5.6	7.3	11.1	14.6
+15 to +11*	4.6	6.2	9.1	12.3	5.6	7.3	11.1	14.6
+20 to +16**	4.6	6.2	9.1	12.3	5.6	7.3	11.1	14.6

* Factors assume only 12 in. of edge insulation.
** Factors assume edge insulation extends down only to bottom of slab.
Note: If no edge insulation is used, calculate heat loss at 0.237 watt/ft of exposed edge per deg TD.

Definitions

R-value: The amount of thermal resistance contributed by insulation when it is installed in a ceiling, wall or floor.

Outdoor design temperature: The lowest outdoor temperature at which the heating system is expected to maintain the indoor design temperature. This is usually considerably higher than the lowest temperature on record for the area; value may be obtained from local electrical utility.

Indoor design temperature, or control point: The temperature which is to be maintained in the heated space —usually 70F for residences in this country.

Design temperature difference (TD): The difference between the outdoor and indoor design temperatures.

Table 6.—Heat loss through windows (Watts/sq ft per deg TD)

No. of glass panes	Description	No. of air spaces	Width of each space (in.)	Heat-loss factor
1	Single glass	None	——	.331
2	Window with usual storm sash	1	1½	.220
	Sealed unit		¼	.185
	Sealed unit		½	.167
	Very tightly fitted storm sash, no vents		1½	.132
3	Sealed unit	2	¼	.126
	Sealed unit		½	.111

Table 7.—Heat loss through solid wood doors (Watts/sq ft per deg TD)

Nominal thickness (in.)	Actual thickness (in.)	Heat-loss factor: Exposed door	Heat-loss factor: With storm door*
1	25/32	.188	.108
1¼	1 1/16	.161	.100
1½	1 5/16	.144	.094
1¾	1⅜	.141	.091
2	1⅝	.126	.082
2½	2⅛	.106	.076
3	2⅝	.091	.067

* 50% glass and thin wood panels.

Table 8.—Heat loss through exposed-beam ceilings with built-up roofing (Watts/sq ft per deg TD)

Preformed roof insulation above deck (in.)	Type of roof deck: Flat metal	Wood 1 in.	Wood 2 in.	Wood 3 in.	Preformed slab; wood fiber & cement binder 2 in.	Preformed slab; wood fiber & cement binder 3 in.
0	.264	.141	.094	.067	.061	.044
½	.117	.085	.064	.050	Insulation not used	
1	.076	.061	.050	.041		
1½	.056	.047	.041	.035		
2	.047	.041	.035	.029		
2½	.038	.032	.029	.026		
3	.032	.029	.026	.023		

placed in the hall. (Where embedded cable is used, however, such spaces are usually heated.)

Closets are normally calculated as part of the room into which they open; room heaters will keep closet temperatures at a comfortable level.

Tables 1, 2 and 3 give heat-loss factors for representative residential constructions at various degrees of insulation. Most insulating products are now being labeled with R-values designating their installed thermal resistance.

Infiltration of outside air may be estimated in terms of "air changes per hr," meaning the number of times per hr the entire heated volume of air is replaced by fresh air. It is common practice to assume ¾ air-change per hr for residential electric heating, although ½ change or less is common for tight construction. Insulated basements which are primarily below grade and have no doors to the outside will have low infiltration rates—as low as 1/10 air change per hr with tight, weatherstripped window sash, and probably no more than ¼ change with no weatherstripping. Formula D and Table 4 may be applied in evaluating heat loss due to infiltration.

Example

Sample calculations are given here for a single-floor frame residence built over a ventilated crawl space. Preliminary data on areas, volume, and heat-loss factors are tabulated for convenience and to show how they were obtained. Room-by-room calculations make use of these values to find the room heat losses and the required heater capacities.

Calculations are also shown for the same floor plan over a heated basement and on a concrete slab. With a heated basement, there will be no floor loss to the basement; however, the basement wall and floor-slab losses must be calculated in addition to the various infiltration and window losses.

Room-by-room calculations

Room	Area x heat-loss factor=heat loss Sq ft x watts/sq ft=watts

LIVING ROOM

Walls	198 × 1.75	= 347
Ceiling	337 × 1.26	= 425
Floor	337 × 1.33	= 448
Windows	78 × 9.24	= 721
Door	20 × 6.58	= 132
Infiltration	2696* × 0.28**	= 755

Total heat loss = 2828
Suggested heater rating = 3.0 kw

DINING ROOM

Walls	40 × 1.75	= 70
Ceiling	137 × 1.26	= 173
Floor	137 × 1.33	= 182
Windows	12 × 9.24	= 111
Door	20 × 6.58	= 132
Infiltration	1096* × 0.28**	= 307

Total heat loss = 975
Suggested heater rating = 1.0 kw

KITCHEN

Walls	168 × 1.75	= 294
Ceiling	117 × 1.26	= 147
Floor	117 × 1.33	= 156
Windows	8 × 9.24	= 74
Infiltration	936* × 0.28**	= 262

Total heat loss = 933
Suggested heater rating = 1.0 kw

BATH

Walls	42 × 1.75	= 74
Ceiling	42 × 1.26	= 53
Floor	42 × 1.33	= 56
Windows	6 × 9.24	= 55
Infiltration	336* × 0.28**	= 94

Total heat loss = 332
Suggested heater rating: A 500-watt heater will satisfy heating requirements;-but, since quick pickup is often desirable, a 1-kw heater is recommended.

* cu ft   ** watts/cu ft per deg TD

BEDROOM 1

Walls	232 × 1.75	= 406
Ceiling	252 × 1.26	= 318
Floor	252 × 1.33	= 335
Windows	16 × 9.24	= 148
Infiltration	2016* × 0.28**	= 564

Total heat loss = 1771
Suggested heater rating = 1.75 kw

BEDROOM 2

Walls	200 × 1.75	= 350
Ceiling	201 × 1.26	= 253
Floor	201 × 1.33	= 267
Windows	16 × 9.24	= 148
Infiltration	1608* × 0.28**	= 450

Total heat loss = 1468
Suggested heater rating = 1.5 kw

BEDROOM 3

Walls	52 × 1.75	= 91
Ceiling	135 × 1.26	= 170
Floor	135 × 1.33	= 180
Windows	12 × 9.24	= 111
Infiltration	1080* × 0.28**	= 302

Total heat loss = 854
Suggested heater rating = 1.0 kw

HEAT LOSS SUMMARY (KW):

Room	Walls	Clg	Floor	Wind	Doors	Infilt	Total
LR	347	425	448	721	132	755	2828
DR	70	173	182	111	132	307	975
K	294	147	156	74	....	262	933
Bath	74	53	56	55	....	94	332
BR1	406	318	335	148	....	564	1771
BR2	350	253	267	148	....	450	1468
BR3	91	170	180	111	....	302	854
Total	1632	1539	1624	1368	264	2734	9161

Basement heat loss with fully heated basement instead of crawl space:

Assume ground water temperature = 50F
Basement walls are 1 ft above grade, 6 ft below
Walls are furred in and insulated to R5
There are three 2-sq-ft, wood-frame, single-glass windows in above-grade walls.

Infiltration:
Volume = 1221 x 7 = 8547 cu ft
At ¼ air change, heat loss (Formula D, Table 4) = 8547 x .00132 x 70 = 790 watts

Windows:
Area = 2 x 3 = 6 sq ft
TD = 70 − 0 = 70 deg
Heat loss (Formula A, Table 6) = .331 x 6 x 70 = 139 watts

Walls (above grade):
Length of outside wall = 2 (33 + 37) = 140 ft
Area = 1 x 40 − windows = 140 − 6 = 134 sq ft
TD = 70 − 0 = 70 deg
Heat loss (Formula A, Table 2) = .037 x 134 x 70 = 347 watts

Walls (below grade):
Area = 6 x 140 = 840 sq ft
TD = 70 − ½ (0 + 50) = 45 deg
Heat loss (Formula A, Table 2) = .037 x 840 x 45 = 1399 watts

Floor:
Area = 37 x 33 = 1221 sq ft
TD = 70 − 50 = 20 deg
Heat loss (Formula C) = .0293 x 20 x 1221 = 716 watts
Total basement heat loss = 3391 watts.

Floor loss with house on slab at grade level instead of over crawl space:

Assume edge of slab insulated to R6.

Length of exposed slab × heat-loss factor = heat loss

Room	ft		×	watts/ft	= watts	Room	ft		×	watts/ft	= watts
Living room	(13 + 24)	37	×	5.3	= 196	Bedroom 1	(16 + 15)	31	×	5.3	= 164
Dining room	(9 + 0)	9	×	5.3	= 48	Bedroom 2	(15 + 12)	27	×	5.3	= 143
Kitchen	(9 + 13)	22	×	5.3	= 117	Bedroom 3	(8 + 0)	8	×	5.3	= 42
Bath	(6 + 0)	6	×	5.3	= 32					**Total slab loss**	**= 742**

INSULATION R-VALUES

The concept of designating thermal insulation effectiveness by R/numbers was introduced about five years ago to facilitate adaptation of the All-Weather Comfort Standard, proposed at about the same time. (A portion of this Standard is given in Table 10.) Widespread acceptance of these values makes it imperative for electric heating specifiers and installers to be familiar with their significance and use.

Comparing insulating materials by any single characteristic—thickness, density, conductivity, etc.—can be misleading and lead to erroneous conclusions. On the other hand, the actual thermal resistance to the flow of heat measured by standard testing procedures can be expressed by a single numerical value which is determined by all these inherent characteristics and which accurately describes the insulating performance.

The resulting R/numbers simplify specifications and calculations since they include, in addition to the resistance of the insulation itself, any resistance imparted to the section by the creation of air spaces or surface films. (Table 9 shows nominal resistances added by both reflective and nonreflective surface films and air spaces.)

Manufacturers' Designations of R/numbers on their insulation take many forms. An example is shown here. The manufacturer's descriptions of the products have been replaced by A, B, C, etc. Note that some products (C, CR and D) have varying R/numbers, depending on whether they are used in the ceiling, floor or wall. This is due to the direction of heat flow (up, down or horizontal) and whether or not an air space is created. The reflective backing of CR and DR is responsible for R/numbers higher than those shown for C and D, respectively, since the reflective backing creates film surfaces and air spaces with resistances greater than those created by insulation without reflective backing. Where R/numbers are not shown opposite a particular product, that product is not intended for that application. Circled values are those which will satisfy All-Weather Comfort Standard requirements.

R / NUMBERS					
Product	Ceiling		Walls	Floor	
	Win.	Sum.	All year	Win.	Sum.
A	(24)	24	-	-	-
B	-	-	(13)	-	-
CR	15	19	-	(19)	15
C	13	13	(11)	(13)	13
DR	-	-	(11)	-	-
D	9	9	(8)	(9)	9
E	-	-	(7)	7	7
R = reflective backing					
Win. = winter			Sum. = summer		

Technical Terms involved in the formulation and use of R/numbers are few and simple. Watts and Btu per hour (Btuh) are both used to represent rate of heat flow. Quantitatively, 1 watt = 3.413 Btuh and conversely, 1 Btuh = 0.293 watt. Heat loss through a building section is thus represented either by Btuh/sq ft per degree temperature difference or by watts/sq ft per degree TD. These two expressions are commonly called the U-factor and W-factor, respectively. The mathematical relationships between these conductance values and thermal resistance are shown here.

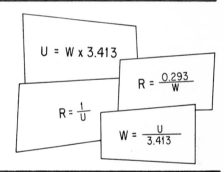

$$U = W \times 3.413$$

$$R = \frac{0.293}{W}$$

$$R = \frac{1}{U}$$

$$W = \frac{U}{3.413}$$

Location of an insulating product in the building section has much to do with the thermal performance, or R/number, to be expected. Assume that insulation type C in the above table is installed in the stud spaces of a frame wall, as shown here. By means of tests, it is established that the insulating batt itself has a mass thermal resistance of 11. Although an air space is created in the wall space, it is less than ¾ in. (an air space is assumed to have negligible resistance unless it is at least ¾ in. wide); hence no air-space resistance is created with the insulation in the wall. Also, since building materials enclose the insulation both inside and out, no surface of the insulation will be exposed to the air, and no surface resistance will be introduced by the insulation. The net installed resistance created by the insulation is thus 11, giving the insulation a value of R/11 installed in the wall.

With the same insulating batt placed between floor joists, however, an air space is created between the subfloor and the insulation, and the bottom surface of the insulation is exposed to the crawl space or unheated basement below. For an insulating batt without a reflective backing, the air space and the exposed surface provide 1.1 and 0.9 units of resistance, respectively (from Table 2), for a total installed resistance of 13.1. The insulation thus has a value of R/13 when used in the floor. (Manufacturers' instructions usually will include the specification that the product must be installed with a ¾-in. or 1-in. minimum air space where construction permits.)

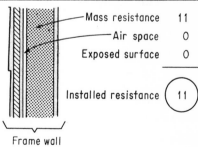

Mass resistance 11
Air space 0
Exposed surface 0

Installed resistance (11)

Frame wall

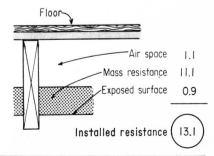

Floor

Air space 1.1
Mass resistance 11.1
Exposed surface 0.9

Installed resistance (13.1)

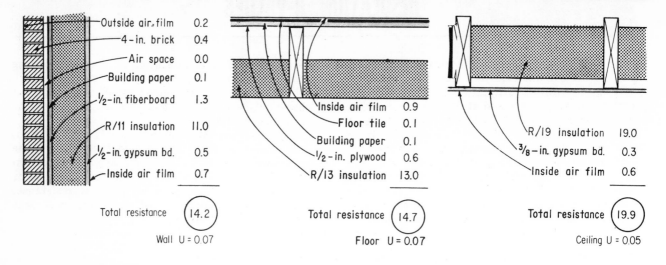

Outside air film	0.2
4-in. brick	0.4
Air space	0.0
Building paper	0.1
½-in. fiberboard	1.3
R/11 insulation	11.0
½-in. gypsum bd.	0.5
Inside air film	0.7

Total resistance (14.2)

Wall U = 0.07

Inside air film	0.9
Floor tile	0.1
Building paper	0.1
½-in. plywood	0.6
R/13 insulation	13.0

Total resistance (14.7)

Floor U = 0.07

R/19 insulation	19.0
⅜-in. gypsum bd.	0.3
Inside air film	0.6

Total resistance (19.9)

Ceiling U = 0.05

Typical Building Sections employing frame construction illustrate how insulation with the proper R/number can bring the wall, ceiling, or floor up to All-Weather Comfort Standard (AWCS) requirements. Each of the section components (brick, sheathing, etc.) contributes a definite amount to the overall thermal resistance of the section; the insulation must supply the balance.

The AWCS recommends a maximum U of 0.07 for frame walls with 4-in. studs (see Table 10). This represents an overall resistance of 1/0.07 or 14.3. The construction components of such a wall have a resistance of 0.2 + 0.4 + 0.1 etc., or a total of 3.2. The insulation must supply 14.3—3.2 or about 11.1. Insulation with a resistance of R/11 will be needed.

The floor section shown has a resistance of about 1.7. Installation of R/13 insulation brings the total to 14.7, the reciprocal of which is about 0.07, the AWCS recommended U-value for frame floors. Similarly, the ceiling shown has a resistance of about 1.0; insulation rated R/19 is needed to bring the total to 1/0.05 or 20. Note that in both the floor and ceiling examples shown, the resistance of the insulation surface and that of the air space is included in the insulation rating.

In computing the overall resistance of building sections, values are sufficiently accurate when carried to one decimal place, as shown. R/numbers of insulation are expressed to the nearest whole number; U-values of building sections are rounded off to two decimal places.

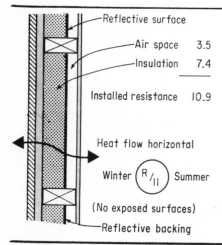

Reflective surface	
Air space	3.5
Insulation	7.4
Installed resistance	10.9

Heat flow horizontal

Winter (R/11) Summer

(No exposed surfaces)

Reflective backing

Reflecting Backing on insulating batts significantly affects the resistance rating of surface films and air spaces. The R/number system takes these effects into account and eliminates much detailed computation. In the sample R/number table previously given, insulation types DR and C both have a rating of R/11 in walls. Type DR is not as thick as type C; its mass resistance is only 7.4 as compared with 11 for typpe C. It has a reflective backing on one side, however, which when facing an air space creates an air-space resistance of 3.5. The sum of the two is 10.9, or R/11. Again, no insulation surface is exposed to room air or outdoor air, so no surface resistance is counted as part of the insulation installed resistance.

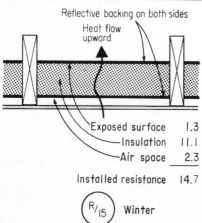

Reflective backing on both sides

Heat flow upward

Exposed surface	1.3
Insulation	11.1
Air space	2.3
Installed resistance	14.7

(R/15) Winter

Direction of Heat Flow and reflectivity of surface films and air spaces are responsible for the difference in summer and winter R/numbers when reflective backings are used on the insulation. In the previous example, with insulation installed in the wall, both heat loss in winter and heat gain in summer involved the horizontal flow of heat, with no change in resistance. The R/11 value thus applies all year. Heat flow through the ceiling, however, is up during the winter and down during the summer. The R/15 batt shown here has two reflective surfaces, one facing the attic space and the other facing the air space formed between the insulation and the ceiling gypsum board or plaster. The mass insulation value of 11 added to surface and air space resistances taken from Table 2 gives the total winter installed resistance of 14.6, or R/15. It should be kept in mind that even though both surfaces have reflective backings, only one is intended as the vapor barrier, and it must face the interior space.

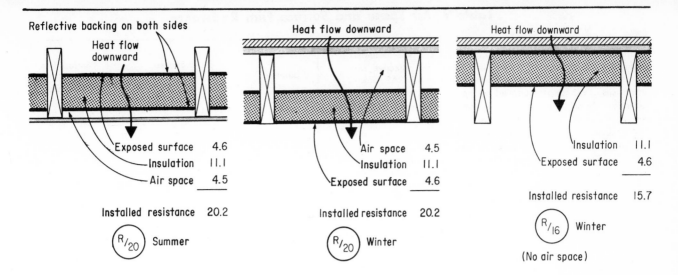

Summer Values of R/numbers for insulation installed in the ceiling will be greater than winter values because of the greater resistance of surface films and air spaces to heat flow downward, especially when reflective surfaces are involved (see Table 9). In the preceding example with heat flow up, the exposed reflective surface and air space had resistance values of 1.3 and 2.3, respectively—a total of 3.6. For the ceiling shown above, with heat flowing down into the room from the attic space, these values are now 4.6 and 4.5, a total of 9.1. Added to the insulation mass resistance of 11.1, the summer installed resistance is now 20.2, or R/20, as compared with R/15 for winter use. (Despite the computed value of R/20, this product is still labeled R/19 to conform with the standardized use of R/19 and R/24 values for ceilings.)

Installed in the floor, the situation is reversed. Heat flow is down in the winter, as shown above, and up in the summer. The R/numbers for the same insulating batt therefore are correspondingly reversed: R/20 (R/19) in the winter, R/15 in the summer, assuming that proper air spaces are provided in both cases.

The importance of the air space is illustrated by the above floor sections. If this R/20 batt is installed with one of its surfaces up against the subfloor as shown, the 4.5 resistance units of the air space are lost, and the insulating value is reduced to R/15. Heating cost estimates are made using computed heat losses based on expected insulation performance. Negligence in following installation recommendations will cause such estimates to be exceeded.

Blown Insulation which is supplied in bags may be installed to provide specific R/numbers through regulation of its installed thickness and the area covered per bag. Information, such as that shown in the table (right), is stamped on each bag. Thus if a 1750-sq-ft ceiling is to be insulated to R/19 with this product, the amount of insulation required will be

$$\frac{1750}{35} \text{ or 50 bags,}$$

leveled out between joists to a depth of 5¾ in. The "weight" column would not be used by the installer; it serves as a check for anyone inspecting the job for conformance to specifications. If the above 1750-sq-ft ceiling has been done correctly, therefore, one or more square feet of the insulation scooped up and placed on a scale should check out to weigh one lb per sq ft. In the table shown, the circled numbers would be filled in by the manufacturer to suit the product contained in the bag.

Insulation blown into walls, assuming that the 3⅝-in. stud space is filled, results in a value of about R/11 using mineral wool, and bags are marked to indicate the wall area (for example, 35 sq ft) covered per bag.

BLOWN INSULATION			
R/	Minimum thickness	Maximum coverage	Weight
R/24	Not less than 7 in.	Not more than 30 sq. ft.	Not less than 1.2 lb./sq. ft.
R/19	Not less than 5¾ in.	Not more than 35 sq. ft.	Not less than 1.0 lb./sq. ft.
R/13	Not less than 4 in.	Not more than 50 sq. ft.	Not less than 0.7 lb./sq. ft.
R/9	Not less than 2½ in.	Not more than 80 sq. ft.	Not less than 0.4 lb./sq. ft.

Table 9. Air Space and Surface Film Resistance

Values given in this table may be used in the calculation of installed R/numbers for any insulating products (see examples below and on preceding pages). Resistances of reflective and nonreflective surface films were taken from the *ASHRAE Guide*; resistances of air spaces, supplied by the National Mineral Wool Insulation Association, are values calculated from research reports. These values, modified slightly since the introduction of the R/number system about five years ago, are normally rounded off to one decimal place in use.

To be effective, air spaces formed by the installation of the insulating material must be at least ¾ or 1 in. thick, as shown in the table. Surface films contribute to the R/number only when one surface of the insulation is exposed.

Direction of heat flow	Air Spaces			Surface Films	
	Thickness	Resistance		Resistance	
	(in.)	Refl.	Nonrefl.	Refl.	Nonrefl.
Up	1	2.30	0.88	1.32	0.61
Horizontal...	¾	3.48	1.01	1.70	0.68
Down	1	4.49	1.08	4.55	0.92

Table 10. All-Weather Comfort Standard

Maximum Heat-Loss Values*

Degree-Days	Watts/sq ft	Btuh/sq ft
Over 8000	10.6	36
7001 to 8000	10.0	34
6001 to 7000	9.5	32
4501 to 6000	9.2	31
3001 to 4500	8.9	30
3000 and under	8.4	29

* Based on an infiltration rate of ¾ air change per hr. Values are expressed in watts and Btuh per sq ft of floor area of the space to be heated, measured to the outside of exterior walls.

These tables contain data from the All-Weather Comfort Standard which aid in specifying insulation quantities to assure comfort to the occupants, low initial equipment costs, and low operating costs.

Although residential construction practices vary to some extent, the resistance of uninsulated floors, walls and ceilings is a comparatively small part of the total resistance after insulating, so that the few general categories represented in the table may be applied in practice with good results.

It should be noted that ceiling and floor insulation requirements are increased when wall insulation is restricted because of the nature of construction materials used. It is expected that adoption of the recommendations given in the table at left will result in an installation conforming with the limits imposed by the table of maximum heat-loss values.

Recommended Thermal Performance Values*

Building section	Type of wall construction		
	Frame		Masonry
	Siding, shingle or masonry veneer exterior		8-in. lightweight block or brick cavity
	4-in. studs	2-in. studs	
Ceilings	U = 0.05 R/19 W = 0.015	U = 0.04 R/24 W = 0.012	U = 0.04 R/24 W = 0.012
Opaque walls	U = 0.07 R/11 W = 0.021	U = 0.11 R/6 W = 0.032	U = 0.12 R/4 W = 0.035
Floors over vented crawl spaces	U = 0.07 R/13 W = 0.021	U = 0.05 R/19 W = 0.015	U = 0.05 R/19 W = 0.015
Floors over unheated basements	U = 0.09 R/9 W = 0.026	U = 0.07 R/13 W = 0.021	U = 0.07 R/13 W = 0.021
Concrete slabs on grade	R/5	R/5	R/5

* U values are given in Btuh/sq ft per deg TD.

W values were calculated from the U values and inserted as a convenience, expressed in watts/sq ft per deg TD.

R/numbers are installed resistance values of thermal insulation which, when applied according to the manufacturer's instructions, will limit U values of the section to those shown.

General Application of R/System

Using information supplied by the manufacturer and Table 9 above, an installed R/number can be calculated for any insulating product. Building materials, insulating and otherwise, are tested and rated according to their ability to conduct heat. This thermal conductivity, k, is expressed as Btuh per sq ft per deg TD per inch of thickness. The thermal resistance per inch of thickness would thus be 1/k, and the resistance of any thickness would be 1/k times the thickness in inches. Adding to this value any applicable air space or surface film resistance gives the installed R/number.

Example: A manufacturer of organic fiber insulation claims a k-factor of 0.25. A reflective foil-wrapped batt of this material 3 in. thick is installed between floor joists over a vented crawl space with a 1-in. air space between the insulation and the floor. What is its installed R/number?

Mass resistance:	$1/0.25 \times 3 = 12.0$	
Air space, reflective, heat flow down:	4.5	
Surface film, reflective, heat flow down:	4.6	
	Total: $\overline{21.1}$ = R/21	

Example: A 2-in. rigid fiberboard with a k-factor of 0.38 is cemented to the inside of a basement wall. Its nonreflective inside surface is left as the interior finish of the basement. What is its installed R/number?

Mass resistance:	$1/0.38 \times 2 = 5.3$	
Air spaces: none	0	
Surface film, nonreflective, heat flow horizontal:	0.7	
	Total: $\overline{6.0}$ = R/6	

OPERATING COST

Reasonably correct estimates of expected annual operating costs are still of significant importance to the promotion and sale of electric heat; hence an appreciation of the factors affecting cost and an understanding of estimating methods in current use are part of the required preparation.

The NEMA Formula

After the gross heat loss has been obtained for each room in the house, the sum of the room losses will give the total house heat loss. Expressed in kilowatts, this figure may be used, together with the design temperature difference and normal annual degree-days for the area involved, in the "NEMA Formula" to get an approximation of the annual energy consumption in kwhr.

The accuracy of the result depends entirely upon the choice of the correction factor "C" used in the formula. This factor must account for many variables in construction and living habits, as well as a "built-in" error in the degree-day concept; hence unless it is applied judiciously, its accuracy could be a matter of luck. Most electric utilities supplying heating loads have adopted one or more values of "C" for use in their areas, depending upon the type of installation involved. An average value is often given as 17.0 but it is admittedly conservative for most applications in well insulated houses and usually yields estimates above the actual energy consumption.

The NEMA Formula
For Estimating Annual Heating Energy

$$\text{Annual kwhr} = \frac{\text{gross heat loss (kw)} \times \text{degree-days} \times \text{C}}{\text{design temperature difference}}$$

Degree-days to be used are calculated to the 65F base, as reported by the U. S. Weather Bureau.

C = Correction factor, obtained from local electrical utility.

In the example illustrated,

$$\text{Annual kwhr} = \frac{9.161 \text{ kw} \times 5000 \text{ DD} \times 17}{70} = 11,124 \text{ kwhr}$$

Cost = 11,124 kwhr × \$.015/kwhr = \$167.

The Degree-Day

Degree-days represent the annual summation of the daily differences between the mean temperature and 65F when the mean temperature is less than 65F. This relation was developed as a device for estimating combustible fuel requirements, based on the observation that residential heating was not generally needed until the outdoor temperature dropped below 65F, where the indoor temperature was kept in the vicinity of 70F.

The daily mean temperature is that temperature midway between the lowest and highest temperatures recorded for the day:

$$\text{mean temperature} = \frac{\text{max. temp} + \text{min. temp}}{2}$$

For a mean temperature of 40F, the degree-days for that day would be 65-40 or 25 degree-days. If during a heating season there were d days having the same mean temperature t, the total degree-days represented by these days would be

$$d (65 - t).$$

The summation of d (65 — t) for all values of t during a normal year, using the number of days represented by each, gives the normal annual degree-days.

Since 65F is used as the basis of calculations, normal degree-days are said to be calculated to the base 65F. If it were known that heating was not needed until the outdoor temperature dropped below 55F, as is often true for industrial or commercial applications, degree-days used for estimating would have to be calculated to the base 55F. This temperature above which no heat is required is also known as the "balance" temperature; it signifies the temperature at which the design heat losses just equal the extra heat gains from the sun, occupants, lighting, appliances, etc.

Thus degree-days to any base b may be expressed as the summation of d (t_b — t) over the complete heating season.

Location	Heating Season	Heating Days	Ave. Mean Temp, F	Degree-Days	Outside Design Temp, F
ALABAMA					
Anniston*	Oct 15–Apr 24	192	50.3	2820	12
Birmingham*	Oct 15–Apr 25	193	50.6	2780	12
Mobile	Nov 2–Apr 1	151	54.9	1529	22
Montgomery	Oct 25–Apr 10	168	53.4	1954	18
ARIZONA					
Flagstaff*	Aug 12–Jul 5	328	42.1	7525	— 4
Phoenix	Nov 5—Apr 2	149	55.0	1492	36
Yuma	Nov 15–Mar 7	113	56.6	951	38
ARKANSAS					
Fort Smith*	Oct 16–Apr 20	187	48.0	3188	6
Little Rock*	Oct 17–Apr 21	187	49.1	2982	8
CALIFORNIA					
Eureka	. . . .	365	52.3	4632	32
Fresno*	Oct 16–Apr 25	192	51.8	2532	32
Independence	Sept 25–May 23	241	49.1	3832	12
Los Angeles	Nov 2–May 10	190	57.4	1451	41
Sacramento	Oct 16–May 14	211	52.7	2600	30
San Diego*	Oct 22–Jun 2	224	58.0	1574	43
San Francisco	. . . .	365	56.6	3069	37
San Jose	Oct 7–Jun 7	244	55.1	2410	38
COLORADO					
Denver	Sept 15–Jun 7	266	43.7	5673	—12
Grand Junction*	Sept 25–May 23	241	41.0	5796	— 3
Pueblo*	Sept 17–May 31	257	42.8	5709	—14
CONNECTICUT					
Bridgeport*	Sept 19–Jun 5	260	42.3	5896	— 1
Hartford*	Sept 12–Jun 2	264	41.7	6139	— 2
New Haven*	Sept 14–Jun 8	268	42.5	6026	0
DELAWARE					
Wilmington*	Sept 27–May 19	235	44.1	4910	0
DISTRICT OF COLUMBIA					
Washington	Oct 2–May 12	223	45.9	4258	10
FLORIDA					
Jacksonville	Nov 10–Mar 21	132	56.6	1113	28
Miami	Dec 4–Mar 13	100	63.3	173	35
Pensacola	Nov 3–Apr 2	151	55.5	1435	24
Tampa*	Dec 1–Mar 3	93	57.8	674	36
GEORGIA					
Atlanta	Oct 14–Apr 25	194	50.5	2811	11
Augusta*	Oct 23–Apr 12	172	52.6	2138	20
Macon*	Oct 23–Apr 9	169	52.9	2049	20
Savannah*	Oct 28–Apr 9	164	54.6	1710	24
IDAHO					
Boise*	Sept 9–Jun 12	277	43.7	5890	—10
Lewiston*	Sept 13–Jun 8	269	44.6	5483	—12
Pocatello*	Sept 4–Jun 20	290	40.9	6976	—17
ILLINOIS					
Cairo	Oct 11–Apr 29	201	46.3	3756	0
Chicago*	Sept 21–May 29	251	39.9	6310	—11
Peoria*	Sept 22–May 27	248	40.5	6087	—13
INDIANA					
Evansville*	Oct 4–Jun 15	255	47.9	4360	— 4
Fort Wayne*	Sept 18–May 30	255	40.3	6287	— 7
Indianapolis	Oct 2–May 18	229	42.6	5134	— 8
Terre Haute*	Sept 28–May 20	235	42.2	5366	— 6
IOWA					
Charles City	Sept 10– May 31	264	36.6	7504	—21
Davenport	Sept 24– May 21	240	39.6	6091	—12
Des Moines	Sept 23– May 23	243	39.2	6274	—13
Sioux City*	Sept 16– May 26	253	37.3	7012	—16
KANSAS					
Concordia	Oct 2–May 19	230	41.9	5323	—11
Dodge City	Oct 2–May 20	231	43.1	5058	— 9
Topeka	Oct 4–May 13	222	42.8	4919	— 8
Wichita*	Oct 7–May 14	220	44.2	4571	— 6
KENTUCKY					
Bowling Green*	Oct 4–May 16	225	46.0	4279	2
Lexington*	Oct 1–May 21	233	43.6	4979	— 2
Louisville	Oct 6–May 10	217	45.3	4279	— 2
LOUISIANA					
New Orleans	Nov 10–Mar 24	135	56.3	1175	26
Shreveport*	Oct 26–Apr 6	163	52.0	2117	14
MAINE					
Eastport	. . . .	365	42.4	8246	— 9
Portland*	Aug 27–Jun 25	303	39.7	7681	— 9
MARYLAND					
Baltimore	Sept 8–May 13	248	48.1	4203	8
MASSACHUSETTS					
Boston*	Sept 17–Jun 5	262	42.9	5791	0
MICHIGAN					
Alpena	Aug 25–Jun 25	305	38.5	8073	—10
Detroit*	Sept 17–Jun 2	259	40.3	6404	— 4
Escanaba	Aug 22–Jun 27	310	37.1	8657	—18
Grand Haven	Aug 31–Jun 19	293	41.4	6915	— 3
Grand Rapids	Sept 16–Jun 2	260	40.1	6474	— 4
Houghton	Aug 9–Jul 6	332	38.0	8964	—18
Lansing*	Sept 9–Jun 3	268	38.9	6982	— 8
Marquette	Aug 24–Jul 1	312	37.7	8529	—16
Sault Ste. Marie*	Aug 8–Jul 15	342	37.3	9475	—19
MINNESOTA					
Duluth	Aug 21–Jul 5	319	35.3	9474	—27
Minneapolis*	Sept 11–May 31	263	35.1	7853	—23
Moorhead	Aug 23–Jun 16	298	34.0	9315	—29
St. Paul*	Sept 11–Jun 1	264	35.4	7804	—23
MISSISSIPPI					
Meridian*	Oct 17–Apr14	180	52.0	2333	14
Vicksburg	Oct 26–Apr 8	165	52.9	2000	15
MISSOURI					
Columbia*	Sept 29–May 17	231	42.9	5113	— 9
Hannibal	Sept 24–May 29	239	43.1	5248	—12
Kansas City*	Oct 5–May 12	220	42.8	4888	— 8
St. Louis	Oct 8–May 10	215	44.2	4469	— 5
Springfield*	Oct 1–May 19	231	44.7	4693	— 5

Asterisks indicate airport stations; others are city office stations.
Average temperature = 65—(degree-days/heating days).
Outside design temperature given is that which is likely to recur once every 13 years
as the minimum daily mean temperature.

Location	Heating Season	Heating Days	Ave. Mean Temp, F	Degree-Days	Outside Design Temp, F
MONTANA					
Billings*	Sept 4–Jun 16	286	40.2	7106	−31
Havre	Aug 29–Jun 22	298	37.4	8213	−39
Helena	Aug 20–Jul 3	318	39.4	8126	−39
Kalispell*	Aug 17–Jul 5	323	40.1	8055	−31
Miles City*	Sept 7–Jun 13	280	37.1	7822	−35
NEBRASKA					
Lincoln	Sept 27–May 21	237	40.3	5865	−15
North Platte*	Sept 15–Jun 1	260	39.8	6546	−15
Omaha*	Sept 24–May 20	239	39.2	6160	−17
Valentine	Sept 12–Jun 5	267	38.5	7075	−21
NEVADA					
Reno*	Sept 4–Jun 26	296	44.6	6036	3
Winnemucca*	Sept 4–Jun 17	287	42.8	6369	−9
NEW HAMPSHIRE					
Concord*	Aug 29–Jun 15	291	38.8	7612	−11
NEW JERSEY					
Atlantic City	Sept 29–May 30	244	45.6	4741	−8
Elizabeth	Sept 20–May 24	247	43.5	5302	2
New Brunswick	Sept 17–May 30	256	43.9	5404	4
Plainfield	Sept 16–Jun 1	259	43.6	5535	4
Somerville	Sept 18–May 29	254	43.1	5586	2
Trenton	Sept 25–May 21	239	43.8	5068	2
NEW MEXICO					
Albuquerque*	Oct 3—May 12	222	45.2	4389	8
Roswell*	Oct 8–May 3	208	48.5	3424	4
Santa Fe	Sept 1–Jun 15	287	43.9	6063	3
NEW YORK					
Albany	Sept 15–May 28	256	40.3	6319	−9
Binghamton*	Aug 30–Jun 16	291	39.1	7537	−7
Buffalo*	Sept 10–Jun 9	273	40.0	6838	−5
Ithaca	Sept 4–Jun 9	279	40.9	6719	−4
New York	Sept 28–May 26	241	44.0	5050	5
Oswego	Sept 9–Jun 15	280	40.1	6975	−7
Rochester*	Sept 9–Jun 6	271	39.7	6863	−4
Syracuse*	Sept 13–Jun 2	263	40.2	6520	−10
NORTH CAROLINA					
Asheville	Sept 29–May 19	233	47.5	4072	5
Charlotte*	Oct 9–Apr 30	204	49.3	3205	14
Hatteras	Oct 23–May 3	193	52.6	2392	21
Raleigh	Oct 12–May 1	202	49.8	3075	14
Wilmington*	Oct 19–Apr 24	188	52.6	2323	20
NORTH DAKOTA					
Bismarck*	Aug 31–Jun 16	290	33.9	9033	−31
Devils Lake	Aug 27–Jun 22	300	31.9	9940	−32
Grand Forks	Aug 15–Jun 23	313	33.8	9764	−31
Williston	Sept 1–Jun 19	292	33.9	9068	−35
OHIO					
Cincinnati	Oct 4–May 14	223	44.7	4532	−3
Cleveland	Sept 23–May 29	249	42.0	5717	−5
Columbus	Sept 27–May 22	238	42.8	5277	−3
Dayton*	Sept 25–May 25	243	42.0	5597	−4
Sandusky	Sept 23–May 29	249	41.5	5859	−4
Toledo*	Sept 16–May 31	258	40.2	6394	−5
OKLAHOMA					
Oklahoma City	Oct 16–Apr 27	194	46.9	3519	−1
OREGON					
Baker	Aug 25–Jul 4	314	42.4	7087	−14
Portland	Sept 16–Jun 18	276	50.0	4143	10
Roseburg	Sept 13–Jun 19	280	50.3	4122	19

Location	Heating Season	Heating Days	Ave. Mean Temp, F	Degree-Days	Outside Design Temp, F
PENNSYLVANIA					
Erie	Sept 20–Jun 4	258	41.3	6116	−3
Harrisburg*	Sept 22–May 20	241	43.2	5258	4
Philadelphia	Oct 2–May 17	228	45.2	4523	6
Pittsburgh	Sept 28–May 19	234	43.4	5048	−3
Reading	Sept 26–May 21	238	43.7	5060	3
Scranton	Sept 15–May 30	258	41.6	6047	−2
RHODE ISLAND					
Block Island*	Sept 13–Jun 19	280	44.1	5843	7
Providence	Sept 18–Jun 1	257	43.2	5607	1
SOUTH CAROLINA					
Charleston	Oct 28—Apr 10	165	54.3	1769	22
Columbia	Oct 19—Apr 17	181	52.4	2284	19
SOUTH DAKOTA					
Huron*	Sept 12–Jun 3	265	29.8	7902	−21
Pierre	Sept 4–Jun 17	287	39.2	7420	−22
Rapid City*	Sept 5–Jun 17	286	26.3	7535	−22
TENNESSEE					
Chattanooga*	Oct 8–May 4	209	48.8	3384	8
Knoxville*	Oct 8–May 4	209	47.8	3590	5
Memphis	Oct 19–Apr 22	186	48.8	3006	6
Nashville*	Oct 11–May 2	204	47.8	3513	3
TEXAS					
Abilene*	Oct 22–Apr 14	175	49.8	2657	7
Amarillo*	Oct 2–May 17	228	45.9	4345	−2
Corpus Christi*	Nov 15–Mar 15	121	56.6	1011	23
Dallas*	Oct 27–Apr 6	162	51.0	2272	8
El Paso*	Oct 19–Apr 19	183	50.6	2641	20
Fort Worth*	Oct 27–Apr 10	166	50.8	2361	8
Galveston	Nov 13–Mar 29	137	56.2	1211	23
Houston	Nov 8–Mar 25	138	55.8	1276	19
Palestine	Oct 30–Apr 7	160	52.6	1980	11
San Antonio*	Nov 5–Mar 29	145	54.1	1579	19
UTAH					
Salt Lake City	Sept 20–May 29	252	43.3	5463	−1
VERMONT					
Burlington*	Sept 3–Jun 10	281	37.0	7865	−17
Northfield	Aug 8–Jul 1	328	38.6	8719	−19
VIRGINIA					
Cape Henry	Oct 12–May 12	213	49.5	3307	17
Lynchburg*	Sept 29–May 12	226	46.6	4153	11
Norfolk	Oct 13–May 7	207	49.9	3119	15
Richmond	Oct 6–May 9	216	47.8	3720	11
Wytheville	Sept 13–Jun 2	263	45.9	5022	3
WASHINGTON					
Seattle	Aug 28–Jul 2	309	50.6	4438	15
Spokane*	Aug 31–Jun 27	301	42.2	6852	−16
Tacoma	Aug 13–Jul 9	331	50.3	4866	15
Tatoosh Island	....	365	49.3	5724	18
Walla Walla	Sept 20–May 27	250	45.6	4848	−12
WEST VIRGINIA					
Elkins*	Sept 12–Jun 6	268	43.5	5773	−4
Parkersburg	Sept 30–May 18	231	44.4	4750	−1
WISCONSIN					
Green Bay*	Sept 2–Jun 12	284	35.9	8259	−20
La Crosse*	Sept 10–May 31	264	36.0	7650	−20
Madison	Sept 13–Jun 3	264	37.3	7300	−19
Milwaukee	Sept 15–Jun 12	271	39.4	6944	−17
WYOMING					
Cheyenne*	Aug 26–Jun 28	307	40.4	7562	−19
Lander*	Aug 29–Jun 22	298	37.1	8303	−30
Yellowstone Park	....	365	38.8	9554	−34

Electric Heating Equipment

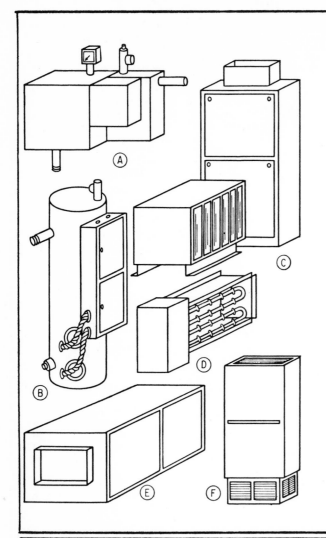

CENTRAL SYSTEMS distribute heat from a centrally located source by means of circulating air or water. Compact electric boilers (A) mounted on wall of basement, utility room, or closet furnish hot water to convectors or embedded pipe, incorporating controls and circuit protection. Immersion heating elements may be stepped in one at a time to provide capacity corresponding to heat loss. Typical systems run to 24 kw. Larger boilers (B) with associated controls and circuiting can take advantage of lower off-peak electricity rates by heating water during off-peak periods, storing it in insulated tanks, and circulating it as needed to convectors or radiators. Capacities to 40 kw are available; higher ratings may be ordered. Packaged heat pumps may be used as a split system with the condenser unit isolated from the compressor and evaporator unit (C), or all may be contained in one enclosure. Since the heat pump both heats and cools, its capacity is usually chosen to correspond with the cooling load, and auxiliary resistance heat is used to make up any difference between the cooling and heating load, if required. Cooling capacities from 1½ to 10 tons are readily available, although higher ratings may be obtained.

Duct insert heaters (D) are used as auxiliary heat for heat pumps, as a central heat source for use in a forced air duct, or as local heat mounted in the delivery duct to individual rooms or areas. Capacities range from ½ to 1000 kw, sizes from 6 in. square to 10 by 12 ft. Units normally include such auxiliaries as thermal overload protection, contactors, sequencing switches, and fan interlocks.

Electric furnaces (E) including blower, resistance heating coils, filter, and associated controls may be operated in a horizontal or vertical position in a basement, closet or attic. Capacities range from 7 to 35 kw; elements are energized in steps as required. Free-standing version (F), rated 12 kw, uses no ducts and is intended for central heating of cabins and other small homes.

WALL HEATERS are designed for surface or recessed mounting, with or without built-in thermostats. Residential models range in rating from 500 to 4000 watts. Recessed types (A & B) vary in size from about 8 by 10 in. to 20 by 24 in. Forced-air models (A) may include fan speed control and provision for use of fan for recirculating air without heat. Coiled wire elements are usually used. Radiant or natural convection units (B) may have tubular elements as shown, ceramic cones wound with nichrome wire, or conductive glass panels. Projection into room varies from ⅜ in. to about 2½ in.

Rugged utility heaters (C) rated 500 and 1000 watts have perforated enclosure and are designed for surface mounting in basements, garages and playrooms. Forced air units with quiet-running blower (D) may be inserted between studs of existing wall through small hole in plaster or gypsum board. Only grille is visible in room. Panel heaters (E) similar to those used on ceilings are surface-mounted; some models are set into enclosing frame. Cornice heaters (F) mounted at junction of wall and ceiling radiate directly at angle to room below; convection currents also set up warm air layer along ceiling which radiates downward. Wall insert heater (G) fits between studs. Warm room air at ceiling is drawn in through upper grille by fan, passed through heating coils, and discharged into room through lower grille. After wall finishing has been applied, only grilles are visible. Thermostat is included.

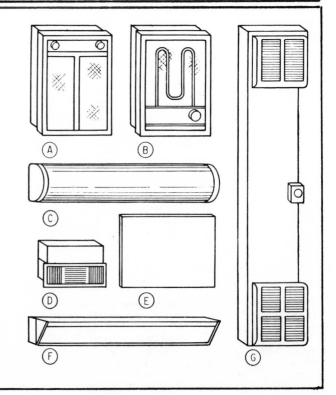

LARGE-AREA CEILING PANELS can be installed to make the entire ceiling a heat source. There are several advantages of this approach to in-space heating. The heaters are completely inconspicuous, being entirely integrated into the building structure itself. There are no moving parts and no maintenance. And, what is often most important, the location of the heaters places no restrictions upon the placement of furniture in the rooms below. While slightly higher heat losses may be expected because of the rather large area of higher temperature adjacent to the cold attic or outdoor air, the practice of using greater insulation thicknesses in the ceiling usually makes this difference insignificant.

Most common ceiling system uses heating cable embedded in plaster or between two layers of gypsum board. Cable comes on reels, is stapled to layer of gypsum lath. Nonheating ends are brought up through panel and down through wall to thermostat or relay. In plastered ceiling, finish plaster is applied over cable. In drywall construction, cable is first completely covered with plaster; finish gypsum panels are then nailed in place, taped, and painted. Cable may be obtained in many lengths and spaced to satisfy room heating capacity requirements. Average heat dissipation is about 2¾ watts/ft of length.

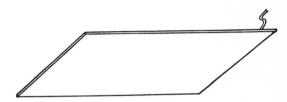

This system has a heating-wire element embedded in a ⅝-in. tapered edge gypsum board 4 ft wide and from 4 to 12 ft long, rated at about 15 watts/sq ft, 240 volts. Panels are nailed to ceiling joists; joints are taped in the usual manner. Branch circuit connection is made to leads on rear of panel.

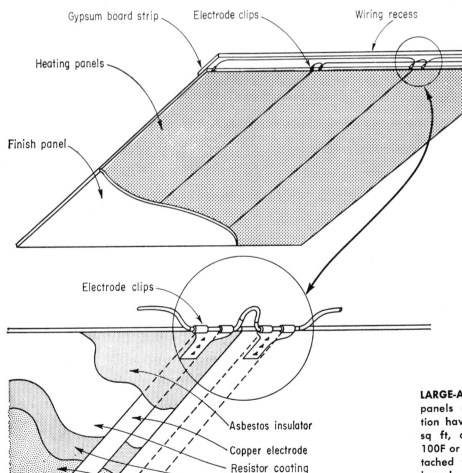

DETAIL OF PANEL AND CONNECTIONS
(shown without finish panel)

LARGE-AREA conductive gypsum board panels designed for 120-volt operation have a heat output of 15 watts/sq ft, operating at temperatures of 100F or lower. Special bushings are attached to gypsum strip to terminate branch circuit conduit or cable; conductors are brought down into wiring recess and secured to electrode clips with a pressure-type connection. Points on clip pierce copper electrodes and conduct current to resistive coating.

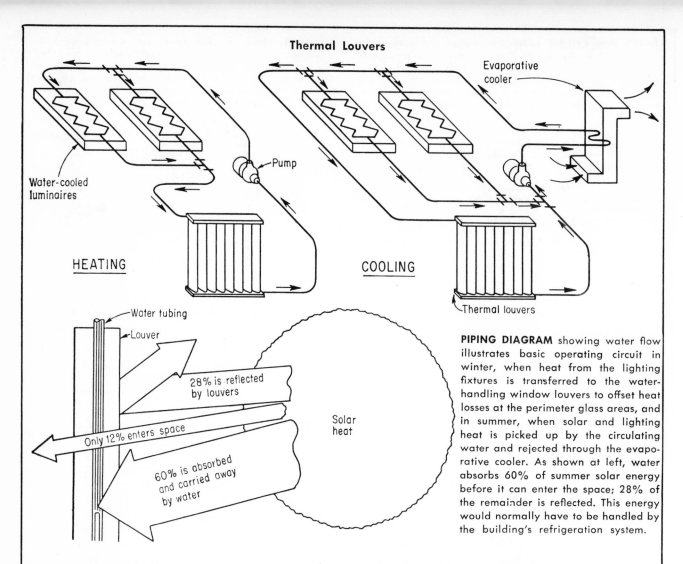

Thermal Louvers

HEATING

COOLING

Water-cooled luminaires

Pump

Evaporative cooler

Thermal louvers

Water tubing

Louver

28% is reflected by louvers

Only 12% enters space

60% is absorbed and carried away by water

Solar heat

PIPING DIAGRAM showing water flow illustrates basic operating circuit in winter, when heat from the lighting fixtures is transferred to the water-handling window louvers to offset heat losses at the perimeter glass areas, and in summer, when solar and lighting heat is picked up by the circulating water and rejected through the evaporative cooler. As shown at left, water absorbs 60% of summer solar energy before it can enter the space; 28% of the remainder is reflected. This energy would normally have to be handled by the building's refrigeration system.

An example of engineering pioneering in heat recovery and utilization is the recent development of thermal louvers to control solar energy and aid in the redistribution of lighting heat. The operating principle is simplified above. Heart of the system is the adjustable vertical aluminum louver units fitted to the inside of the building's glass. The louver blades have a central hollow core through which water is circulated. During the summer, the louvers intercept up to 88% of the solar energy passing through the glass, 60% being absorbed by the circulating water. The water also passes through the specially designed lighting fixtures, picking up about 70% of the ballast and lamp heat. The water is pumped through an evaporative cooler, where its temperature is reduced before recirculating.

In the winter, when perimeter areas need heat, transfer is accomplished from interior lighting units to the louvers by the circulating water, this time bypassing the evaporative cooler. The louvers then act as radiators/convectors to offset heat loss at the window area.

HYDRONIC VALANCE system (A), designed for mounting at junction of wall and ceiling, produces layer of warm air which radiates heat to space below. During the summer, chilled water can be circulated for effective cooling of the space. Floor insert heaters (B) are frequently used in front of glass walls or sliding glass doors. Recessed between frame floor joists or embedded in concrete slab, the unit distributes heat by natural convection. Capacities range from 500 to 2000 watts. Under-cabinet heater (C) is designed specially for use below kitchen base cabinets. Only 3½ in. high and rated 1000 watts, the heater makes use of what is often the only kitchen space available. Heat from permanently sealed-in water is distributed by quiet-running fan. Tempered air inlet (D) incorporating a 1400-watt resistance element takes air from attic space and introduces it into living area. It is intended to provide controlled infiltration and to reduce excess humidity.

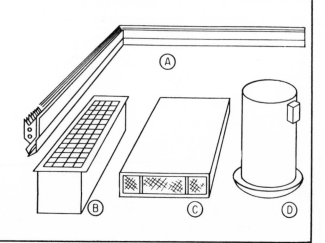

CEILING HEATERS and small panels concentrate higher heat densities than large-area ceiling panel systems.

(A and C) Heaters resembling lighting luminaires in appearance are surface-mounted on ceiling, although some are designed for T-bar or pendant-suspension. Heat source in most models is conductive glass or fiberglass; ratings vary from 600 to 1500 watts at standard voltages. Sizes range in width from 6 to 20 in. and in length from 18 to 48 in.

(B) Metal panels 2 by 4 ft and 2 by 5 ft in size and rated 500 to 750 watts may be surface-mounted on ceiling or dropped into T-bar channels. Typical construction includes a continuous foil-type element adhered in an overall pattern to the insulated rear side of an aluminum pan. Overall thickness is 1 in. or less; heater usually incorporates ½ to ¾ in. of built-in thermal insulation.

(D) Fixture mounting one to three screw-base-type-infrared lamps is used primarily in bathrooms for quick heat and may be controlled either by a thermostat or wall switch. Lamps are rated 250 watts; canopy mounts over ceiling wiring box for connections. Unit may also incorporate fan for bathroom exhaust.

(E) Combination heating/lighting fixture or heating/lighting/exhaust fan units are used for bathrooms or other small rooms. Center heating element is usually conductive glass rated 1000 to 1450 watts; up to 200 watts in incandescent lighting may be included in end panels. Unit may include

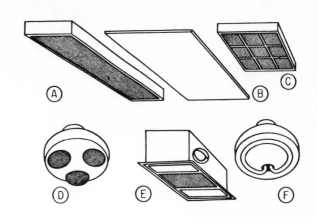

exhaust fan ducted to outdoors which draws air from room through periphery of heater. Small circulating fan may be included to keep air moving over heating element.

(F) Small-room ceiling heater may have tubular resistance element or quartz tube; ratings are from 600 to 1250 watts. Unit may depend entirely upon radiation and natural convection to dissipate its heat or may incorporate a circulating fan.

INDUSTRIAL, commercial and institutional applications are served with wall and baseboard units of special rugged design and with larger capacities. Cabinet convectors (A) rated up to 4 kw with natural convection are used in entranceways, vestibules, corridors, lobbies, laboratories and classrooms. Units may be recessed or surface-mounted, projecting 3 to 6 in. into room. Overall dimensions measure up to about 2 ft in height, 4 ft in length. Forced-air models have ratings to 30 kw, with typical dimensions 25 in. high, 6 to 13 in. deep, 2 to 7 ft long. Unit forced-air heaters (B) for industrial use incorporate means for bracket or pipe suspension from ceiling or building structure. Sizes range to 26 in. high, 33 in. wide, and 22 in. deep for capacities up to 45 kw. Larger ratings to 120 kw (C) provide complete or supplemental heating and ventilating for gymnasiums, supermarkets, warehouses, bowling alleys, etc., in sizes up to 3 by 9 by 10 ft.

Sill-line units (D) resemble large baseboards, are available from about 120 to 700 watts per ft of length, and are usually surface-mounted on outside walls beneath the windows. Made in widths from 2 to 8 ft, they are readily adaptable to modulating control with a step controller. Self-contained forced-air unit ventilators (E) have connections to bring in outside air and are widely used in classrooms and in large multi-room buildings for decentralized comfort conditioning. Unit may also include a chiller and thus provide heating, ventilating and cooling. Typical ratings are from 1.3 to 36 kw in sizes 26 to 32 in. high, 4 to 9 ft long, and 13 to 16 in. deep.

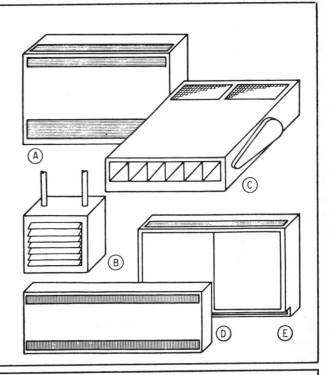

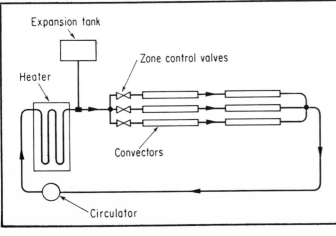

Expansion tank

Zone control valves

Heater

Convectors

Circulator

HYDRONIC SYSTEMS using compact electric boilers, provision for zone control, and sequence switching of elements are now available in several designs. Circulator pumps heated water (about 200F) to radiators, convectors, or embedded floor piping in closed loops. Parallel-connected immersion elements in boiler can provide any required capacity. Significant present market is the conversion of oil- and gas-fired hot water systems installed during World War II. Space occupied by previous fuel-fired boiler and made available because of small size of electric unit can be important sales advantage. Introduction of small heat exchanger takes care of domestic water supply.

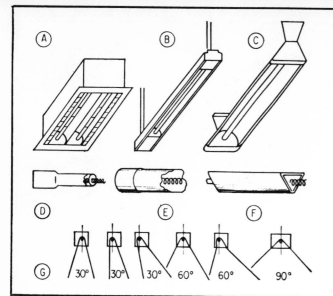

INFRARED HEATERS permit fast-response high-temperature radiation, particularly applicable where it is difficult or impractical to maintain air temperatures at comfortable level. One- or two-lamp fixtures may be recessed into ceiling or canopy (A), suspended by pipe or chain (B), or mounted with brackets (C). Element may be a quartz lamp (D), quartz tube (E), or metal sheath (F). Quartz lamp coiled resistance element operates in vacuum; output contains about 6% visible light; lamp operates at 4000F. Quartz tube is not evacuated; operates at 1200 to 1800F with dull orange-red glow. Metal sheath element has good resistance to impact, vibration and splashing; operates at 1200 to 1500F with dull red glow.

Reflectors are available to provide wide variety of beam spreads, both symmetrical and asymmetrical (G). In general, narrow beam spreads are desirable for higher mounting heights to insure concentration of primary radiation at working level. Infrared heaters are used primarily in industrial, outdoor, and semi-enclosed locations, although more decorative models are available for use in residential bathrooms, laundry rooms, etc.

HYDRONIC BASEBOARD has been introduced using a central water source but employing individual heating elements within the baseboard units themselves. Units containing the heating elements are followed by straight convectors without heaters as required to provide sufficient surface area for the dissipation of the generated heat. Each loop or zone has its own circulator and one or more thermostats; baseboard units are connected by ¾-in. tubing. To provide for further regulation of heat output, convectors have built-in dampers which may be adjusted manually. Heating elements, rated 1 to 5 kw, are chosen or combined to match the heat loss of the space.

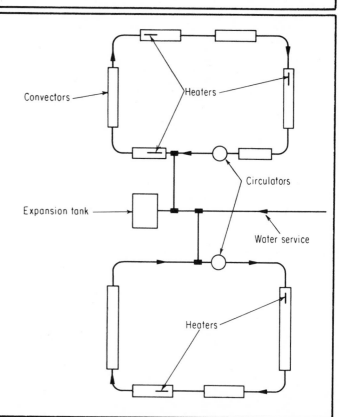

COMPLETE COMFORT, including heating, cooling, air cleaning, fresh air ventilation, humidification, and dehumidification as needed are features of one electric comfort conditioning system. Central unit installed in basement, garage or laundry contains air filter, humidifier, cooling coil, and central heating bank. Heater tempers air supply to individual room forced-air baseboard units. Additional heater contained in each baseboard unit is actuated by thermostat to provide heat required in excess of that furnished by central bank and for "reheat" in summer when dehumidification, but not full cooling, is needed.

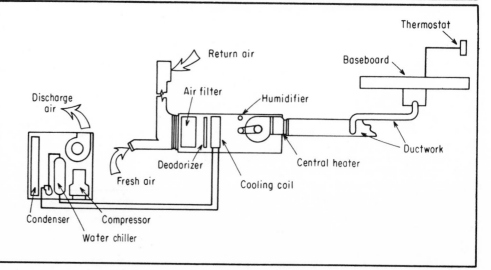

INTERNAL-SOURCE HEAT PUMP

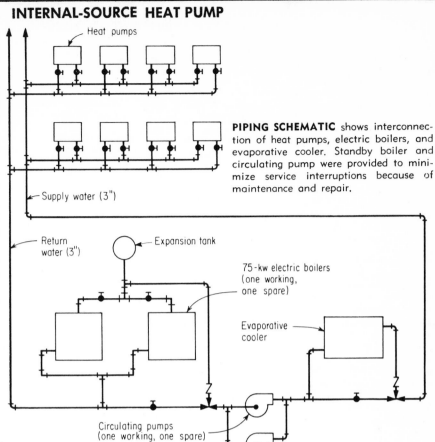

A somewhat different approach to the redistribution of energy for heating and cooling utilizes unitary water-to-air heat pumps; but, instead of drawing heat from a well or other water source, the system employs a two-pipe (supply and return) closed loop of circulating water which acts as both a source of heat and a heat sink.

Each heat pump, its capacity chosen to match the cooling load of the local area it serves, discharges tempered air by means of short ducts and diffusers directly into the occupied space. On the cooling cycle, heat is transferred from the air to the refrigerant and then to the circulating water. On the heating cycle, heat is drawn from the water by the refrigerant and transferred to the air.

Obviously, the system may be used most advantageously where there are areas with large amounts of excess heat as well as areas simultaneously requiring heat. This condition could exist because of high lighting levels (or other sources of heat gain) in interior spaces or because of high solar gains through glass on the sunny side of the building with the shady side calling for heat. Since there will be times when the excess available heat is insufficient to satisfy the heat-loss requirements, an electric boiler is usually provided to add heat to the circulating water as necessary. (Hot water from a storage tank, heated off peak, may also be used.) During the summer time, or whenever the temperature of the water exceeds usable maximum values, the water is diverted through an evaporative cooler to reject excess heat.

The system has several advan-

PIPING SCHEMATIC shows interconnection of heat pumps, electric boilers, and evaporative cooler. Standby boiler and circulating pump were provided to minimize service interruptions because of maintenance and repair.

tages. The nonrefrigerated circulating water is maintained at temperatures ranging between approximately 70 and 95F, and hence the piping need not be insulated. It is a decentralized system; maintenance of any single unit will not affect operation of other units. Any heat pump may be removed quickly by disconnecting the water tubing, power input and discharge air duct collar. A defective unit may be replaced immediately by a spare with

little loss of service. Since the circulating water is maintained at a relatively constant temperature, each unit always has its full capacity of heating or cooling available. Life expectancy will be greater than conventional units because the compressor is inside the building and not exposed to the weather. Of compact size, the units may be located in closets, ceiling plenums, or other available spaces close to the areas to be heated and cooled.

BASEBOARD HEATERS vary widely in shape, size, type of heating element, and rating. Sections are available in lengths up to 10 ft rated from 100 to 3000 watts and may be joined to form longer units (A). Sizes of enclosures vary from 4 to 9 in. high and 1¾ to 2¾ in. deep. Accessories available include thermostat sections (B), convenience receptacles (C), summer-winter sections incorporating a receptacle for a room air conditioner and double-throw switch to change from heating to cooling (D), a section for housing a low-voltage thermostat relay (E), and inside-outside corner sections to permit continuous runs of baseboard around corners (F). Baseboards incorporate some form of thermal protection such as the capillary linear control indicated by the arrow (G). This control breaks the circuit if there is any buildup of heat anywhere along the heater, such as would occur if a blanket fell across the baseboard. Existence of label (H) on heater or carton is assurance that baseboard has been laboratory tested and verified by NEMA to meet performance standards designed for optimum comfort.

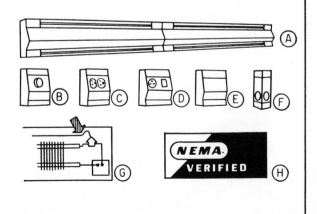

Baseboard Heaters

ELEMENT TYPES and configurations vary widely with baseboard models. Major objectives in design are: to provide maximum area of radiation for transfer of heat from element to air stream and movement of maximum air volume at low velocities to reduce heating of enclosure; to project heated air into room and away from wall to minimize wall streaking; and to allow for lateral movement of element to avoid noises of expansion and contraction.

The "watt-density" of a baseboard is defined as the concentration of heat per unit area of element, expressed in electrical terms as watts per sq in. The total surface area available for heat transfer depends on heater design and determines the operating temperature of the element. Thus "watts per sq in.," and not "watts per ft of length," is the most reliable factor for judging desirable operating characteristics of a baseboard heater. Since the information necessary for such comparisons is not readily available, adherence by the manufacturer to NEMA's equipment standards and approval under its new testing program become increasingly significant to the consumer.

Baseboard sections are available in lengths of 1 to 10 ft with ratings of 100 to 3000 watts. Sizes of enclosures vary from 4 to 9 in. high and 1¾ to 2¾ in. deep. Accessories available include thermostat sections, inside and outside corner sections, blank sections, convenience receptacles, and "heat-cool" selector switch sections designed to permit wall or window air conditioners to be fed from baseboard receptacles.

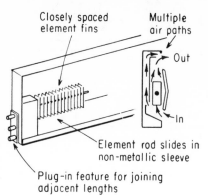

Closely spaced element fins

Multiple air paths

Out

In

Element rod slides in non-metallic sleeve

Plug-in feature for joining adjacent lengths

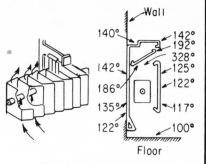

Wall

140° 142° 192° 328° 125° 122° 117° 100°

142° 186° 135° 122°

Floor

Swept-back fins in one model produce these typical operating temperatures (deg F) at room temperature of 83 F

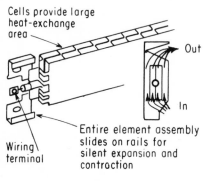

Cells provide large heat-exchange area

Out

In

Wiring terminal

Entire element assembly slides on rails for silent expansion and contraction

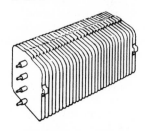

Cast aluminum fins with multiple embedded element rods provide large surface area and low surface temperatures

---

Radiant Heating Systems

A WIDE VARIETY of heater types is classed as "radiant." Steel ceiling panels are available for recessed or surface mounting in sizes of 2 by 4 ft and 2 by 5 ft with ratings of 500 and 700 watts respectively. Hermetically sealed aluminum ribbon-type element is terminated in junction box and connected to suitable leads in flexible metallic conduit for connection to branch circuit. Recessed, these units project only about ½ in. below the ceiling surface. Similar surface-mounted panels, 2 by 4 ft and rated 500 watts, are available in glass with electrically conductive coating on upper side.

Surface-mounted glass-panel heaters which project 2 in. from ceiling are made in sizes of 18 by 18 in. (600 watts) and 24 by 24 in. (1000 watts). Modular design permits heaters to be mounted side-by-side in rows, squares, or other patterns as required.

Radiant glass heaters with conductive coatings for wall, baseboard, or ceiling mounting use spring-loaded carbon contacts on two edges to carry branch-circuit current to glass coating, which transfers generated heat to glass by conduction.

Heating cable, used in both ceilings and floors, consists of a single copper alloy conductor covered with extruded thermoplastic insulation and enclosed by a tough nylon jacket. Such cable is also factory-assembled into mats of various widths and lengths to provide 10 to 15 watts/sq ft, depending upon voltage, for supplementary heat in floor slabs of bathrooms, playrooms, basements, garages, etc.

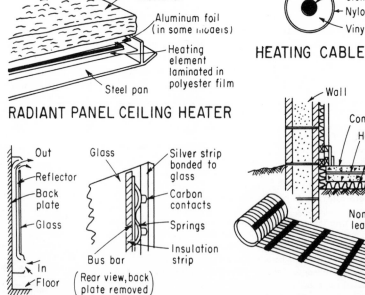

Thermal insulation

Aluminum foil (in some models)

Heating element laminated in polyester film

Steel pan

RADIANT PANEL CEILING HEATER

Wire heating element

Nylon jacket

Vinyl insulation

HEATING CABLE

Out

Reflector

Back plate

Glass

In

Floor

Glass

Silver strip bonded to glass

Carbon contacts

Springs

Insulation strip

Bus bar

(Rear view, back plate removed)

RADIANT GLASS WALL HEATER

Wall

Concrete floor

Heating mats

Insulation

Non-heating leads

FLOOR HEATING MATS

Line-Voltage Thermostats

SEVERAL TYPES of line-voltage thermostats are in use. Single-pole units serve single-stage heating needs. Double-pole units are used when the thermostat must fulfill the requirements for a disconnecting means for the heater (NEC Sec. 422-29). Modulating controls used with two-stage heaters provide two levels of heat. One set of contacts is designed to close ½ to 1½ degrees below the other. Under moderate conditions the contact with the higher setting operates one stage of the heater. When the heat furnished by this single stage is not sufficient, the temperature drops and the second set of contacts energizes the second heater stage.

Two broad categories of line-voltage thermostats include those with exposed sensing elements and those with enclosed elements. It is claimed that the exposed element is more sensitive to heaters having a high percentage of radiant heat, since radiation from all directions is able to reach the element.

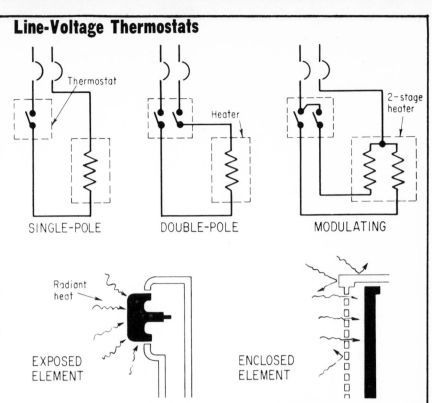

SINGLE-POLE   DOUBLE-POLE   MODULATING

EXPOSED ELEMENT   ENCLOSED ELEMENT

Low-Voltage Thermostats

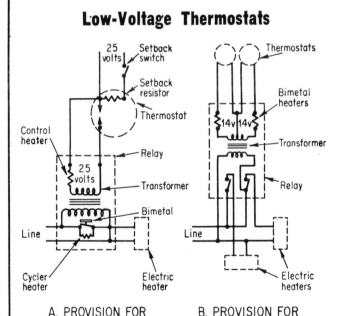

A. PROVISION FOR NIGHT SETBACK

B. PROVISION FOR TWO CIRCUITS

THERMOSTAT-RELAY combinations illustrate two operating principles. (A) Thermostat contacts energize control heater of relay, using relay transformer as source of power. Heating effect of control heater varies with relative length of "on" and "off" time of thermostat contacts. Cycler heater is energized when load switch is open. Bimetal load switch operation depends on total heat furnished by combined effect of control and cycler heaters. Closing setback switch in central control panel heats setback resistor; thermostat contacts close around 62F instead of 70F. (B) This relay may be used to control two heaters from one thermostat or two heaters from two thermostats. When only one thermostat is used, the transformer center tap is not used. Heating of bimetal heaters closes load switches.

Dual-Voltage System

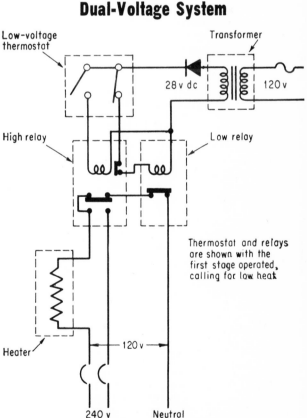

Thermostat and relays are shown with the first stage operated, calling for low heat.

TWO-STAGE LOW-VOLTAGE THERMOSTAT is used in this control circuit to provide either full or half voltage to the heater. At half voltage, heater delivers ¼ rated heat. At first call for heat, first stage of thermostat energizes "low" relay, connecting heater across 120 volts. When weather becomes more severe and heat supplied is inadequate, room temperature drops. Second stage of thermostat, set ½ to 1 deg below first stage, energizes "high" relay, which disconnects "low" relay and connects heater across 240 volts.

Humidity Controls

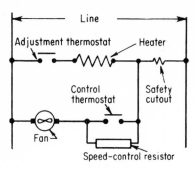

VENTILATING UNIT

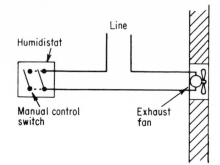

HUMIDISTAT CONTROL

TEMPERED FRESH AIR ventilator and humidistat-controlled exhaust fan both serve to keep relative humidity down in electrically heated homes. The ventilator, installed in the ceiling, discharges heated fresh air into the living space in accordance with the setting of an adjustable thermostat. The slight pressurization resulting helps reduce infiltration of cold outside air and keep the air in continuous gentle motion, reducing stratification. The control thermostat shown cuts in resistor to reduce speed when outside air temperature drops below 35F.

The humidistat contains a control dial marked in percent relative humidity. Setting the control to the desired humidity level causes the exhaust fan to operate when this level is exceeded, inducing increased infiltration of outside air with low moisture content. Humidistat is available with built-in manual control switch as shown to permit operation of fan to control cooking odors, etc.

Input Controllers

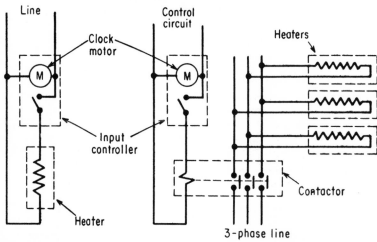

LINE-VOLTAGE CONTROL

PILOT CONTROL OF 3-PHASE CIRCUIT

INFRARED HEATERS are more easily controlled by varying the "on" time using input controllers, or percentage timers, rather than conventional thermostats. The device shown includes a clock mechanism which alternately opens and closes the circuit to the heater according to the setting on the dial on the face of the unit. These controllers cycle about twice a minute; e.i., there are two "on" periods and two "off" periods each minute. The dial is set to the percent on-time desired.

If the heater current exceeds the rating of the controller, the controller may be used as a pilot device to operate a contactor which in turn switches the heaters.

Quartz lamp heaters do not lend themselves to this type of control because of the high visible output.

Motorless units are also available whose switching action depends upon the expansion and contraction of a thermal element.

DEMAND LIMIT CONTROL

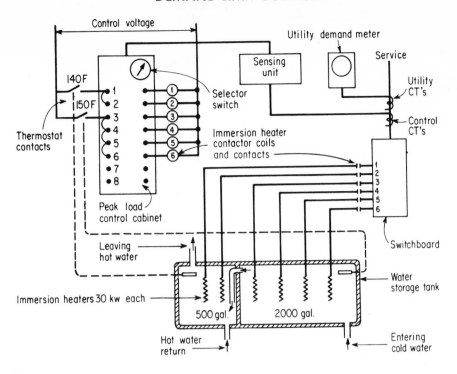

WATER HEATER ELEMENTS in 2500-gal storage tank make up six steps of deferrable load under peak load control. In this application, two "quick-recovery" elements receive highest priority; however, they ask for power only when the water in entire tank drops below 140F.

Electrical utility demand charges in commercial rate schedules could be a major hurdle in justifying an all-electric installation over combustible fuels. However, engineers designing such systems now have an ally in a recently introduced control device to limit system electrical demand, thus reducing demand costs, and in many cases operating energy costs as well.

This peak load control is applicable wherever any part of the connected load is deferrable—i.e., may be disconnected for short periods without adverse effects upon the system as a whole. It is particularly effective controlling electric water heating loads because of the great heat-storage capacity of water.

Essentially, the control consists of a set of current transformers mounted on the service bus or cable, a sensing unit mounted close to the current transformers, and a control cabinet where all circuit connections are made. The unit is equipped to handle eight steps of load, although controls for additional steps may be provided by an auxiliary unit. The control cabinet contains a selector switch which is set to the overall

system demand in kw which is not to be exceeded. Pilot devices (thermostats, etc.) and contactors controlling the deferrable load are connected to terminal strips in the control cabinet. Circuits are numbered from 1 through 8, any number of which may be used, the highest priority loads connected to the lowest numbers.

In operation, the actual system load monitored by the sensing unit is electronically compared with the selector switch demand setting. If the system load equals or exceeds the setting, the deferrable loads connected to the control remain de-energized. If the demand is less than the setting, however, the control begins "scanning" the deferrable loads step by step, in order of priority, and energizes in turn those whose thermostats are "asking" for power, until the available kw capacity is used up. If the system demand then increases due to the non-deferrable load (the load not connected to the control), all connected deferrable loads will be dropped out and reinstated a step at a time, highest priority first, to the extent of the available capacity.

It is important that the selector switch be set properly. If it is set too high, it will permit the deferrable load to contribute to the peak demand and increase costs. If it is too low, it will restrict operation of the deferrable loads unnecessarily. Demand charges, of course, are set by the peak kw demand. Once this peak is reached and recorded on the utility's demand meter, subsequent utilization of capacity up to and including this peak amount in the same billing period will not add to the demand charges. Therefore, maximum use may be made of the controlled loads if the control selector switch matches the peak recorded demand at any given time. Original switch settings may be arrived at from the connected load and anticipated diversity. Initial operation of the plant or building with the switch set quite low will provide more accurate information. A monthly visual check of the demand meter reading and readjustment of the selector switch will optimize results; however, seasonal checks should suffice in most cases once a system demand pattern has been established.

PROTECTION against excessive heat due to an obstruction such as a pillow or blanket inadvertently placed against the heater and restricting air circulation is provided by linear controls. Liquid-filled capillary is sealed at time of manufacture with a slight vacuum, holding diaphragm in position shown in (A). Spring holds contacts closed, and heating element is energized.

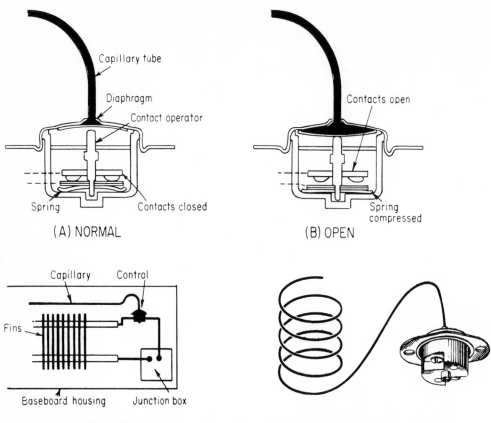

(A) NORMAL   (B) OPEN

Any buildup of heat anywhere along the capillary tube, which extends the length of the baseboard, causes liquid to heat up and eventually boil, increasing pressure within tube and snapping diaphragm into position (B). This forces contact operator downward against spring, breaking contacts and deenergizing element. When liquid cools, diaphragm snaps back to position (A), closing contacts. Cycling continues until obstruction is removed. Contacts will also open if capillary tube develops a leak, since loss of vacuum will move diaphragm to position (B).

Some models incorporate a reset button, making it necessary for the homeowner to press the button to return the contacts to the closed position and restore heating. It is presumed that any obstruction will be noticed and removed at this time.

Installation

Provisions specifically applicable to electric comfort heating were added to the National Electrical Code in 1953, special attention being warranted by the use of heating equipment in direct contact with or as an integral part of the structure itself. These provisions, included in Article 422 under Appliances, were concerned primarily with heating cables embedded in ceilings and floors and the effect of high ambient temperatures on circuit wiring. Except for minor editorial changes and a few additional provisions, these same rules appear as Part E of Article 422 in the 1965 edition of the code.

Ceilings

Surface temperatures of ceilings containing heating cable embedded in plaster or sandwiched between layers of gypsum board normally reach the vicinity of 100 to 120F when installed in accordance with manufacturers' recommendations. (Section 422-42 of the code limits such temperatures to a maximum of 150F.) Branch circuit wiring in the attic or rafter space above the heated ceiling may be affected by this higher temperature, depending upon the thermal resistance of the insulation and/or structural materials between the wiring and the heated surface; and upon the amount of ventilation in the attic.

Code Tables 310-12 and 310-14, which give normal allowable current-carrying capacities of copper and aluminum conductors, also include correction factors to be applied when ambient temperatures

Conductor Derating

a. No insulation
Conductors installed in an uninsulated joist space must be at least 2 in. above ceiling. Ambient temperature is considered to be 50 C (122 F). (NEC Sec. 422-47c)

b. 2 in. of insulation
Conductors installed above insulation at least 2 in. thick require no correction for temperature. (NEC Sec. 422-47b)

c. More than 2 in.
Conductors installed within insulation must be at least 2 in. above ceiling. Ambient temperature is considered to be 50 C (122 F). (NEC Sec. 422-47a)

Ceiling joists

Thermal Insulation

2 in. min.

2 in.

2 in.

Branch circuit wiring

Ceiling cable

CIRCUIT WIRING above heated ceiling may require derating where build-up of heat may affect conductor insulation.

in excess of 30C (86F) are anticipated under normal operation. Since this temperature is normally exceeded immediately above heated ceilings or ceiling panel heaters, the code stipulates in Section 422-47 the conditions under which the correction factors of Tables 310-12 and 310-14 are to be used. These conditions are shown at right. It should be noted that the wiring referred to is *any* wiring in a position to be affected by the heat, whether or not it is associated with the heating system.

The extent to which the conductors' allowable current-carrying capacities are reduced when subject to the required correction is shown by the accompanying table. Obviously, there is a distinct advantage to installing all conductors sufficiently removed from the heated surface.

Additional clearance requirements are specified by the code to insure against an excessive buildup of heat due to an obstruction. Ceiling cable or panels must be separated by at least 8 in. from lighting fixtures and outlet and junction boxes (Sec. 422-50). It is advisable to allow extra clearance around ceiling lighting fixtures; a subsequent replacement could be considerably larger than the original fixture. This same section requires at least a 2-in. separation between

panels and cables and ventilating openings or other openings in the room surface, allowing for rims of registers, etc., after installation.

Heating cable may not be installed in closet ceilings or over cabinets which extend to the ceiling, such as those usually located in the kitchen (Sec. 422-49b). Each of these provisions is intended to prevent the trapping of heat and a consequent buildup in temperature.

Sec. 422-49b also specifies that cables shall not be installed under walls or partitions or over walls or partitions which extend to the ceiling, except that "single runs of cable may pass over partitions where they are embedded."

The intent here is to avoid repeated crossings of cable over (or under) partitions, since radiation from these sections would be restricted or the cable would be unnecessarily exposed to possible physical damage. While the code specifically speaks of partitions, the same reasoning would apply to arches, exposed ceiling beams, etc.

However, there are times when a small ceiling area (such as over a dressing room or entryway) is separated from a larger room by such an arch or beam, yet it is impractical to install a separate heating cable and control. The above-quoted exception was intended as a solution to this problem. A typical

floor plan of such a situation is shown on the next page with two methods of getting the heating cable past the partition or beam. In the upper sketch the cable is brought up into the attic space, through a porcelain tube, and back down through the gypsum board. Plaster is then forced into the tube and puddled over the exposed cable and tube in the attic. This should be the same plaster or joint cement that is used between the two layers of gypsum board. (In no case should insulating plaster be used.)

In the lower sketch a hole is drilled through the top plate of the partition (or beam) and a porcelain tube pressed into the hole. Plaster is packed into the tube after the heating cable has been passed through. In both cases, the plaster serves to conduct heat away from the cable, avoiding hot spots and possible burnouts.

A third possibility is to cut the heating cable at the partition and solder in a length of non-heating lead. This conductor may be brought into the attic space and over the partition without plastering, although it should be provided with protection against physical damage.

Each of these methods is of course subject to the approval of the local inspecting authority. The best solution is to use a separate

Allowable Current-Carrying Capacities at 30C, 40C, and 50C Ambient Temperatures

Copper Conductors						Size AWG	Aluminum Conductors					
Insulation							Insulation					
R, RU, RUW, T, TW			RH, RUH, RH-RW, RHW, THW, THWN				R, RU, RUW, T, TW			RH, RUH, RH-RW RHW, THW, THWN		
Carrying Capacity (amperes)*							Carrying Capacity (amperes)**					
30C	40C	50C	30C	40C	50C		30C	40C	50C	30C	40C	50C
15	12.3	8.70	15	13.2	11.25	14	...	....	.....	...	....	.....
20	16.4	11.60	20	17.6	15.00	12	15	12.3	8.70	15	13.2	11.25
30	24.6	17.40	30	26.4	22.50	10	25	20.5	14.50	25	22.0	18.75
40	32.8	23.20	45	39.6	33.75	8	30	24.6	17.40	40	35.2	30.00
55	45.1	31.90	65	57.2	48.75	6	40	32.8	23.20	50	44.0	37.50
70	57.4	40.60	85	74.8	63.75	4	55	45.1	31.90	65	57.2	48.75
80	65.6	46.40	100	98.0	75.00	3	65	53.3	37.70	75	66.0	56.25
95	77.9	55.10	115	101.2	86.25	2	75	61.5	43.50	90	79.2	67.50
110	90.2	63.80	130	114.4	97.50	1	85	69.7	49.30	100	88.0	75.00

heating cable assembly for the smaller ceiling area, if one can be obtained with a rating close to the room's heat loss, connecting it in parallel with the cable of the larger room. The single thermostat thus controls both cables. Care must be taken to choose the thermostat location so that the non-heating leads of both cables will reach it.

Separate shorter cable lengths can also be used in a large room where the ceiling is divided by exposed beams. However, it will usually be desirable to control the entire ceiling by a single thermostat, so that two or more junction boxes may be necessary for the interconnection of the several cable assemblies. Whether the boxes would be considered accessible if located in the attic space is a question which would have to be answered locally.

Adjacent cable runs in plaster or between two layers of gypsum board must be no closer to each other than 1½ in., must not exceed 2¾ watt per ft, and must be secured at least every 16 in. (Sec. 422-52).

Stapling guns are usually used for the purpose; the guns are designed to apply the staples with just the right amount of pressure to hold securely without damage to cable insulation. Heating cable is usually run parallel with the ceiling joists, with slightly wider spacing between adjacent runs directly below the joists to provide space for nailing the lower layer of gypsum board and thus reduce danger of nailing into the cable. (This is not a consideration in all-plaster installations, of course; a uniform spacing may be used.) The cable thus crosses the joists only near the walls. Its location should be made clear to the workmen installing the gypsum board so that no nails are used at those points. It is usual to keep cable at least 6 in. away from all walls to avoid nailing hazards.

Walls

Code Sec. 422-48 covers clearances of wiring in walls. While not specifically stated, this section was intended to apply to *heated* walls. The installation of heating cables in walls is prohibited by Sec. 422-52a; however, a heated wall could conceivably result through the application of some subsequently developed and approved wall covering, molding, etc., in which case there would be a code rule to cover it. The provisions of this section were not intended to be applied to conductors behind such equipment as wall heaters and baseboard heaters, since such units are designed

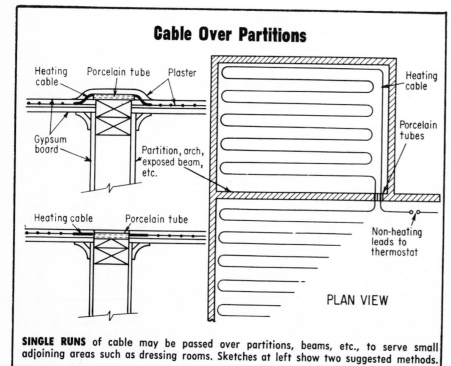

Cable Over Partitions

Heating cable · Porcelain tube · Plaster · Gypsum board · Partition, arch, exposed beam, etc. · Heating cable · Porcelain tube

Heating cable · Porcelain tubes · Non-heating leads to thermostat

PLAN VIEW

SINGLE RUNS of cable may be passed over partitions, beams, etc., to serve small adjoining areas such as dressing rooms. Sketches at left show two suggested methods.

to reflect heat forward and minimize rear surface temperatures. However, logic dictates that the ambient temperatures behind such heaters will be greater than elsewhere in the wall. In the absence of a specific interpretation on this point, it is possible that an inspector may feel justified in requiring conductors immediately behind such heaters to be derated; hence such areas should be avoided.

Sec. 422-48a requires wiring in outside walls to be located outside the thermal insulation. This provision antedated the prevalent practice of filling the entire stud space with insulation; hence compliance may be impossible. Attempting to meet this requirement by fastening cables to the sheathing at the rear of the stud space in outside walls is an undesirable solution, since the cable in such a position would be subject to physical penetration by nails driven into the sheathing from the outside in fastening shingles or other siding material.

The intent of this provision is to insure air circulation about the conductors. In a completely insulated wall there will not be adequate circulation; hence any conductors installed within thermal insulation should be considered as operating in an ambient of 50C.

Installation restrictions may be imposed on specific heating equipment by Underwriters' Laboratories which are not covered by the code. Some baseboard heaters, for example, are marked "Mount bottom of heater ¾ in. above floor." This is to insure that rugs will not restrict the air inlet at the bottom of the heater. Wood blocking or molding at least ¾ in. thick may be installed beneath the baseboard for additional support and to keep dirt from accumulating in the space.

Another example is a wall insert heater marked "Do not install so that bottom of heater is less than 2 ft above floor." Such markings are required by UL as a fire preventive measure when their so-called "furniture tests" indicate the need. Since a homeowner may reasonably object to having a heater installed that high on a wall, the installer should be familiar with any restrictions which may affect the placement of the specific heaters intended for the job. Many heaters are available which are not restricted in this manner.

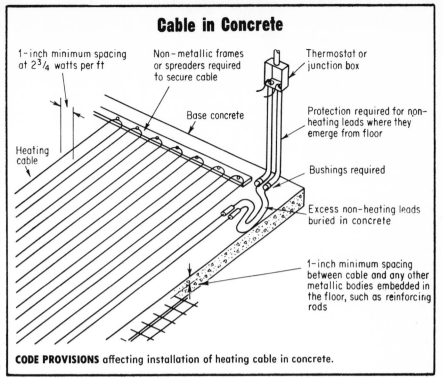

Cable in Concrete

1-inch minimum spacing at 2³/₄ watts per ft

Non-metallic frames or spreaders required to secure cable

Base concrete

Heating cable

Thermostat or junction box

Protection required for non-heating leads where they emerge from floor

Bushings required

Excess non-heating leads buried in concrete

1-inch minimum spacing between cable and any other metallic bodies embedded in the floor, such as reinforcing rods

CODE PROVISIONS affecting installation of heating cable in concrete.

Floors

The provisions of Code Sec. 422-54 covering heating cable in concrete floors are summarized in an accompanying drawing.

Par. (a) states: "Adjacent runs of cable not exceeding 2¾ watts per ft shall be installed not less than 1 in. on centers." There has been considerable difference of opinion as to whether this was meant to prohibit the use of heating cables which exceed 2¾ watts per ft. Some members of the Code-Making Panel covering this section have indicated that "there was no bar to the recognition of heating cable with a rating in excess of 2¾ watts per ft, provided the cable was tested under the spacings proposed for its use and found acceptable." Many inspectors have seen fit to permit higher wattages at increased spacings, and many such installations are now in use, however most cable available for the purpose is designed for 2¾ watts per ft at rated voltage.

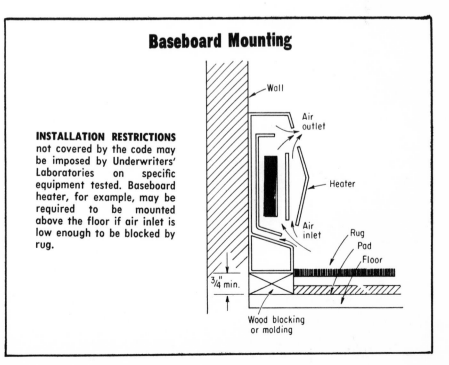

Baseboard Mounting

Wall

Air outlet

Heater

Air inlet

Rug

Pad

Floor

¾" min.

Wood blocking or molding

INSTALLATION RESTRICTIONS not covered by the code may be imposed by Underwriters' Laboratories on specific equipment tested. Baseboard heater, for example, may be required to be mounted above the floor if air inlet is low enough to be blocked by rug.

Par. (b) requires cables to be "secured in place by non-metallic frames or spreaders or other approved means while the concrete or other finish is applied." Metallic supports such as those commercially available for use in roadways or sidewalks are not to be used in floor spaceheating installations. Lumber is often used, although a more common method is to staple the cable directly to the base concrete after it has set about four hours. It was not the intention that this code paragraph prohibit the use of metal staples; this method has been tested by Underwriters' Laboratories and found acceptable. The object was to reduce the possibility of short circuits because of continuous metallic conducting materials spanning several adjacent cable runs.

Par. (c): "A spacing of at least 1 in. shall be maintained between the heating cable and other metallic bodies embedded in the floor." This is self-explanatory; again, the intent is to reduce the possibility of contact between the cable and such conducting materials as reinforcing mesh, water pipes and air ducts.

Par. (d) requires leads to be protected where they leave the floor "by rigid metal conduit, electrical metallic tubing, or by other approved raceways extending to the junction box," and Par. (e) adds that bushings shall be used where the leads emerge in the floor slab. These provisions refer to the non-heating leads which connect the branch circuit home run to the heating cable. The splices connecting the nonheating leads to the cable are always buried in the concrete. About 6 in. of leads are left available in the junction box; any remaining length of non-heating lead is buried in the concrete. The conductors should not be shortened. This applies even though the non-heating leads are Type UF cable. Sec. 339-3 (e) (8) does prohibit the use of UF embedded in poured cement, concrete or aggregate; however, these heating cable assemblies are tested by UL and listed as suitable for such use. Sec. 339-3 (d) was revised in the 1963 Code to recognize the use of single-conductor Type UF for such a purpose, stating that UF "shall be of the multiple conductor type except where recognized under the provisions of Sec. 422-44." (This section requires heating cables to be furnished with factory-assembled non-heating leads at least 7 ft long and consisting of conductors and wiring approved for general use or for the purpose.)

It is common practice to test the continuity of the heating cable while the covering layer of concrete is being laid using an ohmmeter, ammeter, or a lamp. A simple method is to connect a 7½-watt, 120-volt lamp in series with the heating cable for continuous indication during the pour.

Standards

The National Electrical Code covers approval of electrical equipment in Section 90-8:

"Examination of Equipment for Safety. For approval of specific items and materials covered by the code, examinations for safety should be made under standard conditions, and the record made generally available through promulgation by organizations properly equipped and qualified for experimental testing, inspections of the run of goods at factories, and service-value determination through field inspections. This avoids the necessity for repetition of examinations by different examiners, frequently with inadequate facilities for such work, and the confusion that would result from conflicting reports as to the suitability of devices and materials examined for a given purpose."

Underwriters' Laboratories, Inc., one of the best known of such testing organizations, publishes annually three volumes listing commercially available electrical equipment which they have tested and which at the date of publication meets their standards. The volume listing electric comfort heating equipment, *Electrical Appliance and Utilization Equipment List*, is brought up to date each May, with bi-monthly supplements appearing between annual issues.

Equipment listed is voluntarily submitted for test by the respective manufacturers. UL personnel test the heaters for compliance with *Standards for Safety, Electric Space-Heating Equipment, UL 573*. This publication, developed by UL in cooperation with the electric heating industry, is available to manufacturers as a basic guide for the use of their designers. A full report of the completed test is furnished the manufacturer. Acceptable equipment is listed; unacceptable equipment must be modified and resubmitted for further tests if the manufacturer desires eventual listing of that particular piece of equipment.

The manufacturer also agrees to a follow-up service determined by UL and carried out periodically to see that subsequent production of the listed item continues to conform to requirements. There are two follow-up services applicable to different equipment types. Electric central furnaces, boilers, duct heaters and baseboard are covered under "Label Service." Under this service, UL inspectors visit the manufacturer's factory periodically, sometimes several times a month, to examine his current production of listed equipment. This equipment is identified by means of labels issued to the manufacturer by the local UL inspector and affixed to the equipment by the manufacturer.

The remaining heater types (wall units, portables, etc.) are listed under "Reexamination Service," which involves one or more trips a year by UL personnel to the manufacturer's plant. No labels are furnished by UL for this service, although manufacturers may of their own choosing, purchase reexamination service markers from UL and affix them to their listed equipment. Listing is

How to Determine Heating Cable Spacing

The following formulas may be used to determine nominal spacing between adjacent runs of ceiling heating cable. They are not exact, since they do not take into account the length of the ends of the loops or the return run to the thermostat location. However, this is on the safe side; i.e., it will tend to leave some ceiling area toward the end which is more sparsely covered by cable instead of having an excess with no place to put it. Judgment must be used toward the end to increase the spacing slightly so as to end up at the thermostat location. Most cables will have a marker at the mid-point of the roll. When it appears, approximately half the ceiling should be covered.

PLASTERED CEILINGS

The following formula will give the nominal spacing between adjacent cable runs:

$$s = \frac{12 (A - U)}{L}$$

where

s = spacing between adjacent cable runs (in.)
A = total ceiling area (sq ft)
U = area of ceiling which is not to be covered by cable (sq ft)
L = total length of cable to be used (ft)

The result should be rounded off to the nearest smaller ¼ in. for ease of measurement. The area "U" includes the clearance strip of 6 in. all around the edge of the ceiling at the walls plus any significant area which is to be kept free of cable for air distribution registers, lighting fixtures, etc.

GYPSUM BOARD CEILINGS

To permit the covering layer of gypsum board to be nailed to the ceiling joists without the danger of piercing the cable, a space at least 2½ in. wide beneath each joist should be kept free of cable. This means that the total number of runs must be divided among the number of joist spaces. Assuming the cable is installed parallel with the joists, the number of runs per joist space and their spacing will be

$$n = \frac{iL}{12 (A - U)} \quad \text{and} \quad s = \frac{i - 2.5}{n - 1}$$

where n = number of cable runs per joist space
i = joist center-to-center spacing (in.)
A = total ceiling area (sq ft)
U = area of ceiling which is not to be covered by cable (sq ft)
L = total length of cable to be used (ft)
s = spacing between adjacent runs (in.)

EXAMPLE: After making heat-loss calculations, it is decided that a heating cable 655 ft long is required to be installed on a ceiling 16 ft by 14 ft. A 6-in. clearance is to be maintained between the cable and the walls; a space 2 ft square is to be kept free of cable in the center of the ceiling for a lighting fixture. Determine the spacing to be used between runs for (a) a plastered ceiling, (b) a gypsum board ceiling with joists on 16-in. centers, and (c) a gypsum board ceiling with joists on 24-in. centers.

SOLUTION: (a) Plastered ceiling:
Area of ceiling:

$$A = 16 \times 14 = 224 \text{ sq ft.}$$

Area not covered by cable

2 strips 0.5 × 16 =	16 sq ft
2 strips 0.5 × 13 =	13 sq ft
Fixture area =	4 sq ft
Total = U =	33 sq ft

Substituting in formula:

$$s = \frac{12 (A - U)}{L} = \frac{12 (224 - 33)}{655}$$

$$s = \frac{12 \times 191}{655} = 3.5 \text{ in.}$$

(b) Gypsum board ceiling, joists on 16-in. centers.
As above, $A = U = 224 = 33 = 191$ sq. ft.
Number of runs per joist space:

$$n = \frac{iL}{12 (A - U)} = \frac{16 \times 655}{12 \times 191} = 4.57 \text{ (Use 5.)}$$

Spacing between adjacent runs:

$$s = \frac{i - 2.5}{n - 1} = \frac{16 - 2.5}{4} = 3.4 \text{ in. (Use 3¼ in.)}$$

(c) Gypsum board ceiling, joists on 24-in. centers.
Number of runs per joist space:

$$n = \frac{iL}{12 (A - U)} = \frac{24 \times 655}{12 \times 191} = 6.86 \text{ (Use 7.)}$$

Spacing between adjacent runs:

$$s = \frac{i - 2.5}{n - 1} = \frac{24 - 2.5}{6} = 3.6 \text{ in. (Use 3½ in.)}$$

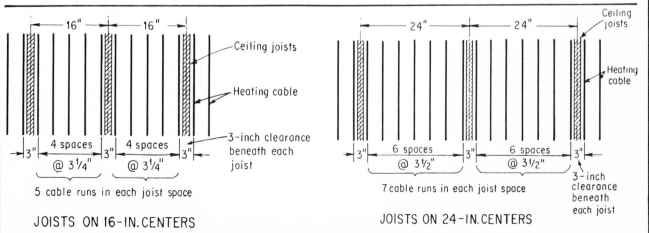

JOISTS ON 16-IN. CENTERS

JOISTS ON 24-IN. CENTERS

repeated annually under Reexamination Service as long as the item continues to conform. Investigation is also made of any reports from inspectors, other manufacturers, etc., of listed products thought not to be in compliance with applicable requirements, and appropriate action taken where necessary.

Typical items of concern to UL testing personnel include protection against contact with live parts, insulation resistance, provisions for grounding, capacity of switches and other controls, effects of over-voltage and under-voltage, and protection against fires from overheating of combustible materials near the heaters. Such tests are made not from the standpoint of successful operation of the heaters, but from the standpoint of safety. Listing of electric heating equipment, like that of all other tested products, indicates only that the equipment conforms with the minimum specified standards designed to protect the public against personal injury, loss of life, and damage to or loss of property.

Performance Standards

Although economics and other forces have caused various types of heating equipment of different manufacture to develop marked similarities so that safety standards could be formulated and applied, the mere fact that a product is listed does not mean that it is equal in performance to others of its type listed. Accordingly, it follows that competition will give rise to equipment which, while satisfying minimum safety requirements and thus bearing a UL label, may leave something to be desired in the way of performance.

Installation of such deficient equipment results ultimately in customer dissatisfaction and complaints, a headache for the contractor and utility, and a black eye for the electric heating industry. The electric utility, lacking practical criteria for judging heater performance, often finds it expedient to set up its own standards in an attempt to circumvent such problems. This could result in scores of independent sets of standards and divergent requirements which would be almost impossible for heater manufacturers to fulfill.

To provide unity and direction in this regard, the Electric Comfort Heating Section of NEMA has set up NEMA Standards Publication No. HE 2-1962, *Electric Comfort Heating Equipment*. It covers definitions, performance standards, and test methods applicable to heating equipment of the types used principally in residences. Its main concern is the control of temperature developed on and around the heater. Excessive temperatures, apart from the fire hazard, affect the comfort produced and the durability of the heater itself and increase the probability and extent of wall streaking.

The NEMA standards specify maximum allowable operating temperatures, whereas UL standards require only that under certain test conditions fire does not result. To make their standards more useful to the electrical contractor, inspector, utility, homeowner, or any other interested party, NEMA has entered into a contract with Electrical Testing Laboratories (ETL), New York City, to test heating equipment for conformance with the NEMA standards. A *NEMA Directory of Electric Baseboard Heating Equipment* has been published listing those product lines which have been tested and found to be in conformance with Standard HE 2-1962.

Thus for the first time there is available an authoritative, reliable guide for use in the field to insure more satisfactory heating installations through the uplifting of manufacturing standards in general. Although this initial directory is restricted to baseboard equipment, plans are being made for the extension of the testing program to other heater types.

Lighting design

THE art and science of modern lighting design is much broader in scope than is generally recognized. It requires a knowledge and understanding of the physics and control of light, of the science of seeing, of the principles of architectural and structural building design, and of the myriad number and types of light sources, luminaires, lighting equipments and components. Also, it requires a knowledge of artistic and esthetic values, of interior design and decoration, and of environmental factors and design, color harmony, and other similar factors, especially when light is to be used as a decorative medium. Thus, the key to lighting design is primarily a recognition of the use to be made of the light, and the development of a clearly defined statement of the lighting problem involved. This becomes all the more difficult, since in most instances people are also involved, and must be considered.

Once the lighting problem has been defined and clearly outlined, the design of a lighting system to fulfill the lighting objectives is not overly complicated. The problem then becomes one of adopting practical procedures which have been developed and well documented in the Illuminating Engineering Society's *Lighting Handbook* (4th Edition), in lighting equipment and light source manufacturers' catalogs and bulletins, and elsewhere.

Presented here is a suggested detailed procedure for the design of modern lighting systems. Many of the factors to be considered have been listed, and some of the decisions to be made are discussed.

Define the lighting problem

Quite logically, the first thing to do in planning a lighting system is to determine, to the extent possible, exactly what the lighting problem is. In general, the lighting problem is dictated by four major factors. 1) physical size and shape of the area; 2) architectural design and structural details; 3) occupancy or end use, of the area; and 4) the type and degree of severity of the seeing tasks which will exist. Inherent in these will be other allied sub-factors, such as: type of environment—dictated by type of occupancy; extent of use of glass facades—dictated by architectural design; etc.

Physical dimensions—Determine the exact size and shape of the area to be lighted. On small projects, this may be a simple single area, defined by width, length, and ceiling height. On larger projects, it will usually consist of an area which can be subdivided into a number of simple individual areas, and each defined separately. Complete area dimensions should be tabulated, and further supported by plan and elevation drawings, when available.

Structural details—Determine the architectural design and structural details. On new projects, these details should be available on architectural and structural drawings, or from the architect or builder. On relighting projects, a visit to the job should be made, and all details noted.

Occupancy—Determine what the area will be used for, and how it will be utilized. For example, if it is to be used for manufacturing, obtain a firm (or tentative, if necessary) layout of departments, machinery, production lines, etc., and a description of type of work which will be done in each department, or area.

Seeing tasks—Determine, and tabulate, the various types of seeing tasks which will exist in the area, or areas. Type of occupancy, layout of the area, and type of work to be done will dictate the type of seeing problems which will be encountered.

Add to the above information any other details that can be determined, such as: ceiling, wall, and floor construction; color and finish of ceiling, walls, and floors; location, size and shape of any columns or other structural details, etc; whether the area will be air conditioned, and type, size, and location of air ducts, diffusers, etc; and other similar details.

Select illumination levels based on severity of visual tasks

Severity of visual tasks	Types of visual tasks	Footcandles (Range)
Easy	Use in areas not involving critical or prolonged seeing, such as conference rooms, inactive files, washrooms, corridors, stairways	30 and Below
Ordinary	Minimum for any visual task requiring more than casual use of the eyes. General lighting level for most interiors involving non-critical seeing.	30–100
Difficult	Average seeing problems, involving regular office work, general industrial work, art displays, etc.	100–200
Very Difficult	Critical seeing tasks extending over prolonged periods, such as fine assembly, inspection, drafting, color grading, etc.	200–500
Most Difficult	Highly critical seeing tasks involving fine assembly, fine inspection, sewing, feature displays, and others.	500–1000
Special Applications	Highly critical, involving precision industrial processes, cloth inspection, surgery, and others.	1000 and up

Select lighting levels needed

In 1958, IES approved and announced a complete revision of their Recommended Levels of Illumination. These lighting levels represent currently recommended practice, and should be followed generally. The lighting levels are expressed in footcandle values for a long list of seeing tasks which exist in commerce, industry, and the home.

While the *quantity* of light provided for any end-use application is important, and should be given serious consideration, it seldom should be the paramount issue, or measure of the adequacy, in the design of a lighting system. Of equal, if not greater importance, is the *quality* of the lighting.

Provide lighting of high quality

In determining the *quality* of the light to be provided for a specific lighting design problem (or set of seeing tasks), there are several factors to be considered and analyzed. These include: 1) end use of the lighting result; 2) visual environment; 3) light control; and many others.

End Use of Lighting Result—Determine whether the light needed is for utilitarian use—light for seeing, or work light, so to speak; or for decorative use—light for decoration, as in a fine restaurant, or hotel lobby, etc. Often the light must be used for both utility (reading a menu in a restaurant, for example) and for decoration (to create a certain decorative effect and mood in the restaurant, for example). The end use of the lighting result will influence to considerable extent the quality of the light needed.

Visual Environment—Analyze the visual environment which is proposed (or which should be recommended by the lighting engineer). Factors which create or influence the visual environment include such items as the physical size of the area, the colors and finishes of the interior (floor, walls, ceilings, presence of glass walls, windows, doors, etc.), and size, colors and finishes of interior furnishings (machines, furniture, draperies, murals, etc.). All of these factors have an influence on the *quality* of the light; or, to look at it from a different viewpoint, the *quality* of the light can be controlled to create the type of visual environment which is desired. This *quality* may be controlled by the judicious selection of light sources, types of luminaires, and types and locations of lighting equipments in general.

Light Control—Visual tasks and lighting *quality* will influence the type of light control to be selected. In other words, the visual tasks and desired *quality* will dictate the choice of diffuse or directional light control, the degree of shielding needed, and similar features. Conceivably, many seeing tasks may call for a combination of light control principles—hence, for lighting equipment which incorporates several types of light control (diffusion, shielding, directional control, polarization etc., all in one luminaire).

Also inherent in light control is glare control. This includes the control or reduction of both direct and reflected glare. The commonly used system for glare appraisal is the Visual Comfort Index system. Thus many lighting equipment manufacturers now provide VCI values for specific luminaires, along with other technical data.

RECOMMENDED SURFACE REFLECTANCES FOR OFFICES

Surface	Reflectance Range (%)
Ceiling finishes	80 – 92
Walls	40 – 60
Furniture	26 – 44
Office machines and equipment	26 – 44
Floors	21 – 39

Source: IES Lighting Handbook

Other factors which affect lighting quality include the color quality of the light which is produced by the light sources, the brightness ratios (see table "Recommended Brightness Ratios for Interior Lighting") which result from the various colors and reflectance values, and other possible glare sources, such as sky glare, or glare from other sources such as windows or glass walls.

Select proper light sources

The heart of any lighting system is the light source, or sources, which convert electric energy into light. The efficiency of the light source, measured in lumens per watt, dictates to considerable extent the overall efficiency for the lighting

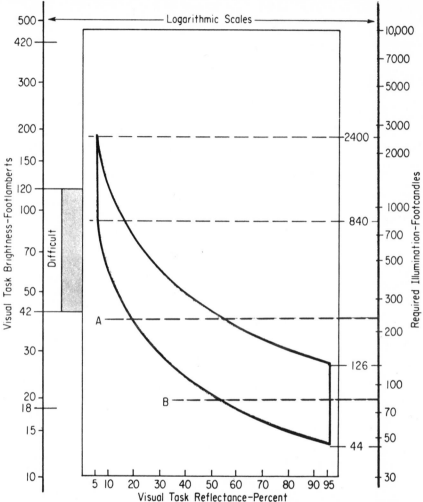

Brightness and Lighting Level Relationship for Difficult Visual Task Category

The above chart is a graphical representation of the data shown in the table "Visual Task Brightnesses and Related Lighting Levels," for seeing tasks classified as "Difficult." Visual task brightnesses are shown in the vertical scale at the left, in footlamberts. Also shown on the logarithmic scale are the brightness ranges for the other four categories of seeing task difficulty.

Visual task reflectance values are shown in percent on the bottom numerical scale, covering practical values ranging from 5% to 95%.

Required illumination for "difficult" visual tasks, or for visual tasks ranging from 42 to 120 footlamberts in brightness, and plotted against visual task reflectance values of 5% to 95%, are shown in the shaded area between the two curves, in footcandles. The footcandle values are plotted against a logarithmic scale (right). Note that footcandle values range from 44 to 126 at 95% visual task re-

flectance, and from 840 to 2400 at 5% visual task reflectance. The bottom curve is for seeing tasks with a visual task brightness of 42 footlamberts; top curve represents seeing tasks with a visual task brightness of 120 footlamberts.

The required illumination for the "very difficult" seeing task category, representing visual task brightnesses between 120 and 420 footlamberts, if plotted on this same chart, would form a shaded area immediately above that shown. Similarly, the required illumination for the "ordinary" seeing task category, representing visual task brightnesses between 18 and 42 footlamberts, if plotted on this chart, would form a similarly shaped shaded area immediately below the one shown.

Professional lighting designers might develop separate charts of this type, one for each seeing task category, for design reference. Or, if drawn to large scale, all data could be shown on one chart.

Footcandle Tables

In 1958, the Illuminating Engineering Society adopted new—and higher—illumination levels for practical visual tasks. These levels were recommended after a study of the Blackwell Report, which stemmed from an eight-year project at the University of Michigan's Vision Research Laboratories. The results of this study, headed by Dr. Richard H. Blackwell, director of the Michigan laboratories, revealed the necessity for higher lighting intensities. The study has been supported since 1950 by the Illuminating Engineering Research Institute, an independent research body of IES.　　All figures used at the right of each column are the currently recommended footcandle levels.

INDUSTRIAL AREAS

AIRPLANE MANUFACTURING
Stock parts:
Production 100
Inspection 200**
Parts manufacturing:
Drilling, riveting, screw fastening 70
Spray booths 100
Sheet aluminum layout and template work; shaping and smoothing of small parts for fuselage; wing sectons, cowling, etc. 100
Welding:
General illumination 50
Supplementary illumination 1000
Subassembly:
Landing gear, fuselage, wing sections, cowling and other large units 100
Final assembly:
Placing of motors, propellers, wing sections and landing gear 100
Inspection of assembled ship and its equipment 100
Machine tool repairs 100

AIRPLANE HANGARS
Repair service only 100

ASSEMBLY
Rough easy seeing 30
Rough difficult seeing 50
Medium 100
Fine 500
Extra Fine 1000

AUTOMOBILE MANUFACTURING
Frame assembly 50
Chassis assembly line 100
Final assembly and inspection line 200**
Body manufacturing:
Parts 70
Assembly 100
Finishing and inspecting 200**

BAKERIES
Mixing room 50
Face of shelves (vertical illumination) 30
Inside of mixing bowl (vertical mixers) 50
Fermentation room 30
Make-up room:
Bread 30
Sweet yeast raised products ... 50
Proofing Room 30
Oven room 30
Fillings and other ingredients ... 50
Decorating and icing:
Mechanical 50
Hand 100
Scales and thermometers 50
Wrapping room 30

BOOK BINDING
Folding, assembly, pasting, etc. ... 70
Cutting, punching and stitching .. 70
Embossing and inspection 200**

BREWERIES
Brew house 30
Boiling and keg washing 30
Filling (bottles, cans, kegs) 50

CANDY MAKING
Box department 50
Chocolate department:
Husking, winnowing, fat extraction, crushing and refining, feeding 50
Bean cleaning and sorting, dipping, packing, wrapping 50
Milling 100
Cream making:
Mixing, cooking and molding 50
Gum drops and jellied forms 50
Hand decorating 100
Hard candy:
Mixing, cooking and molding 50
Die cutting and sorting 100
Kiss making and wrapping 100

CANNING AND PRESERVING
Initial grading raw material samples 50
Tomatoes 100
Color grading (cutting rooms) 200**
Preparation:
Preliminary sorting:
Apricots and peaches 50
Tomatoes 100
Olives 150
Cutting and pitting 100
Final sorting 100
Canning:
Continuous belt canning 100
Sink canning 100
Hand packing 50
Olives 100
Examination of canned samples .. 200**
Container handling:
Inspection 200**
Can unscramblers 70
Labeling and cartoning 30

CHEMICAL WORKS
Hand furnaces, boiling tanks, stationary driers, stationary and gravity crystallizers, ... 30
Mechanical furnaces, generators and stills, mechanical driers, evaporators, filtration, mechanical crystallizers, bleaching 30
Tanks for cooking, extractors, percolators, nitrators, electrolytic cells 30

CLAY PRODUCTS AND CEMENTS
Grinding, filter presses, kiln rooms 30
Molding, pressing, cleaning and trimming 30
Enameling 100
Color and glazing—rough work .. 100
Color and glazing—fine work .. 300**

CLEANING AND PRESSING INDUSTRY
Checking and sorting 50
Dry and wet cleaning and steaming 50
Inspection and spotting 500**
Pressing:
Machine 150
Hand 150
Repair and alteration 200**

CLOTH PRODUCTS
Cloth Inspection 2000**
Cutting 300**
Sewing 500**
Pressing 300**

COAL TIPPLES AND CLEANING PLANTS
Breaking, screening and cleaning areas 10
Picking 300**

DAIRY PRODUCTS
Fluid milk industry:
Boiler room 30
Bottle storage 30
Bottle sorting 50
Bottle washers .... —
Can washers 30
Cooling equipment 30
Filling: inspection 100
Gages .... (on face) 50
Laboratories 100
Meter panels ...... (on face) 50
Pasteurizers 30
Separators 30
Storage refrigerator 30
Tanks, vats:
Light interiors 20
Dark interiors 100
Thermometer ..... (on face) 50
Weighing room 30
Scales 70

ELECTRICAL EQUIPMENT MANUFACTURING
Impregnating 50
Insulating: coil winding 100
Testing 100

EXPLOSIVES
Hand furnaces, boiling tanks, stationary driers, stationary and gravity crystallizers 30
Mechanical furnaces, generators and stills, mechanical driers, evaporators, filtration, mechanical crystallizers 30

Tanks for cooking, extractors, percolators, nitrators 30

EXTERIOR AREAS
Entrances:
Active (pedestrian and/or conveyance) 5.0
Inactive (normally locked, infrequently used) 1.0
Vital locations or structures 5.0
Building surrounds 1.0
Active shipping area surrounds . . . 5.0
Storage areas—active 20
Storage areas—inactive 1
Loading and unloading platforms . 20

FLOUR MILLS
Rolling 50
Sifting 50
Purifying 50
Packing 30
Product control 100
Cleaning screens, man lifts, aisleways and walkways, bin checking 30

FORGE SHOPS 50

FOUNDRIES
Annealing (furnaces) 30
Cleaning 30
Core making (fine) 100
Core making (medium) 50
Grinding and chipping 100**
Inspection (fine) 500**
Inspection (medium) 100
Moulding (medium) 100
Moulding (large) 50
Pouring 50
Sorting 50
Cupola 20
Shakeout 30

GARAGES—AUTOMOBILE AND TRUCK
Service garages:
Repairs 100
Active traffic areas 20
Parking garages:
Entrance 50
Traffic lanes 10
Storage 5

GLASS WORKS
Mix and furnace rooms, pressing and lehr, glass blowing machines 30
Grinding, cutting glass to size, silvering 50
Fine grinding, polishing, beveling 100
Inspection, etching and decorating 200**

GLOVE MANUFACTURING
Pressing 300**
Knitting 100
Sorting 100
Cutting 300**
Sewing and inspection 500**

HAT MANUFACTURING
Dyeing, stiffening, braiding, cleaning and refining 100
Forming, sizing, pouncing, flanging, finishing and ironing 200**
Sewing 500**

INSPECTION
Ordinary 50
Difficult 100
Highly difficult 200**
Very difficult 500**
Most difficult 1000**

IRON AND STEEL MANUFACTURING
Open hearth:
Stock yard 10
Charging floor 20

Pouring slide 20
Slag pits 20
Control platforms 30
Mold yard 5
Hot top 30
Hot top storage 10
Checker cellar 10
Buggy and door repair 30
Stripping yard 20
Scrap stockyard 10
Mixer building 30
Calcining building 10
Skull cracker 10
Cinder, dump 0.1
Rolling mills:
Blooming, slabbing, hot strip, hot sheet 30
Cold strip, plate 30
Pipe, rod, tube, wire drawing . . . 50
Merchant and sheared plate 30
Tin plate mills:
Tinning and galvanizing 50
Cold strip rolling 50
Motor room, machine room 30
Inspection:
Blackplate, bloom, billet chipping 100
Tinplate, other bright surfaces . . 100†

LAUNDRIES
Washing 30
Flatwork ironing, weighing, listing and marking 50
Machine and press finishing, sorting 70
Fine hand ironing 100

LEATHER MANUFACTURING
Cleaning, tanning and stretching, vats 30
Cutting, fleshing and stuffing . . . 50
Finishing and scarfing 100

LEATHER WORKING
Pressing, winding and glazing . . . 200
Grading, matching, cutting, scarfing, sewing 300

LOCKER ROOMS 20

MACHINE SHOPS
Rough bench and machine work 50
Medium bench and machine work, ordinary automatic machines, rough grinding, medium buffing and polishing 100
Fine bench and machine work, fine automatic machines, medium grinding, fine buffing and polishing 500**
Extra fine bench and machine work, grinding—fine work 1000**

MATERIALS HANDLING
Wrapping, packing, labeling 50
Picking stock, classifying 30
Loading, trucking 20
Inside truck bodies and freight cars 10

MEAT PACKING
Slaughtering 30
Cleaning, cutting, cooking, grinding, canning, packing 100

PACKING AND BOXING (SEE MATERIALS HANDLING)

PAINT MANUFACTURING
General 30
Comparing mix and standard (see Color Matching) . . . . 200†

PAINT SHOPS
Dipping, simple spraying, firing . . 50
Rubbing, ordinary hand painting and finishing art, stencil and special spraying 50
Fine hand painting and finishing 100
Extra fine hand painting and finishing (automobile bodies, piano cases, etc.) 300**

PAPER BOX MANUFACTURING
General manufacturing area 50

PAPER MANUFACTURING
Beaters, grinding, calendering . . . 30
Finishing, cutting, trimming, papermaking machines 50
Hand counting, wet end of paper machine 70
Paper machine reel, paper inspection and laboratories 100
Rewinder 150

PLATING 30

POLISHING—BURNISHING 100

PRINTING INDUSTRIES
Type foundries:
Matrix making, dressing type . . . 100
Font assembly—sorting 50
Hand casting 50
Machine casting 50
Printing plants:
Color inspection and appraisal . . 200**
Machine composition 100
Composing room 100
Presses 70
Imposing stones 150
Proof reading 150
Electrotyping:
Molding, finishing, leveling molds, routing, trimming 100
Blocking, tinning 50
Electroplating, washing, backing . . 50
Photo engraving:
Etching, staging 50
Blocking 50
Routing, finishing, proofing 100
Tint laying 100
Masking 100

RECEIVING AND SHIPPING (SEE MATERIALS HANDLING)

RUBBER TIRE AND TUBE MANUFACTURING
Stock preparation:
Banbury, plasticating, milling . . . 30
Calendering 50
Fabric preparation:
Stock cutting, bead building 50
Tube tubing machines 50
Tread tubing machines 50
Tire building:
Solid tire 30
Pneumatic tire 50
Curing department:
Tube curing, casing curing 70
Final Inspection:
Tube, casing 200**
Wrapping 50

RUBBERS GOODS—MECHANICAL
Stock preparation:
Plasticating, milling, banbury . . . 30
Calendering 50
Fabric preparation:
Stock cutting, hose looms 50
Molded products and curing 50
Extruded products 50
Inspection 200**

SHEET METAL WORKS
Miscellaneous machines, ordinary bench work 50
Presses, shears, stamps, spinning, medium bench work 50
Punches 50
Tin plate inspection, galvanized . . 200††
Scribing . . . . 200††

SHIP YARDS
General 5
Ways 10
Fabrication areas 30

SHOE MANUFACTURING (LEATHER)
Cutting and stitching:
Cutting tables 300**
Marking, buttonholing, skiving, sorting, vamping and counting . . 300**

Stitching:
Dark materials 300**
Making and finishing:
Nailers, sole layers, welt beaters and scarfers, trimmers, welters, lasters, edge setters, sluggers, randers, wheelers, treers, cleaning, spraying, buffing, polishing, embossing 200

SHOE MANUFACTURING (RUBBER)
Washing, coating, mill run compounding 30
Varnishing, vulcanizing, calendering, upper and sole cutting 50
Sole rolling, lining, making and finishing processes 100

SOAP MANUFACTURING
Kettle houses, cutting, soap chip and powder 30
Stamping, wrapping and packing, filling and packing soap powder .. 50

STAIRWAYS, WASHROOMS AND OTHER SERVICE AREAS ... 20

STONE CRUSHING AND SCREENING
Belt conveyor tubes, main line shafting spaces, chute rooms inside of bins 10
Primary breaker room, auxiliary breakers under bins 10
Screens 20

STORAGE ROOMS OR WAREHOUSES
Inactive 5
Active:
Rough bulky 10
Medium 20
Fine 50

STRUCTURAL STEEL FABRICATION 50

SUGAR REFINING
Grading 50
Color inspection 200

TESTING
General 50
Extra fine instruments, scales, etc. 200**

TEXTILE MILLS (COTTON)
Opening, mixing, picking 30
Carding and drawing 50
Slubbing, roving, spinning, spooling 50
Beaming and slashing on comb:
Grey goods 50
Denims 50
Inspection:
Grey goods (hand turning) 100
Denims (rapidly moving) 500**
Automatic tying-in 150**
Drawing-in by hand 200**
Weaving 100

TEXTILE MILLS (SILK AND SYNTHETICS)
Manufacturing:
Soaking, fugitive tinting, conditioning or setting of twist 30
Winding, twisting, rewinding, and coning, quilling, slashing:
Light thread 50
Dark thread 200
Warping (silk or cotton system) on creel, on running ends, on reel on beam, on warp at beaming .. 100
Drawing-in:
On heddles 200**
On reed 200**
Weaving 100

TEXTILE MILLS (WOOLEN AND WORSTED)
Opening, blending, picking 30
Grading 100**
Carding, combining, recombing, gilling 50
Drawing (white) 50
Drawing (colored) 100
Spinning (frame) (white) 50
Spinning (frame) (colored) 100
Spinning (mule) (white) 50
Spinning (mule) (colored) 100
Twisting (white) 50
Winding (white) 30
Winding (colored) 50
Warping (white) 50
Warping (white) (at reed) 100
Warping (colored) 100
Warping (colored) (at reed) 300**
Weaving (white) 100
Weaving (colored) 200
Grey goods room:
Burling 150**
Sewing 300**
Folding 70
Wet finishing:
Fulling 50
Scouring 50
Crabbing 50
Drying 50
Dyeing 100**
Dry finishing:
Naping 70
Shearing 100**
Conditioning 70
Pressing 70
Inspecting (perching) 2000**
Folding 70

TOBACCO PRODUCTS
Drying, stripping, general 30
Grading and sorting 200**

UPHOLSTERING—AUTOMOBILE, COACH
Furniture 100

WAREHOUSE (SEE STORAGE)

WELDING
General illumination 50
Precision manual arc welding 1000**

WOODWORKING
Rough sawing and bench work .. 30
Sizing, planing, rough sanding, medium machine and bench work, glueing, veneering, cooperage 50
Fine bench and machine work, fine sanding and finishing 100

Notes on Industrial Areas
*Minimum on the task at any time.
**Obtained with a combination of general lighting-plus specialized supplementary lighting. Care should be taken to keep within the recommended brightness ratios. These seeing tasks generally involve the discrimination of fine detail for long periods of time and under conditions of poor contrast. To provide the required illumination, a combination of the general lighting indicated plus specialized supplementary lighting is necessary. The design and installation of the combination system must not only provide a sufficient amount of light, but also the proper direction of light, diffusion, and eye protection. As far as possible it should eliminate direct and reflected glare as well as objectionable shadows.
†The specular surface of the material may necessitate special consideration in selection and placement of lighting equipment, or orientation of the work.
††Special lighting such that (1) the luminous area shall be large enough to cover the surface which is being inspected and (2) the brightness be within the limits necessary to obtain comfortable contrast conditions. This involves the use of sources of large area and relatively low brightness in which the source brightness is the principal factor rather than the footcandles produced at a given point.

INSTITUTIONS

ART GALLERIES
General 30
On paintings (supplementary) ... 30
On statuary and other displays .. 100
(1) Dark paintings with fine detail should have 2 to 3 times higher illumination.
(2) In some cases, much more than 100 foot-candles is necessary to bring out the beauty of statuary.

HOSPITALS
Anesthetizing and preparation room 30
Auditorium:
Assembly 15
Exhibition 30
Autopsy and morgue:
Autopsy room 100
Autopsy table 2500
Morgue, general 20
Central sterile supply:
General 30
Needle sharpening 150
Corridor:
General 10
Operating and delivery suites and laboratories 20
Cystoscopic room:
General 100
Cystoscopic table 2500
Dental suite:
Waiting room:
General 15
Reading 30
Operatory, general 70
Instrument cabinet 150
Dental chair 1000
Laboratory, bench 100
Recovery room 5
Dining room (see Restaurants)
Electroencephalographic suite:
Office 100
Workroom 30
Patients' room 30
Emergency room:
General 100
Local 2000
EKG, BMR and Specimen room:
General 20
Specimen table (supplementary) .. 50
Examination and treatment room:
General 50
Examining table 100
Eye, ear, nose and throat suite:
Dark room 10
Eye examination and treatment room 20
Ear, nose and throat room 20
Exits, at floor 5
Flower room 10
Formula room 30
Fracture room:
General 50
Fracture table 200
Kitchen:
Central 70
Floor, kitchen and pantry 70
Dishwashing 30
Laboratories:
Assay rooms 30
Work tables 50
Close work 100
Laundry:
General 30
Pressers and ironers 70
Sorting 70
Libraries 70
Linen closet 10
Locker rooms 20
Lobby 30
Lounge rooms 30
Maintenance shop:
General 30
Work benches 100

New Tables (cont.)

Paint storage 10
Medical records room 100

Nurses' station:
General 20
Desk and charts 50
Medicine room counter 100
Nurses' workroom 30

Nurseries:
General 10
Examination table 70
Play room, pediatric 30

Obstetrical:
Clean-up room 30
Scrub-up room 30
Labor room 20
Delivery room, general 100
Delivery table 2500
Offices (See Offices)
Parking lot 5

Power plant:
Boiler room 10
Machine room 20
Switchboard room 30
Transformer room 10

Pharmacy:
General 30
Work table 100
Active storage 30
Alcohol vault 10

Private rooms and wards:
General 10
Reading 30
Psychiatric disturbed patients'
areas 10

Radioisotope facilities:
Radiochemical laboratory 30
Up-take measuring room 20
Examination table 50
Retiring room 10

Sewing room:
General 20
Work area 100
Solariums 20
Stairways 20

Storage, central:
General 15
Office 70

Surgery:
Instrument and sterile supply room 30
Clean-up room (instruments) 100
Scrub-up room 30
Operating room, general 100
Operating table 2500
Recovery room 30

Therapy:
Physical 20
Occupational 30
Toilets 10
Utility room 20

Waiting room:
General 15
Reading 30

X-ray room and facilities:
Radiography and fluoroscopy . . . 10
Deep and superficial therapy 10
Darkroom 10
Waiting room, general 15
Waiting room, reading 30
Viewing room 30
Filing room, developed films 30
Storage, undeveloped films 10

HOTELS

Auditoriums:
Assembly only 15
Exhibitions 30
Dancing 5
Bars and cocktail lounges (see
Restaurants)

Bathrooms:
Mirror‡ 30
General 10

Bedrooms:
Reading (books, magazines, news-
papers) 30
Inkwriting** 30
Make-up†‡ 30
General 10
Corridors, elevators and stairs . . 20
Dining areas (see Restaurants)
Entrance foyer 30
Front office 50
Kitchen (see Restaurants)

Laundry:
Washing 30
Flat work ironing 50
Machine and press finishing 70

Linen room:
Sewing 100
General 20

Lobby:
General lighting 10
Reading and working areas 30

Marquee:
Dark surroundings 30
Bright surroundings 50

Offices:
Accounting 150
General 100
Reception 30

Power plant:
Boiler room 10
Equipment room 20
Storerooms 10
Work shops (See Machine Shops
and Woodworking, under Indus-
trial Areas Section)
Museums (See Art Galleries)
Professional Offices (See Hospitals)
Restaurants, lunch rooms, cafeterias

Dining areas:
Cashier 50

Intimate type:
Light environment 10
Subdued environment 3

For cleaning 20

Leisure type:
Light environment 30
Subdued enviroment 15

Quick service type:
Bright surroundings†† 100
Normal surroundings†† 50
Food displays—twice the general
levels but not under 50

Kitchen, commercial:
Inspection, checking and pricing . 70
Other areas 30
*Minimum on the task at all times.
**Pencil handwriting, reading of
reproductions and poor copies require 70 footcandles.
†This may be done in the bathrooms
but if a dressing table is provided
local lighting should provide the
level recommended.
††Including street and nearby establishments.
‡For close inspection, 50 footcandles

OFFICES

OFFICES
Cartography, designing, detailed
drafting 200
Accounting, auditing, tabulating,
bookkeeping, business machine
operation, reading poor reproductions, rough layout drafting . . . 150
Regular office work, reading good
reproductions, reading or transcribing handwriting in hard pencil
or on poor paper, active filing,
index references, mail sorting . . 100
Reading or transcribing handwriting in ink or medium pencil on
good quality paper, intermittent
filing 70
Reading high contrast or well-
printed material, tasks and areas

not involving critical or prolonged
seeing such as conferring, inter-
viewing, inactive files and washrooms 30
Corridors, elevators, escalators,
stairways 20

BANKS:
Lobby:
General 50
Writing areas 70
Tellers' stations 150
Posting and keypunch 150
Regular office work 100

**DEPOTS, TERMINALS AND
STATIONS**
Waiting room 30
Ticket offices:
General 100
Ticket rack and counters 100
Rest room and smoking room . . . 30
Baggage checking 50
Storage 20
Concourse 10
Platforms 20
Toilets and washrooms 30
Drafting rooms (see Offices)

**MUNICIPAL BUILDINGS (FIRE
AND POLICE)**
Office work, corridors, elevators,
stairways, washrooms (see Offices)
Police:
Identification records 150
Jail cells and interrogation rooms 30
Fire Hall:
Dormitory 20
Recreation room 30
Wagon room 30

Post Offices:
Lobby, on tables 30
Sorting, mailing, etc. 100
Storage 20
Files (see Offices)
Corridors and stairways 20

STORES

SHOW WINDOWS
Daytime lighting:
General 200
Feature 1000
Nighttime lighting:
**Main business district—highly
competitive:**
General 200
Feature 1000
**Secondary business districts or
small towns:**
General 100
Feature 500
**Open-front stores (see Display
lighting under Store interiors)**
Store interior:
Circulation areas 30
Merchandising areas:
Service 100
Self-service 200
Showcases and wall cases:
Service 200
Self-service 500
Feature displays:
Service 500
Self-service 1000
Stockrooms 30

(1) Above values are illumination on the
merchandise on display or being appraised.
The plane in which lighting is important
may vary from horizontal to vertical.
(2) Specific appraisal areas involving difficult
seeing may be lighted to substantially higher
levels.
(3) Color rendition of fluorescent lamps is
important. Incandescent and fluorescent
usually are combined for best appearance of
merchandise.
(4) Illumination may often be made non-
uniform to tie in with merchandising layout.

Basic data on electric light sources				
Type light source	Lamp bulb type	Watts per lamp (Range)	Lumens* per watt (Range)	Average rated life (Hours)
Incandescent	Pear shape	150–1500	17–22	750–1000
	Reflector (R)	30–1000	7–18	2000
	Projector (PAR)	75–500	10–12	2000
	Quartz-iodine	300–1500	21–22	2000
	Halogen PAR & R	250–1500	12–17	4000
Fluorescent	Preheat	15–100	40–79	7500–12000**
	Instant start	25–75	70–84	7500–9000**
	Rapid start	30–215	63–81	7500–12000**
Mercury vapor	Clear	100–1000	38–56	24,000
	Color-improved	100–1000	34–55	24,000
Metal halide	High-intensity	400–1000	79–90	6000***
High pressure sodium vapor	Clear	400	105	6000***

* Initial lumens. Does not include watts loss in ballasts for electric discharge lamps.
** Average life, under specified conditions, and based on three burning hours per start.
*** Economic life. Actual life at five hours per start or more will be much longer.

Coefficients of utilization for typical semi-indirect fluorescent luminaire

ρcc	80		70		50	
ρw	50	30	50	30	50	30
RCR	Coefficients of utilization (X.01) for 20% effective floor cavity reflectance					
1	79	76	72	69	58	56
2	70	65	63	59	52	49
3	62	57	57	52	46	43
4	55	49	51	45	41	38
5	49	43	45	40	37	33
6	44	38	41	35	34	29
7	40	34	37	31	30	26
8	36	30	33	27	27	23
9	32	26	30	24	25	21
10	30	24	27	22	23	19

ρcc = Effective Ceiling Cavity Reflectance
ρw = Wall Reflectance

$$\text{RCR} = \text{Room Cavity Ratio} = \frac{5 h_{RC}\,(L + W)}{LW}$$

system in which it is used. It is therefore highly important that the lighting engineer select the light sources for his lighting systems with intelligence and care.

Light source efficiency is not the only factor to be considered, of course. Other factors include such features as color quality of the light (spectral quality), total light output of the lamp, lamp life, lumen depreciation throughout life, stroboscopic effect, amount of heat produced, effect of ambient temperature surrounding the lamp on its efficiency, and several others. All of these factors should be carefully analyzed and considered, and weighted according to their relation to the ultimate lighting result desired, and to the overall lighting cost.

Light sources used for general lighting purposes, including light for decoration, are of three types: incandescent, fluorescent and mercury vapor. Natural daylight may also be a factor in lighting, especially when window and glass wall areas are involved.

Light Source Light Output—The total light output of individual lamp types, measured in total initial lumens, should be considered. The higher the light output of individual lamps, the fewer

RECOMMENDED BRIGHTNESS RATIOS FOR INTERIOR LIGHTING

Condition	Ratio
Between visual tasks and adjacent surroundings Example: White paper and desk top	1 to 1/3
Between visual tasks and more remote darker surfaces Example: White paper on desk & floor	1 to 1/10
Between visual tasks and more remote brighter surfaces Example: White paper on desk and luminaires	1 to 10
Between luminaires and adjacent surfaces in normal field of view	20 to 1
Anywhere within normal field of view Example: Luminaires and floor	40 to 1

These ratios are recommended as maximums: reductions are generally beneficial. See also Fig. 11–8 and Fig. 14–2 in IES Lighting Handbook

RECOMMENDED REFLECTANCE VALUES FOR INDUSTRIAL AREAS

Surface	Reflectance (%)
Ceiling	80
Wall	60
Desk and bench tops	35
Machines and equipment	25 to 30
Floors	not less than 15

Source: IES Lighting Handbook

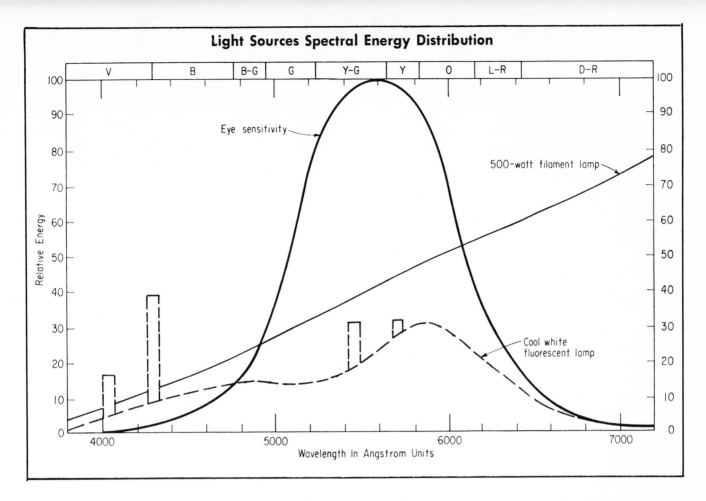

Light Sources Spectral Energy Distribution

V | B | B-G | G | Y-G | Y | O | L-R | D-R

Eye sensitivity

500-watt filament lamp

Cool white fluorescent lamp

Relative Energy

Wavelength In Angstrom Units

the lamps that will be required to produce a given illumination level. Along with the light output, of course, must be considered the physical size of the lamp, and the size of the luminaire that will be required to house the lamp, (or lamps, in the case of multiple-lamp luminaires).

Spectral Quality—Light is radiant energy which constitutes the visible spectrum. It is composed of pure spectral colors, or so-called color regions. In their simplest form, these color regions are divided into nine well-known parts: violet, blue, blue-green, green, yellow-green, yellow, orange, light red and dark red. These nine colors span the entire visible spectrum, which ranges from about 4000 to 7000 Angstrom units (1 Angstrom equals 10 millimicrons). The color of a colored light source has all (or most) of its energy in the spectral region of that color. Green, for example, ranges from about 4900 A° to 5600 A° (see "Light Sources Spectral Energy Distribution"). When appropriate quantities of radiant energy of these different wave-lengths are combined, so-called "white" light (daylight, for example) results.

Each type of light source produces a different "color quality" of light. That is, each type produces radiant energy of different wavelengths, which the eye perceives as a color sensation depending on how the radiant energy is distributed over the visible spectrum. This is true of natural daylight, which varies in "color" throughout the day, and of candles, oil lamps, electric light sources, and others. Thus the lighting designer is working with "color," fundamentally, when he

works with light; and spectral quality of light sources selected for any specific lighting application should be selected on the basis of its appropriate "color quality" for the lighting results required, or desired.

Light sources which produce so-called "white" light have an inherent "color quality," which is expressed in terms of "color temperature," and measured in degrees Kelvin. A light source is said to have a certain color temperature (see table "Color Temperature of Various Light Sources") when its radiation has the identical color characteristics as a black body at this stated temperature. The Kelvin temperature scale has its zero at —273 degrees C, or at —459.4 degrees F, sometimes referred to as absolute zero. Thus the color quality of a cool white fluorescent lamp, rated at 4500°K, for example, is the same as that of a black body heated to a temperature of 4500 degrees above absolute zero. A black body, it should be further noted, is a theoretical object which is assumed to have perfect characteristics for emitting all the colors of the visible spectrum from red to violet, as its temperature is increased from a point where it barely glows a deep red until it reaches a white heat, and eventually its melting point.

Strictly speaking, color temperature should be applied only to light which is generated by heat, such as daylight, or incandescent filament lamps. However, the general practice of light source manufacturers in distinguishing one "white" fluorescent lamp from another by the use of a Kelvin (color temperature) designation, to differentiate between warm and cool "whites," has become quite well known and generally accepted by lighting engineers, and to a lesser extent by the public. Also, the need for balancing the color quality of light (by filters) to match the light response characteristics of color films in color photography, has made the use of color temperature designations of light familiar to millions of professional and amateur photographers. Thus it is a nomenclature of lighting technology which the lighting engineer should recognize and adopt.

In general, incandescent filament lamps produce a yellowish white light. The lower wattage incandescent lamps produce a light that is distinctively yellow, and the higher wattage lamps (operating with a higher filament temperature) produce a "whiter" yellow.

Mercury vapor lamps produce a blue-green "white" light basically, devoid of yellow-orange-red light. By means of phosphor coatings, however, the light source manufacturers have been able to improve the color quality of these lamps, and improved "whites," including a "yellow" lamp, have resulted. Manufacturers' literature should be referred to for complete details.

Fluorescent lamps are purposely made in a variety of "white" colors for use in general lighting applications. These include daylight (6500°K), cool white (4500°K), white (3500°K), and warm white. In addition, there are two "deluxe" lamps —the deluxe cool white, and the deluxe warm white—in which phosphors are used to provide more red and orange radiation and thus more closely approximate a continuous-spectrum light.

Light Control—Incandescent lamps, and mercury vapor lamps to a lesser degree, are considered point sources of light. The light output can thereby be quite accurately controlled by means of reflectors or prismatic glass or plastic reflectors or refractors.

Fluorescent lamps are line sources of light, of fairly large diameter; hence, the light output is fundamentally of a diffuse character. Control of the light output from these lamps is less accurate, and generally limited to shielding, or to further diffusion.

The degree of light control needed, from a light distribution standpoint, to achieve a specific lighting result, thus becomes a factor in the selection of the light source.

Lamp Life—Light sources deteriorate from use, thus have a "rated average life" expectancy.

Incandescent lamps of the large lamp type normally used for general lighting purposes have a rated average life of 1,000 hours, except for certain sizes and types which are rated at 2,000 hours for use in special high bay applications to help reduce maintenance costs, and for certain reflector-type lamps used for show window, floodlighting, and other similar applications.

Rated average life of fluorescent and mercury vapor lamps is a function of the frequency of starting the lamps, as well as number of hours operated. Both are characteristically long-life lamps. Fluorescent lamp life is shown in the chart "Rated Average Life of Fluorescent Lamps."

Rated average life of mercury vapor lamps now ranges from 6,000 to 10,000 hours, for most types, but manufacturers' literature should be checked for exact ratings and lumen maintenance.

An excellent factor for comparing lamp life of one light source with another, and for making economic analyses, is "burnouts per billion lumen hours." This factor may be calculated for any light source by dividing one billion by "average lamp life" in hours times "mean light output" in lumens. This indicates the number of lamps to be purchased and replaced to provide a fixed quantity of light output. Burnouts per billion lumen hours have been shown in the two tables—"Standard Fluorescent Lamps" and "Standard Incandescent Lamps."

Stroboscopic Effect—For most lighting applications, stroboscopic effect, or flicker, is not a problem. However, for certain applications, such as floodlighting a tennis court, or lighting of moving parts in industrial applications, it should be avoided. The stroboscopic effect of filament lamps is too low to be a problem, but may be sufficiently high on electric discharge type lamps to be a problem under certain circumstances. It can usually be minimized enough to be considered practical for use by operating the lamps in a specific area on three separate circuits, each circuit supplied from a separate phase. Another solution is to use high frequency power for the lighting system.

Lighting Load Affects Air Conditioning

1. Heat from a lighting load is measured in —

   Btu's per hour

2. A lighting system produces a Btu per hour heating load equal to —

   Lighting Kilowatts* x 3414

3. Required tons of air conditioning to remove a lighting system heat load is equal to —

   $$\frac{\text{Btu's per hour (from 2)}}{12000}$$

4. One ton of air conditioning capacity will remove the heat for a lighting load of —

   3500 watts

---

*Add both lamp wattage and ballast watts loss for fluorescent lighting systems.

Heat from light sources

All light sources create heat when burning. This heat results from the consumption of electric energy by the lamp, and is directly proportional to the wattage of the lamp. Each watt produces 3.41 Btu per hour, when burning.

As a result of recent coordinated activity between electrical and mechanical engineers, a new technique for handling lighting heat loads has been developed. It is based on the integration of lighting and air conditioning systems. In these new "integrated" systems, air-handling lighting troffers are used, and the lighting heat load is drawn upward into the return air duct system so that it does not enter the occupied room area that is being air conditioned.

Heating with light

On the other hand, lighting heat may help to reduce the heating problem for buildings during winter months. Many electrical and mechanical engineers are thus developing various methods and systems which will utilize the lighting heat load when needed for heating the building, and eliminate the lighting heat load when cooling the building. Such collaboration recently has expanded so that today the team includes the architect, the structural engineer, the heating and ventilating engineer, the electrical and lighting engineer, and the air conditioning engineer. Out of this collaboration, plus considerable research and development work by the lighting industry and the air conditioning industry, a new concept has evolved. This new concept is one of environmental engineering, or the conditioning of space with lighting, heating, cooling, sound control, space flexibility, and other environmental factors.

This expanded use of lighting heralds a new era in environmental design. It provides the opportunity to supply all, or a substantial part, of a building's heat losses with lighting, and control of lighting heat thus becomes necessary for the most effective use.

IES zonal-cavity method

The new 4th Edition (June 1966) of the *IES Lighting Handbook* presents and describes a refinement on the lumen method of calculations. It is the IES Zonal-Cavity Method. With this refinement of the lumen method, the room must be divided into three cavities—ceiling, room, and floor—as indicated in the accompanying drawing. Then, by using the specific reflectances for the surfaces in each of these three cavities, more accurate calculations can be obtained than is possible by the original lumen method of calculations. In addition, with the Zonal-Cavity Method, the effects of room proportions, luminaire suspension length, and work plane height upon the coefficient of utilization (CU) are more accurately accounted for.

The Zonal Cavities are defined as follows:

Ceiling Cavity is the space bounded by the ceiling, the upper walls, and an imaginary plane through the luminaires.

Room Cavity is the space bounded by the plane through the luminaires, the work plane, and the portion of the walls between these planes.

Floor Cavity is the space bounded by the work plane, the lower walls, and the floor.

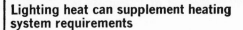

Lighting heat can supplement heating system requirements

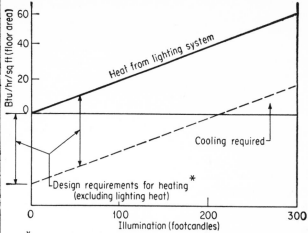

*Prototype example; varies from building to building based on existing climatic and other variable conditions.

HEAT produced by lighting systems was formerly considered a problem, to be solved by the air conditioning engineer. More recently, lighting heat is being utilized to supplement the building's heating system requirements. In many instances, especially when lighting levels in excess of 100 fc are provided, the lighting heat is adequate to heat the entire building. The current trend is to give more and more consideration to thermal load balancing in which lighting heat is used to help reduce both heating and cooling capacity requirements.

In applying the Zonal-Cavity Method of calculations, the proportions of each cavity may be represented by a *Cavity Ratio*. These *Cavity Ratios* may be obtained from a table (see Fig. 9-2, Cavity Ratios, *IES Lighting Handbook*), or from a formula, as follows:

$$\text{Ceiling Cavity Ratio, } CCR = \frac{5h_{CC}(L+W)}{LW}$$

$$\text{Room Cavity Ratio, } RCR = \frac{5h_{RC}(L+W)}{LW}$$

$$\text{Floor Cavity Ratio, } FCR = \frac{5h_{FC}(L+W)}{LW}$$

Where L = room length
W = room width
h = cavity height

with all dimensions being in feet.

Room Cavity Ratios are always required to obtain coefficients of utilization, just as Room Ratios or Room Indices were required by the original Lumen Method of calculations. The *Ceiling* and *Floor Cavity Ratios* are required only to obtain *Effective Cavity Reflectances,* which are now used in coefficient of utilization tables for specific luminaires to establish specific effective cavity reflectance conditions. These effective ceiling or floor cavity reflectance percentages for various reflectance combinations are also provided in table form, by manufacturers of lighting equipment, or in Fig. 9-3 in the *IES Handbook*.

Manufacturers of lighting equipment provide coefficient of utilization tables for each luminaire. These CU tables are for Room Cavity Ratios (RCR) varying from 1 to 10, based on 20% Effective Floor Cavity reflectance, and for various Ceiling Cavity and Wall Cavity reflectances. A typical CU table for a semi-indirect luminaire is shown.

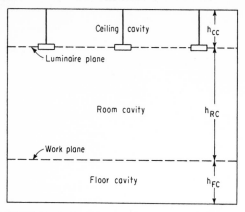

IES Zonal-Cavity Method of Calculations

Ceiling cavity — h_{CC}

Luminaire plane

Room cavity — h_{RC}

Work plane

Floor cavity — h_{FC}

CALCULATING Coefficients of Utilization (CU) for specific luminaires in rooms of specific proportions, and with ceiling, wall and floor reflectances of specific values, is improved in accuracy by dividing the room into three cavities as shown above and then determining the cavity ratio for each as provided for by the IES Zonal-Cavity Method.

When Effective Floor Cavity reflectance varies from the 20% value normally used in manufacturers' CU tables, correction factors for 10% and 30% Effective Floor Cavity reflectances are provided in table form, either by lighting equipment manufacturers, or in Fig. 9-5 of the *IES Lighting Handbook*.

A simple procedure may now be followed to obtain the CU value for the specific luminaire. The procedure for a suspended luminaire is typical:

1. Obtain *Room Cavity Ratio* and *Ceiling Cavity Ratio* by formulas (above), or from table.

2. Obtain *Effective Ceiling Cavity reflectance*, ρcc, from manufacturers' literature, or from Fig. 9-3 in the *IES Lighting Handbook* (note that expected *maintained* ceiling and wall reflectances should be used in selecting the proper column).

3. Obtain CU for expected *maintained* wall reflectance and 20% Effective Floor Cavity reflectance from the CU table for the luminaire. (Interpolate as required for exact RCR and Ceiling Cavity reflectance.)

Calculating lighting levels

After determining the proper coefficient of utilization for a specific luminaire, using the Zonal-Cavity method, lighting levels for the area being considered may be calculated as follows:

Average Maintained Illumination Level—

$$FC = \frac{LL/L \times CU \times LLD \times LDD}{A/L}$$

where FC = footcandles
   LL/L = lamp lumens per luminaire
   CU = coefficient of utilization
   LLD = lamp lumen depreciation factor
   LDD = luminaire dirt depreciation factor
   A/L = area per luminaire (sq ft)

The Lamp Lumen Depreciation (LLD) factor is the percent of initial lumens produced at 70% of rated life. Lamp manufacturers' up-to-date statistics for the particular lamp being considered should be consulted. Fig. 9-6 in the *IES Lighting Handbook* lists the LLD factor for basic types of incandescent, mercury and fluorescent lamps.

The *Luminaire Dirt Depreciation* (LLD) factor covers the accumulation of dirt on the luminaire, depending upon the degree of dirtiness (five degrees, from "very clean" to "very dirty") in the area where it will be used. Luminaires are classified in six categories, each category representing its characteristics of dirt attraction or dirt retention.

Manufacturers of lighting equipment will normally provide an LLD multiplier for each luminaire, along with a CU table and other photometric and test data, based on the use of light sources for which the luminaire is designed. Fig. 9-6 in the *IES Lighting Handbook* may also be used to determine this LLD factor.

Lighting equipment manufacturers will also normally provide an LDD classification of each luminaire on the photometric data sheet for the luminaire. Otherwise, the LDD factor can be determined through a three-step procedure outlined in the *IES Lighting Handbook*.

Step 1 is to determine the atmosphere (one of five degrees of dirt condition) in which the luminaire will operate. This can be done by referring to Fig. 9-8 or Fig. 9-9, in the *IES Lighting Handbook*. The five conditions are—very clean, clean, medium, dirty, and very dirty.

Step 2 is to select the luminaire category (one of six) which most nearly illustrates the luminaire's characteristics of dirt attraction or of dirt retention.

Step 3 is to follow the applicable dirt condition curve (determined in Step 1) on the appropriate luminaire category chart (Fig. 9-7 of the *IES Lighting Handbook*) to the proper vertical line for "elapsed time in months" of the planned cleaning cycle. The intersection of the "dirt condition curve" and the "vertical line" will represent the LDD factor which can be read on the vertical axis of the chart.

The LLD and LDD factors are essentially refinements on the *maintenance factor* (MF) used in the original Lumen Method of lighting calculations. Having determined these two factors, as outlined above, they may be used in the Zonal-Cavity method formula to determine the "average maintained illumination" level in footcandles.

It should be noted that Ceiling Cavity Ratios (CCR) become zero for surface-mounted or recessed luminaires; also, that CU tables are based on 20% Effective Floor Cavity reflectance only. Correction factors are available (Fig. 9-5, *IES Lighting Handbook*) for 10% and 30% Effective Floor Cavity reflectances.

In making these calculations, the values may be related to the total area of the project, to the area per luminaire, or to the area per bay or other convenient or practical subdivision.

Color in lighting

Color is a most important consideration in lighting design. Yet, it is usually one of the most neglected factors.

All light has color, including daylight. There is no such thing as colorless light. Also, all objects, surfaces, and materials on which light falls (except black) have color.

The lighting engineer should consider color in lighting from two standpoints. First, he should consider the color of the light being used, or as pro-

COEFFICIENTS OF UTILIZATION FOR TYPICAL LUMINAIRES

Luminaire Type	Distribution and Maximum Spacing	Ceiling Walls Room Ratio	80%		50%	
			50%	30%	50%	10%
			Coefficients of Utilization			
Direct Lighting						
1-Lamp Aluminum Troffer Baffled	0% Up 60% Down 0.8 x MH	1.0 1.5 2.5 4.0	.43 .50 .55 .59	.40 .47 .53 .57	.42 .49 .54 .56	.37 .44 .50 .54
3-Lamp 24'' Troffer Diffusing Plastic	0% Up 60% Down 0.9 x MH	1.0 1.5 2.5 4.0	.37 .45 .52 .56	.31 .40 .48 .54	.35 .43 .49 .54	.27 .35 .43 .50
Mercury Aluminum High Bay	0% Up 70% Down 0.9 x MH	1.0 1.5 2.5 4.0	.48 .57 .64 .68	.45 .53 .61 .66	.47 .55 .62 .66	.42 .50 .58 .63
Mercury Porcelain High Bay Ventilated	0% Up 75% Down 1.0 x MH	1.0 1.5 2.5 4.0	.50 .59 .67 .74	.46 .55 .64 .70	.49 .58 .66 .71	.42 .52 .61 .67
Mercury Prismatic High Bay	0% Up 70% Down 0.6 x MH	1.0 1.5 2.5 4.0	.67 .73 .78 .81	.63 .70 .75 .79	.64 .69 .74 .76	.60 .65 .70 .74
Semi-Direct Lighting						
4-Lamp Enclosed Diffusing Plastic	10% Up 50% Down 1.0 x MH	1.0 1.5 2.5 4.0	.27 .34 .40 .45	.23 .30 .37 .41	.25 .30 .36 .40	.19 .25 .32 .36
2-Lamp Porcelain Industrial Reflector	10% Up 70% Down 1.0 x MH	1.0 1.5 2.5 4.0	.47 .60 .71 .78	.41 .54 .65 .74	.45 .56 .66 .73	.36 .48 .59 .67
2-Lamp Bare Lamp Channel	10% Up 80% Down 1.0 x MH	1.0 1.5 2.5 4.0	.46 .58 .69 .77	.38 .51 .63 .72	.42 .53 .64 .71	.33 .44 .55 .64
Direct — Indirect Lighting						
Multilamp Metal Panels and Louvers	30% Up 35% Down 1.1 x MH	1.0 1.5 2.5 4.0	.31 .37 .44 .50	.27 .33 .41 .47	.28 .32 .39 .42	.22 .27 .34 .39
2-Lamp Metal Sides Louver Shielding	45% Up 35% Down 1.2 x MH	1.0 1.5 2.5 4.0	.37 .46 .57 .63	.30 .40 .51 .59	.32 .38 .47 .51	.24 .31 .40 .45

TYPES OF LIGHTING SYSTEMS

ICI* Light Distribution	Type of Luminaires	Type of Mounting	Lighting System Classification
Direct 90% to 100% Downward	Recessed	In Ceiling	Recessed (Inc. or Fl.)
	Individual Unit Continuous Row	On Ceiling	Surface Mounted Direct
	Individual Unit Continuous Row	On Ceiling	Suspended Direct
	Luminous Architectural Elements	On Ceiling, Side Walls, or Columns	Architectural
	Decorative Ornamental	On Ceilings or Walls	Ornamental
	Large-Area Low-Brightness	Recessed in Ceiling	Luminous Element
	Diffuser Ceilings Louver Ceilings	From Ceilings	Translighted Ceiling
Semi-Direct 60% to 90% Downward	Individual Unit Continuous Row	On Ceiling	Surface Mounted Semi-Direct
	Individual Unit Continuous Row	On Ceiling	Suspended Semi-Direct
	Luminous Cornice	On Wall near Ceiling	Architectural
General Diffuse 40% to 60% Downward	Individual Unit	On Ceiling	Suspended
	Continuous Row		Direct-Indirect
Semi-Indirect 60% to 90% Upward	Individual Unit Continuous Row	On Ceiling	Suspended Semi-Indirect
	Luminous Cove Wall Bracket With Downward Component	On Wall	Semi-Indirect
	Luminous Ornamental	On Ceiling	Suspended Semi-Indirect
Indirect 90% to 100% Upward	Individual Unit Continuous Row	On Ceiling	Suspended Indirect
	Wall Urns Cove Pedestal Ceiling Soffit**	On Wall On Wall or In Ceiling Floor or Counter Top In Ceiling	Indirect Cove Indirect Indirect**

International Congress on Illumination approved classification of lighting systems according to a range of distribution of total light output upward or downward, in percentages as shown. A more detailed classification, as given here, has been found through practice to be more practical.
**According to ICI practice, soffit lighting might be classified as "direct". In actual practice, it is normally referred to as "indirect," since it is actually a form of cove lighting.

duced by the light sources. This applies to daylight, so-called "white" electric light, or colored light. Secondly, he should consider the color of the objects being lighted, including walls, floors, machines, merchandise, people, etc. Every object on which light falls also has color. And this color, as perceived by the eye, will be influenced by the color of the light which falls upon it.

There is available a new color guide which every lighting engineer should have in his files. It is "Color and the Use of Color by the Illuminating Engineer," which has been prepared by the Color Committee of the IES, and is available from the IES headquarters office. This guide presents a full discussion of all phases of color as it relates to interior lighting, along with simple rules which should be followed.

Flexible Control

Electric lighting is now an essential commodity in our way of life. It is in use 24 hours a day, every day, throughout the nation. It is used to light our homes, our places of work, our recreation areas, our streets and highways, tunnels, bridges, outdoor signs, monuments, airports, gasoline service stations, restaurants, theatres, night clubs, etc.

The need for higher lighting levels generally has been recognized. Footcandle levels will be approximately doubled over the next few years from existing levels, especially in retail stores, offices, drafting rooms, and industrial plants.

In view of the increasing levels of illumination, and of the expanding use of electric lighting, the need for greater flexibility in lighting control be-

comes evident. This need is perhaps greatest for home lighting systems, where it is desirable to create a variety of lighting effects, ranging from low level decorative and mood lighting to high level illumination for reading, sewing, playing cards, and similar activities. Such lighting flexibility also becomes desirable for multi-purpose auditoriums, gymnasiums, school classrooms, and for restaurants, exhibit halls, hotel lobbies, banquet halls, private offices, and many others.

Lighting flexibility can be obtained by either of two basic methods. One method is to use multiple switch control to a single multiple-lamp luminaire, or to a multiple-lamp area such as a luminous ceiling. The other method is to use a dimmer system on all of the lighting circuits. With new and improved dimming devices becoming available, the dimming method is automatically becoming more practicable for lighting systems wherever multiple lighting effects may be desired. Included in the new dimming devices are new and improved methods for dimming fluorescent lighting systems over a broader range of intensities.

Available Power

Part and parcel of lighting system design is the wiring system which provides the electric power to operate it. In general, this includes the branch circuit wiring, switching, dimmer control, etc. back to the lighting panels, which serve as a practical point of divisional responsibility. Actual design of the branch circuit wiring system may be done either by the lighting engineer, or by the electrical system design engineer in full cooperation with, and under the direction of, the lighting engineer.

In the interest of lighting economics, however, the lighting engineer should go still further. In cooperation with the electrical engineer, he should investigate and analyze the type of electric power which is available for serving the lighting load, especially on lighting projects involving loads of 50 kw and above, or on many special lighting applications such as athletic field houses, large gymnasiums, armories, banks, air conditioned concentrated-work production areas, etc.

This analysis should include a study of the various voltage and phase combinations available from the electric utility service normally in use, and in the case of exceptionally large lighting loads, of any other electric power service which might be made available on a special basis. Voltages which are now in common usage for lighting systems are given in the table "Lighting System Voltages," for standard 60 cycle power and for high frequency power systems. Once the lighting engineer has completed his basic lighting layout design, he is in a position of being able to make economic studies to determine the most economical electrical distribution system for the specific electrical loads and length of runs for sub-feeders and branch circuits involved.

Lighting System Voltages

(Single Phase—Volts)		
60 Cycle		High Frequency
Incandescent Filament Lamps	Electric Discharge Lamps	Fluorescent Lamps
28–32 110–125 220–240	110–125 200–216 220–240 240–280 440–480*	400** * 600**

*Mercury lamp transformers.
**Phase-to-phase voltage, with grounded neutral to provide less than 300 volts to ground (NEC).

Most economic studies over the past few years have shown substantial savings for systems utilizing higher voltages (especially 277-volt lighting systems served by a 480/277-volt 3-phase 4-wire service). Also, many recent studies have shown that higher-frequency power for lighting (360, 400, 840, 1500 cycle systems) offer economic and other advantages.

As higher lighting levels are adopted, the importance of higher voltage distribution systems, and especially of higher frequency electric power at 400 volts or 600 volts, increases. The use of high frequency power has the distinct advantage of reducing the heat load for air conditioned areas of up to 20%, and savings are further reflected in total capacity requirements for air conditioning equipment.

Practicality

After completing a lighting system design, it is always a good idea to study it objectively before proceeding with its recommendation or specification. Such study should be made to provide a measure of its economy and practicality.

One of the first things to do, as a precautionary measure, is to double-check all calculations. In making this check, all dimensions should also be verified. Further, the conclusions reached for each of the above nine steps should again be gone over briefly and verified, based on the final proposed lighting system design.

Every lighting system affects other mechanical, electrical, or structural details. Thus the proposed system should be further analyzed to determine that it is practical from these standpoints. Some of the checks which should be made include:

Electrical load—Calculate the total electrical load required for the lighting system, including the watts loss in ballasts, or auxiliaries. Translate this into "watts per sq ft", and compare it with standard, or normal, practice.

Air conditioning—Determine the impact of the electrical load for lighting on the air conditioning system. This factor will normally be handled by the air conditioning engineer, but if the electrical load is considerably higher than normal, it will mean that air conditioning capacity must be installed to take care of it. Such additional capacity should logically be charged against the lighting system in making economic studies. In view of the higher lighting levels being recommended by the Illuminating Engineering Society, as adopted in 1958, this factor will grow in importance as the new lighting levels are adopted and put into use.

Another factor of importance in connection with air conditioning systems is to check for interference between air diffusers, air ducts, etc., and luminaires or lighting equipment. The lighting engineer must, of necessity, work closely with the air conditioning engineer to resolve such problems of equipment mounting locations.

Heat Dissipation—Since many of the modern lighting systems are of the recessed, or built-in types, it may be found practical and advisable to consider methods for dissipating heat loads from lighting equipment by means of special ventilating systems for the lighting units, so that the lighting system heat load does not become a part of the air conditioning problem. Many studies are already being made on this problem, and this approach should be considered for lighting systems which generate excessive amounts of heat.

Conflict With Other Devices — The proposed lighting system should be checked for interference with any structural details, or with sprinkler systems, public address systems, etc. Preliminary analysis of the proposed lighting system will at least reveal possible conflicts between the lighting system and these other factors, and aid the lighting engineer in resolving them with the architect or allied trades engineers.

From the owner's viewpoint, both first cost and annual operating cost will be of interest. The lighting engineer should develop estimates for each, on as accurate a basis as possible, and be prepared to discuss these costs in detail.

Supplementary Lighting

Applied lighting practice over the past 20 years or more (especially since the introduction of the fluorescent lamp in 1938) has been to provide general lighting, of more or less uniform footcandle levels, in stores, offices, classrooms, production areas, etc. Illumination levels installed have ranged from about 20 footcandles up to 50 and 75 footcandles for these purposes, with many installations over the past four or five years ranging to 100 footcandles and above, depending on the degree of severity of the seeing tasks involved, and the general acceptance of users of the need for more light.

This practice of installing uniform lighting levels throughout an area replaced the earlier concept, generally in practice in the 1920s and 1930s, of installing low levels of general lighting in an area, and supplementing this low level general lighting with considerably higher lighting levels at the point of work. This so-called "general plus local lighting" approach has been considered more or less obsolete in recent years, except for critical seeing tasks where lighting levels of 200 footcandles and above were used. These tasks involved many applications, however, such as for inspection, fine machining, color work, etc. in industry, and for display lighting in stores, show windows, special exhibits and similar applications. It was found to be desirable and more economical to provide these higher lighting levels for use over small work areas and on displays with supplementary type lighting, superimposed on average level general lighting of suffi-

cient quantity to maintain acceptable brightness ratios in the general field of view of the workers, or viewers of displays.

Supplementary lighting has usually been accomplished with reflector-type units installed close to the work areas, or with reflector spot or flood lamps in suitable fixed or adjustable type holders. Both incandescent and fluorescent units have been used for this purpose.

The point-by-point method of calculation is used to determine estimated footcandle values from individual supplementary lighting units. It is necessary, of course, to have a candlepower distribution curve for the unit being considered. Footcandle values may then be calculated for a point at any angle from the center axis of the unit, or on the axis. Most manufacturers of such equipment also supply charts showing footcandle values over a specified area located a specific distance from the unit, which eliminates the need for time-consuming calculations.

In view of the higher lighting levels now being recommended by the Illuminating Engineering Society for all difficult seeing tasks, it may once again become necessary to adopt the supplementary lighting technique to achieve these new higher lighting levels economically. Lighting engineers may well find it advisable to consider this approach to many of their high lighting level projects, and to study new and better techniques for providing supplementary lighting.

Residential Lighting

Lighting for the home should tie in with family life and activities. Family size, living habits, social activities, sports, hobbies, and similar factors vary greatly. Therefore, wherever practical, home lighting should be custom-designed to meet the specific requirements and individual preferences of the individual family.

Fundamental to home lighting design is the provision for a wide variety of lighting effects, to en-

able the proper environment to be created for each family activity, seeing problem, or decorative treatment. This demands the use of many different lighting techniques and types of lighting devices, with maximum control flexibility. Only through this approach to the home lighting problem can the family begin to approach the many benefits and conveniences of better light for better living.

The principal purpose for lighting in the home is

Residential Outdoor Wiring

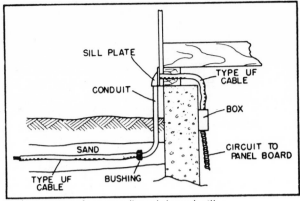

Running circuit from panelboard through sill.

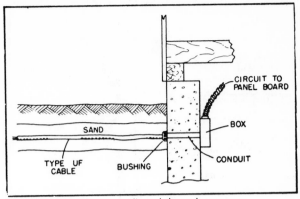

Running circuit from panelboard through masonry.

Capacity

Residential areas planned for outdoor living invariably require capacities in excess of original estimates. Therefore, at least two 20-amp 2-conductor circuits or one 3-wire circuit should be installed, each circuit originating at the panelboard and not as an extension of an existing circuit.

Underground Circuits

Type UF (underground feeder) cable is used extensively for underground circuits, being approved for direct burial without additional protection. Conduit and bushing should be provided as shown to protect cable through masonry and above ground. Enough slack should be left in cable where it enters the building to permit expansion due to temperature changes. Cable should be laid in sand deep enough to avoid damage by spading.

Where there is danger from digging, undue pressure or other abuse, a running board (1 by 2 or larger) should be laid over cable before trench is backfilled. Galvanized rigid steel conduit or equivalent should be used where there is danger from termites or rodents. Any approved moisture-resistant wire may be used where run is entirely within conduit.

Running Circuit to Outside

Circuits may be run from basement panelboard directly through the foundation wall or through the wooden sill above the foundation. The former involves more labor, but the installation is not in evidence from the outside.

Circuits from above-grade panelboards in garages, utility rooms, etc., may be run through the building wall from an interior box. After installation of cable, sealing compound should be used around opening to prevent entrance of moisture or insects.

Overhead Circuits

Open wiring run overhead is often more economical for certain applications (such as floodlighting of sports areas) where proper clearances may be obtained. Service drop, service entrance or approved weatherproof wire may be used.

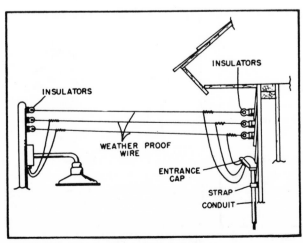

Overhead wiring used for outdoor lighting.

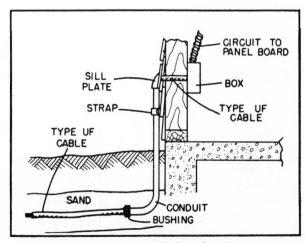

Running circuit from panelboard through wall.

Residential Outdoor Wiring

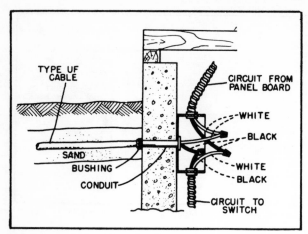

Switch control of outdoor circuit.

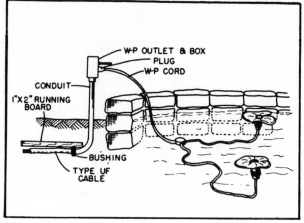

Underwater lighting unit connected to weatherproof outlet.

Switching

Outdoor circuits are most effectively controlled from indoors, although weatherproof switches are available for outdoor mounting at specific play areas, etc. Lights or convenience outlets used for a common purpose (garden lights, recreation area lights, etc.) should be switched as a group. For more flexible multi-point control, a low-voltage remote-control system may be readily adapted.

Fixtures

Play area lights, porch and entrance lights, eave floods, and post and driveway lights should be wired permanently without plug and outlet provisions where practical. Small garden lights, however, are moved frequently to most advantageously set off plants, shrubs and trees and are more easily accommodated through outlets. Similarly, special underwater fixtures for garden pools may be removed and stored during winter months.

Recommended Wire Sizes for Outdoor Circuits

(2-conductor 120v or 3-conductor 120/240v)

Max length (ft)	Wire Size (AWG)	
	15-a fusing	20-a fusing
50	14	12
100	12	12
150	12	12
200	12	10
250	10	10

Maximum Number of Lamps per Circuit

Lamp Watts	15-a circuit	20-a circuit
200	8	10
150	10	14
100	16	20
75	21	27
60	32	40

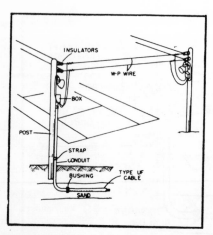

Floodlight fixture for sports area.

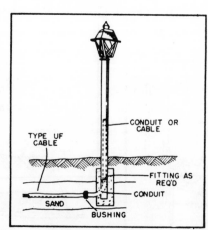

Ornamental post lighting fixture.

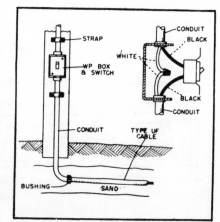

Weatherproof switch located outdoors.

Courtesy General Electric Co., Construction Materials Division

MAINTENANCE STEPS FOR INCREASED LIGHTING LEVELS

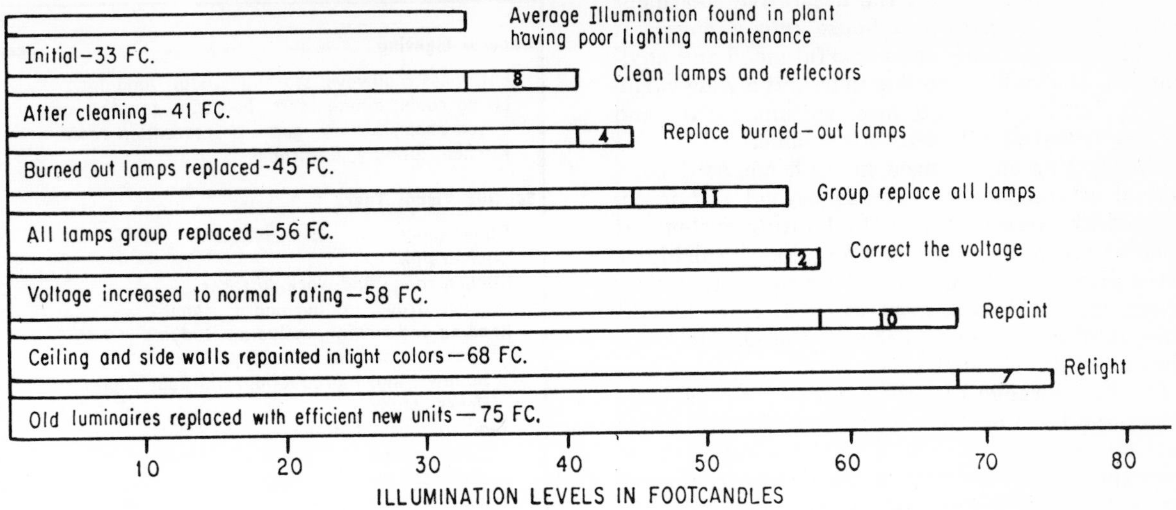

Average Illumination found in plant having poor lighting maintenance

Initial—33 FC.

Clean lamps and reflectors — 8

After cleaning—41 FC.

Replace burned—out lamps — 4

Burned out lamps replaced—45 FC.

Group replace all lamps — 11

All lamps group replaced—56 FC.

Correct the voltage — 2

Voltage increased to normal rating—58 FC.

Repaint — 10

Ceiling and side walls repainted in light colors—68 FC.

Relight — 7

Old luminaires replaced with efficient new units—75 FC.

10 20 30 40 50 60 70 80
ILLUMINATION LEVELS IN FOOTCANDLES

Lighting maintenance is a highly important factor in lighting system design. The above chart illustrates its effectiveness on a typical lighting installation. Increased reflectances, improved brightness ratios, and higher lighting levels may be effected through simple maintenance procedures.

Select luminaires and lighting equipment which include easy maintenance features designed and built into the units by the lighting equipment manufacturers; and provide easy access to all luminaires and lighting equipment.

MAJOR CAUSES OF LIGHT LOSS
In Lighting Systems

Cause of Depreciation	Percent Loss
Lamp Depreciation (End of rated life)	
Incandescent	20
Fluorescent	30
Mercury Vapor	23
Circuit Voltage Depreciation	
With adequate wiring	Negligible
With poor wiring and overloading of circuits	5–20
Luminaire Light Absorption	18–35
Paint Depreciation	
Absorption of light by walls, ceilings, floors and other surfaces	5 (per year)
Dirt and Dust Depreciation	
1-month cleaning intervals	10
3-month cleaning intervals	15
6-month cleaning intervals	20
Cleaned when lamps burn out	30
Lamp Outage Depreciation	Up to 12

TYPES OF MAINTENANCE EQUIPMENT
Used for Lighting Servicing

Equipment	Mounting Height (Feet)			
	To 12	12–18	18–30	Over 30
Catwalk (Or Truss)			X	X
Crane (Where Available)			X	X
Crows-Nest Ladder			X	
Disconnecting Hanger		X	X	X
Portable Maintenance Platform		X	X	
Relamping Bridge			X	X
Step Ladder	X			
Straight Ladder		X		
Telescoping Platform Tower		X	X	

LIGHT SOURCE EFFICIENCIES

Source	Approx Lumens per Watt*
Candle (luminous efficiency equivalent)	0.1
Oil lamp (luminous efficient equivalent)	0.3
Original incandescent lamp (1879)	1.4
60-watt carbon filament lamp (1905)	4.0
60-watt coiled coil tungsten filament lamp (1954)	13.9
1000-watt general service lamp (1959)	23.0
No. 1 photoflood lamp (1959)	34.4
1000-watt Type H12KP (ASA) mercury vapor lamp (1958)	58.0
40-watt cool white fluorescent lamp, lamp only (1959)	77.5

*Initial value, lamp only

to provide comfortable seeing for work, play and relaxation. But it can, and should, be made to serve many other needs. It should enhance the appearance, the atmosphere and the decorative treatment that helps to transform a house into a home. It should create a sunny and cheerful mood and environment. It should be flexible to permit a wide variation in lighting effects to meet varying moods, and for psychological and decorative value.

The lighting environment in the home, as in commercial establishments, extends beyond and is influenced by more than just the lighting system. It includes the walls, ceilings, floors and furnishings. These areas reflect light and cause rooms to appear larger, more cheerful, more colorful, more livable, when medium to light finishes are used. Dark finishes have the opposite effect.

The broad range of light sources, lighting techniques and lighting units makes it possible to select lighting systems which fit family budgets, yet remain appropriate for varying decorative treatments for individual family habits and requirements. When combined with appropriately finished light colors on all interior surfaces, a more satisfactory lighting environment may be expected.

From a lighting design standpoint, the rooms of a house can be divided into two basic groups. For one group, consisting of living room, dining room, bedrooms, den or study, halls and stairway, and recreation or play room, general diffuse illumination should be provided throughout each room, supplemented by local lighting at all furniture groupings or local areas where higher intensities may be needed for difficult seeing problems. Also, provision should be made to use light in these rooms as a decorative medium. For the other group of rooms, consisting of kitchen, bath, laundry, pantry, etc., or service areas, a higher level of general lighting for utilitarian purposes should be planned.

For general illumination, overhead ceiling lights are generally most satisfactory. In the living room, dining room and bedrooms, these should be decorative in character to harmonize with the furnishings, or may consist of coves, valances and cornices where the budget will permit. Recessed spots and floods carefully shielded, may also be used to light murals, pictures, indoor plants or flower arrangements, etc. Lighted ornaments, wall cabinets, etc. may be used as purely decorative devices.

IES Recommended Illumination for Residences

General Lighting	Foot-candles*
Entrances, hallways, stairways, stair landings	10**
Living room, dining room, bedroom, family room, sun room, library, game or recreation room	10**
Kitchen, laundry, bathroom	30

Specific Visual Tasks	
Table games	30
Kitchen sink	70
Kitchen range and work surfaces	50
Laundry, trays, ironing board, ironer	50
Reading and writing, including studying	
Books, magazines, newspapers	30
Handwriting, reproduction and poor copies	70
Desks, study	70
Reading music scores	
Simple scores	30
Advanced scores	70
Sewing	
Dark fabrics (fine detail, low contrast)	200
Prolonged periods (light to medium fabrics)	100
Occasional periods (coarse thread, large stitches, high contrast thread to fabric)	30
Shaving, makeup, grooming; on the face at mirror locations	50

*Minimum on the visual task.
**General lighting for these areas need not be uniform.

In the kitchen, uniform general illumination may be provided by a ceiling lighting system, ranging from a single ceiling unit to a complete wall-to-wall luminous ceiling. Large-area low-brightness recessed panels are an excellent intermediary solution. Supplementary lighting should also be provided over all work areas—food preparation, range, dishwashing center. Recessed incandescent units with concentrated light distribution can be used for some of these areas, and fluorescent wall brackets, or fluorescent strip lighting under cabinets, are also suitable where they can be installed.

In the bathroom both an overhead ceiling luminaire and two wall brackets, one on either side of the mirror, are desirable.

Overhead utilitarian lighting units are desirable in the laundry, in the furnace room, over a work bench, in the garage, and in other similar service areas.

Signals and communications

Design of any system for signal, alarm or communication is closely related to the type of system and to the particular manufacturer's instructions. The many manufacturers of such equipment make available much literature and offer engineering services to assist the electrical designer.

However, the NE Code covers signal and communication systems in Articles 640, 725, 800 and 810, offering standard design data for all types of systems.

Article 640 of the code covers sound recording and reproduction, centralized distribution of sound, public address, speech input systems and electronic organs. Specific provisions are as follows:

1. Power supply connections from the equipment to the building wiring system and between equipment must comply with rules on general power and light wiring.

2. Wiring and equipment for P. A., speech input, radio-frequency and audio-frequency systems and amplifying equipment associated with radio-receiving stations in centralized distribution systems must comply with Article 725.

3. Wireways and auxiliary gutters may be used with conductor occupancy up to 75% of cross-section area, and may be used in concealed places where run in straight lines between wiring boxes.

4. Equipment must be located or protected to guard against physical damage which might create a hazard to life or property.

5. Amplifier output circuits rated not over 70 volts, with open-circuit voltage not over 100 volts, may use Class 2 wiring as set forth in Article 725.

Article 725 of the code covers, among other things, signal circuits. A signal circuit is defined as any electrical circuit which supplies energy to an appliance which gives a recognizable signal. Such circuits include those for door bells, buzzers, code-calling systems, signal lights and the like.

There are two classifications of signal-circuit systems:

1. Class 1 systems—those in which the power is not limited as it is for Class 2 systems.

2. Class 2 systems—those in which power is limited according to maximum open-circuit voltage and maximum rating of overcurrent protection as follows:

A. Max. 15 volts, 5 amps.
B. Max. 30 volts, 3.2 amps.
C. Max. 60 volts, 1.6 amps.

(In any of the three foregoing cases, overcurrent protection may be omitted where the current supply is from a transformer or other device having energy-limiting characteristics and approved for the purpose, or from primary batteries.)

D. Max. 150 volts, 1 amp—provided that such circuits are equipped with current-limiting means other than overcurrent protection which will limit the current as a result of a fault to not more than one amp.

Running circuits for sound systems

Wiring loudspeaker circuits

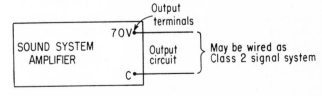

Wireway for sound system

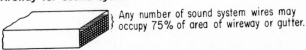

Any number of sound system wires may occupy 75% of area of wireway or gutter.

Class 1 signal wires in raceway

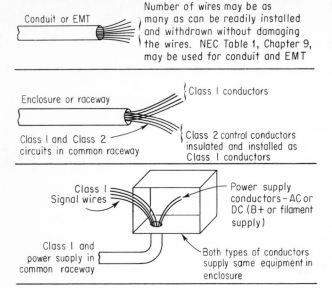

Conduit or EMT — Number of wires may be as many as can be readily installed and withdrawn without damaging the wires. NEC Table 1, Chapter 9, may be used for conduit and EMT

Enclosure or raceway — Class 1 conductors

Class 1 and Class 2 circuits in common raceway — Class 2 control conductors insulated and installed as Class 1 conductors

Class 1 Signal wires — Power supply conductors – AC or DC (B+ or filament supply)

Class 1 and power supply in common raceway — Both types of conductors supply same equipment in enclosure

Class 2 signal wires require separation

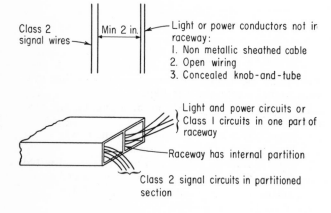

Class 2 signal wires — Min 2 in. — Light or power conductors not in raceway:
1. Non metallic sheathed cable
2. Open wiring
3. Concealed knob-and-tube

Light and power circuits or Class 1 circuits in one part of raceway

Raceway has internal partition

Class 2 signal circuits in partitioned section

Design of Class 1 systems

1. In general, wiring of Class 1 signal systems must be the same as power and light wiring.

2. Conductors are generally limited to minimum of No. 14 but No. 18 or No. 16 may be used if installed in raceway or approved cable or flexible cord and protected at not more than 20 amps.

3. Wires larger than No. 16 must be Type R, T or other approved type. Fixed No. 18 or No. 16 must have insulation at least equal to Type RF-2 or TF. Other conductors with specific approval for the purpose may be used.

4. The number of signal circuit conductors in a raceway may be determined from Table 1, Chapter 9. But, this is not a requirement. The number of wires permitted in a raceway may be as many as can be readily installed and withdrawn without damaging the wires.

5. Signal circuit conductors do not have to be derated according to number in a raceway.

6. When signal conductors are run in raceway with power and light conductors, all conductors must be derated in accordance with Note 8 of Tables 310-12 through 310-15—determining the derating factor on the basis of the number of power and light conductors.

7. Conductors for two or more Class 1 signal circuits may be run in the same raceway—ac and/or dc circuits—if all conductors are insulated for the maximum voltage of any conductor in the raceway.

8. Conductors must be protected against overcurrent in accordance with their current-carrying capacities from Tables 310-12 through 310-15.

Design of Class 2 systems

1. Conductors and equipment on the line side of devices supplying Class 2 systems must conform to rules for general power and light wiring.

2. Class 2 conductors must be insulated and must be separated from conductors of electric light and power circuits as follows:

A. Open conductors must be separated at least 2 in. from power and light conductors not in a raceway, unless separated by a continuous and firmly fixed nonconductor.

B. Class 2 conductors must not be used in any raceway, compartment, outlet box or similar fitting with light and power conductors or with Class 1 signal or control conductors, unless the conductors of the different systems are separated by a partition. But this does not apply to wires in outlet boxes or similar fittings or devices, where power supply conductors are introduced solely for supplying power to the signal equipment to which the other conductors in the enclosure are connected.

C. In shafts, conductors must be separated at least 2 in. from power and light conductors or the conductors of either system must be encased in noncombustible tubing.

D. In hoistways, conductors must be installed in rigid conduit or EMT, except as provided for elevators in Article 620.

E. Conductors run vertically in a shaft or partition must have fire-resistant covering capable of preventing the carrying of fire from floor to floor except where conductors are encased in noncombustible material or located in a fireproof shaft with fire stops at each floor.

3. Overcurrent protection for Class 2 systems must be approved for the purpose.

4. A transformer supplying a Class 2 system must be approved for the purpose and be restricted in rated output to not more than 100 volt-amperes.

Industrial buildings

Industrial plants require a variety of signaling and communication systems, some having individual control equipment, and others interconnected or combined at one point to be supervised by the plant superintendent or the guard personnel:

Fire alarm

Fire alarm systems should be of the closed-circuit supervised type. City and State ordinances should be checked regarding requirements. Generally noncoded systems are limited to small plants, since they only transmit a general alarm and do not indicate the location of the operated station. Coded systems are preferable.

Fire detection

Automatic fire detection systems may be used separately or combined with the manual fire alarm systems.

DEFINITIONS OF TERMS USED IN SOUND WORK

ACOUSTICS . . . . The auditory characteristics of a room resulting from the production, transmission, reception or effects of sound within it.

ACOUSTIC FEEDBACK . . . . The transfer of sound from the loudspeaker back into the microphone in such a manner as to create an annoying squeal or howl.

ACOUSTIC TREATMENT . . . . . . The use of special sound absorbing material to reduce echos and to control reverberation.

AMPLIFIER . . . . In a sound system this usually refers to a device of electronic components used to strengthen the originating signal from a microphone or record player to the point where it will operate loudspeakers.

BAFFLE . . . . Most commonly used synonymously with loudspeaker housing and may be a suspended, or surface or recessed, ceiling or wall mounting device made of wood, plastic or metal, in which a loudspeaker is housed.

BOOSTER AMPLIFIER . . . . An amplifier designed to boost the level of a signal from a pre-amplifier to provide power for driving loudspeakers.

DECIBEL . . . . A unit used to measure the relative loudness of sound. Engineers employ the complex term also to designate power or voltage ratios.

GAIN . . . . Usually expressed in decibels, this term is applied to indicate the increase in voltage or power output over the voltage or power input.

HIGH IMPEDANCE . . . . Literally the total opposition that a circuit offers to the flow of alternating current. Primarily used in the sound field as an important characteristic of amplifiers, microphones and accessories.

LOSS . . . . A term usually expressed in decibels to indicate the decrease of voltage or power output from voltage or power input.

LOW IMPEDANCE . . . . See High Impedance. Usually applies to 500 ohms or less.

MICROPHONE . . . . A device which converts sound waves into corresponding audio-frequency electrical energy.

MIXER . . . . Usually a pre-amplifier which permits several microphones, record player and/or radio tuner to be combined through volume controls. The suitably mixed signal is then usually fed to the input of a booster amplifier.

MONITOR LOUDSPEAKER . . . . . A small loudspeaker mounted in a console or cabinet rack (or adjacent to these) which provides an audible indication of the sound level of the system and which permits preliminary adjustment of the amplifier output before distribution to remote loudspeakers.

PRE-AMPLIFIER . . . . Frequently used synonymously with mixer, although it may be designed to provide for increasing the level of only one input signal.

REPRODUCER . . . . The cartridge mounted in the tone arm which tracks the record grooves by means of a stylus (needle), picking up the electrical signal equivalent of the music or sound which was recorded.

VOLUME LEVEL INDICATOR . . . . A device (meter, neon bulb, etc.) which permits the operator of a sound system to determine visually the sound level output. Usually incorporated in consoles, cabinet racks and pre-amplifiers.

Two Types of Line-Matching Transformers

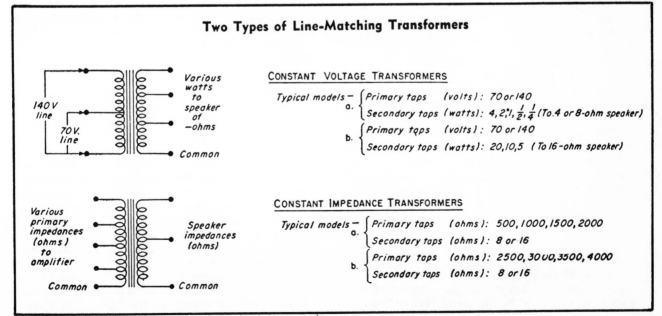

CONSTANT VOLTAGE TRANSFORMERS

Typical models —
a. Primary taps (volts): 70 or 140
Secondary taps (watts): 4, 2, 1, $\frac{1}{2}$, $\frac{1}{4}$ (To 4 or 8-ohm speaker)

b. Primary taps (volts): 70 or 140
Secondary taps (watts): 20, 10, 5 (To 16-ohm speaker)

CONSTANT IMPEDANCE TRANSFORMERS

Typical models —
a. Primary taps (ohms): 500, 1000, 1500, 2000
Secondary taps (ohms): 8 or 16

b. Primary taps (ohms): 2500, 3000, 3500, 4000
Secondary taps (ohms): 8 or 16

When combined with manual fire alarm systems of the coded type, automatic fire alarm systems may be interconnected by using electrically tripped transmitters. In this way a separate and distinguishable signal may be given for these protected areas.

Watchman's systems

Watchman's supervisory systems should be of a type which will require the watchmen on the various tours to produce a record in the superintendent's or chief guard's quarters at the start and at the finish of each tour. It should also contain provisions for the calls to be made to each station and in sequence. Extra features may be included in these systems, such as a delinquency indicator which will signal the chief guard when a watchman is delayed in arriving on time at a station. Or a telephone jack and a pilot lamp at each station may be provided so that communication may be had between headquarters and the outlying points. The telephone jack is used for plugging in a handphone which is equipped with cord and plug, while the lamp is used to notify the watchman along the tour that he is to call the central point. All tour stations must be located at remote points to insure complete coverage of the premises.

Sprinkler systems

These alarm systems are used to signal when sprinkler heads open, when noticeable leaks occur, when waterflow valves operate in either dry or wet systems, when post indicator valves operate or are left open or when the shut-off valves are placed in a sub-normal position. All of these valves are equipped with contacts so that an alarm will be transmitted to either audible signals, annunciators or a combination of same. A supervisory control panel or an annunciator should be provided.

A coded signal may be transmitted to the signal devices of a coded fire alarm system by interconnecting the sprinkler system wiring through an electrically tripped transmitter. These transmitters should be connected to separate supervised circuits on the fire alarm control panel.

Smoke detection

These systems are used to detect smoke in ventilating, air-conditioning and dust-collecting ducts. It may also provide for disconnecting the air blower motor, and to close dampers in various sections of the duct system to prevent spreading of fire.

This is accomplished by means of photo-electric systems wherein the light source directs a beam to a photo-electric cell across the interior of the ducts. The photo-electric equipment may be adjusted to operate when the smoke in the ducts reaches a predetermined density. The control equipment transmits the signal to annunciators together with an audible alarm at the guard's quarters, and may also be interconnected with the manual fire alarm system.

Thermostatic detectors may be installed in the ducts to indicate abnormal rise in temperature.

Burglar alarms

Burglar alarm systems may be used to protect all doors, windows, elevator openings, skylights, etc. This is accomplished by the use of various types of spring contact, switches, foil tape and networks of wired lattice-work. Photo-electric equipment may be used to protect stockrooms, toolrooms, filerooms and loading platforms. Safes and cabinets may be protected by special electrified enclosures or capacity alarms. All signals should terminate in a control cabinet at the chief guard's quarters.

Door alarms

Such systems are used to signal the guard room when certain restricted areas have been entered or vacated by individuals. The doors are provided with contacts which operate lamps or drops in annunciators. An audible signal such as a bell or buzzer is provided at the supervisory location with isolating switches for each circuit. In addition it is desirable to operate a large bell adjacent to each door.

Hold-up alarms may be used in the disbursing office using special pushbuttons, foot and knee contactors at desks and counters.

Paging

Paging systems are used to call and locate individuals for answering telephones, attending meetings, etc. In general these systems may be either of the coded, sound or visual type.

The coded type consists of a code transmitter with audible signals such as bells, horns, chimes or mild-toned sounders and the associated controls.

A sound system consists of one or more microphones, a number of loud-speakers and the associated amplifier equipment.

The visual system used in laboratories and offices consists of a keyboard, lamp annunciators and the necessary control equipment for flashing the lamps and operating a buzzer signal when desired.

Code signals are assigned to the personnel in the coded system. Code numbers are assigned in the visual type of system.

Clock and program systems

These are used for indicating the time of day and operating signal devices such as bells or horns at pre-determined times such as starting and stopping work, rest periods, lunch periods, etc. In addition they may also include time stamps, employees' time recorders, elapsed time or job recorders, etc. These systems may be provided with synchronous-motored movements or minute-impulse movements.

Intercom

Intercommunicating telephone systems may be provided in various forms, and the selection should be based upon the practical requirements.

There are cases in small plants where a 2-station or pair of telephones are desired to converse between two points. For larger installations up to about ten stations, where only one conversation is found necessary at one time, the common-talking selective ringing system may be used. In systems requiring a greater number of stations the selective-talking selective-ringing type should be used. Where it is desired to have a small number of telephones supervised from one location, and only one pair of conversations is desired at one time, a master common-talking system is frequently found satisfactory. For large systems the manual switchboard or the automatic dial type systems should be used.

P. A. systems

Public address sound systems may be used throughout the plant for paging, radio programs, recordings, announcements and entertainment derived from a centralized system. Loudspeakers of the proper type and size are distributed throughout the premises with the wiring to the control center.

Other systems

There are many systems which may be used in manufacturing processes. Liquid level indicators supervise the high and low levels of liquid contents in tanks, cisterns, reservoirs. Pressure indicators supervise all measurable forms of pressure such as air, oil, water and steam. Temperature indicator systems supervise liquid and area temperatures.

Commercial buildings

Modern office and commercial buildings, whether located in large or small cities are faced with similar basic problems insofar as protection and expediency is concerned.

Fire systems

Fire alarm systems of the manual type should be installed for the protection of the general public and the employees within the building. Such systems may be of the same type as outlined for industrial buildings.

Fire alarm systems of the automatic type should be installed at all points where records or files are kept or stored. These systems are composed of a quantity of equally distributed thermostatic detectors grouped into zones and wired to annunciator control boards, or combined with the manual fire

alarm system through electrically tripped transmitters.

Fire-line signal systems are similar to standard coded fire alarms of the closed-circuit type with the addition of manually operated signal stations which are installed on alternate floors of tall buildings. These manual stations have hinged doors, are equipped with special cylinder locks, and are composed of closed-circuit strap keys which are used exclusively by members of the fire department to transmit signals to the pump room.

The coded and the manual stations are all connected in series. The bells are of the single stroke type and are located in the pump room, elevator shafts and at all points required by the local fire prevention authorities. This feature may also be added to pre-signal fire alarm systems in which case the initial operation of the pre-signal station transmits the coded signals on the fire line or pilot bells. The second operation of the pull lever in conjunction with the insertion of a special plug or key in the station will operate the general alarm on all bells.

Fire-line telephone systems are composed of a master station telephone located in the pump room, sub-master station telephones located in the auxiliary pump room and at the building entrance, and outlying telephones located on each of the other floors. These systems are of the common-talking type.

The master and the sub-master telephones are provided with pushbuttons to selectively call each other. The master station is also provided with a loudspeaker type receiver mounted into the instrument housing. A handset with a long extension cord is included which will enable the operator of the pump to remain at his post. Vibrating bells of 6-in. size are used as audible signals on these telephones. The outlying telephones are provided with pushbuttons for selectively calling the master and the sub-master telephones.

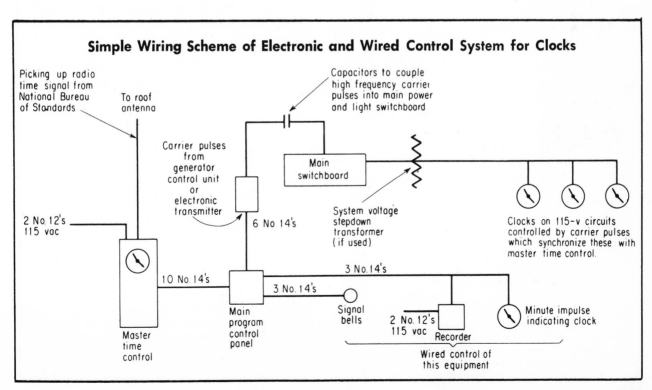

Simple Wiring Scheme of Electronic and Wired Control System for Clocks

"IN" AND "OUT" SYSTEM

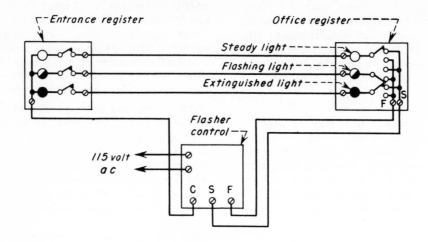

Entrance register

Office register

Steady light

Flashing light

Extinguished light

F   S

Flasher control

115 volt a c

C   S   F

CLOCK AND PROGRAM SYSTEM

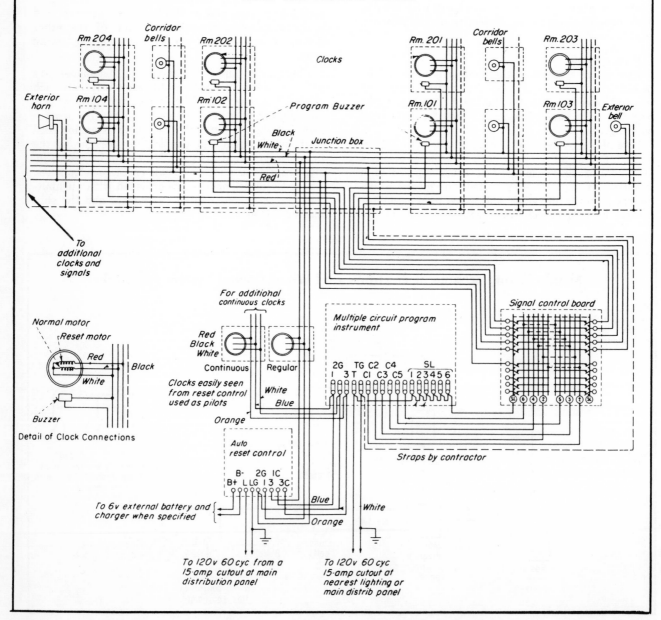

Rm 204

Corridor bells

Rm 202

Clocks

Rm. 201

Corridor bells

Rm. 203

Exterior horn

Rm 104

Rm 102

Program Buzzer

Black

White

Junction box

Red

Rm.101

Rm 103

Exterior bell

To additional clocks and signals

Normal motor

Reset motor

Red

Black

White

Buzzer

Detail of Clock Connections

For additional continuous clocks

Red
Black
White

Continuous

Regular

Clocks easily seen from reset control used as pilots

White

Blue

Orange

Auto reset control

B-   2G   IC
B+ L LG I 3 3C

To 6v external battery and charger when specified

Multiple circuit program instrument

2G   TG C2 C4   SL
I   3 T CI C3 C5   1 2 3 4 5 6

Signal control board

Straps by contractor

Blue

White

Orange

To 120v 60 cyc from a 15-amp cutout at main distribution panel

To 120v 60 cyc 15-amp cutout at nearest lighting or main distrib panel

PHOTO-ELECTRIC SMOKE DETECTOR
INSTALLED IN AIR DUCT

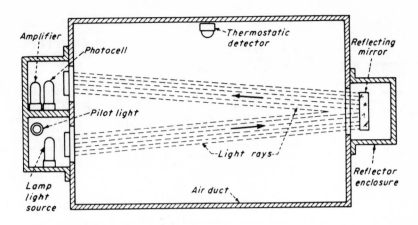

LAYOUT OF TYPICAL PHOTO-ELECTRIC
DOOR OPERATING SYSTEM

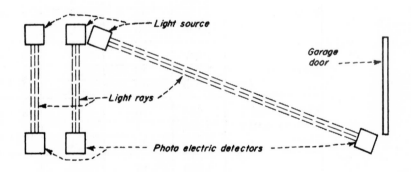

INTERLOCKING DOOR SYSTEM FOR LABORATORIES

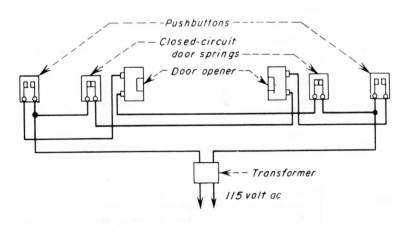

DESIGN CONSIDERATIONS

Following is an outline of usual factors involved in laying out paging, public address and music distribution systems:

I. LOUDSPEAKERS

A. Number of speakers (depends upon size, shape and type of area)
1. One or a few, each operating at high output (high-level speaker system)
2. Relatively large number, each operating at low output (low level speaker system)

B. Types of speakers
1. Cone speakers in wall-mounted, ceiling-mounted, or suspended-baffle enclosure
2. Horn speaker (trumpet, projector horn, re-entrant horn, etc)

C. Amplifier connection
1. Direct connection to amplifier output taps corresponding in impedance value (ohms) to impedance value (ohms) of a single speaker or of a number of speakers in series, parallel, or series-parallel
2. Connection to amplifier constant-voltage output taps (70, 100, 140 volts, etc) through constant-voltage line-matching transformers
3. Connection to amplifier high-impedance output taps (250 or 500 ohms) through constant-impedance line-matching transformers

D. Placement of speakers
1. Assure uniform loudness (eliminate dead or hot spots)
2. In churches, theatres and auditoriums, place speakers well forward of microphones to prevent feedback (squeeling)
3. Minimize reverberation (sound bouncing around)

II. AMPLIFIERS

A. Power output
1. Typical ratings: 6, 10, 15, 30, 50, 70, 100, 125, 250 watts
2. Output required depends upon size and type of area to be covered by sound system (see accompanying table)

B. Number and types of inputs (terminals for connecting high- and/or low-impedance microphones, record player or radio tuner)

C. Output taps (impedance values)
1. Direct connection: 4-, 8- and 16-ohm taps
2. Constant-voltage line transformer connection: 70-, 100- or 140-volt taps
3. Constant-impedance line transformer connection: 250- and/or 500-ohm taps

D. Special functions
1. Record player built into amplifier housing
2. Amplifier, microphone and speakers in carrying case (portable system)

E. Controls
1. Tone
2. Anti-feedback

F. Remote volume controller (plug-in unit for use at distance from amplifier)

G. Power source
1. 110-125 vac, 60 cycles
2. 115 vac, 25 cycles
3. 115 vdc
4. 6 or 12 vdc

H. Amplifier mounting
1. Portable, with protective cage
2. Panel-mounted, for installation on rack

I. Cost (increases with power rating and fidelity of reproduction)

J. Separate preamp unit (for one or more remotely located power or booster amplifiers)

K. Custom assemblies (amplifier, preamp, radio tuner, record player, or other input devices mounted in vertical cabinet rack or console cabinet)

III. INPUT DEVICES

A. Microphones
1. Crystal, dynamic or velocity
2. Omni-directional, bi-directional, or uni-directional (cardioid)

B. Record player (automatic or manual)

C. Tape player

D. FM-AM radio tuner

E. Tone generator
1. To produce tone signal for factory work shifts, lunch periods, etc.
2. Electronic siren for alarm applications
3. To simulate sound of large bell in church belfrys

TYPICAL SYSTEM DATA FOR VARIOUS APPLICATIONS

Application	Sq. Ft. Area	Amplifier Rating (Watts)	Number of Speakers	Type of Speakers
Auditoriums	2,000	15	2	12" Cone in Wall Baffles
	5,000	30	2	12" Cone in Wall Baffles or
	15,000	50	4	12" Projector Horns
Ballrooms	2,000	15	4	
	4,000	30	4	12" Cone in Wall Baffles
	10,000	50	6	
Churches	1,000	10	2	10" Cone in Wall Baffles
	4,000	15	2	12" Cone in Wall Baffles
	15,000	30	4	
Classrooms, Offices and Stores	500	10	1	8" Cone in Wall Baffle
	2,000	15	2	10" Cone in Wall Baffles
	8,000	30	4	
Factories	1,000	15	2	12" Projector Horns
	4,000	30	4	
	8,000	50	4	Re-Entrant Horns
	40,000	100	10	
Funeral Parlors	1,000	10	1	
	4,000	15	4	12" Cone in Wall Baffles
	10,000	30	8	
Restaurants and Night Clubs	1,000	15	2	
	5,000	30	6	12" Projector Horns
	10,000	50	12	
Stadiums and Gymnasiums	3,000	15	2	12" Cone in Wall Baffles
	10,000	30	4	Re-Entrant Horns
	50,000	100	8	

NOTES:

1. Values given in table are averages—not minimums or maximums.

2. Number of speakers and amplifier power rating should be increased where background noise is higher than normal for the type of area.

3. Although wall baffles are indicated for cone speakers, ceiling-recessed or suspended baffles are frequently advantageous.

4. Acoustically "live" areas generally require lower speaker sound levels.

5. Number of speakers will vary with shape of the plan view of the area.

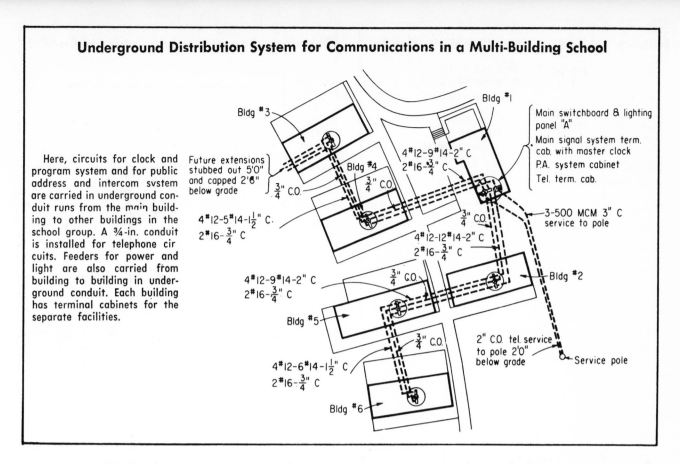

Here, circuits for clock and program system and for public address and intercom system are carried in underground conduit runs from the main building to other buildings in the school group. A ¾-in. conduit is installed for telephone circuits. Feeders for power and light are also carried from building to building in underground conduit. Each building has terminal cabinets for the separate facilities.

Other systems

Sprinkler alarm systems are also used. However, in office buildings these systems are usually installed in storage spaces and other hazardous locations where a deluge is found necessary to prevent the spread of a fire. It is not usually considered where water might completely damage the contents in a given location.

Smoke detection systems may be used in the various duct systems in ventilating and air-conditioning the building and may be applied as outlined under industrial buildings.

Protective alarms are provided in numerous forms to protect doors, windows, floors, ceilings, etc. from intrusion.

Call systems are widely used and are of many types. Individual return-call systems, in which push-buttons and a buzzer may be combined in one block for calling back and forth, are used between two points. Other systems may be composed of push-button blocks on desks, counters, etc., which will operate lamps or drops in annunciators, and pilot or return signals such as lamps on the originating calling station.

Electric door locks are used on doors to be supervised, with operation from pushbuttons at specified locations. Electric door closers may be used and operated from pushbuttons where executives desire to close the doors for privacy.

Clock and program systems may be used in an entire building if occupied by one concern, or by the tenants occupying individual floors.

Garage ramp systems are composed of photoelectric equipment and arranged so that the doors will automatically open to permit an automobile or other vehicle to enter. A double ray is used so that the beams will not be affected or interrupted by a person who may be passing. A diagonal ray may also be used to prevent the door from lowering while the vehicle is still in the ramp. A bell signal may be located in the garage to advise attendants that a vehicle is to enter.

Intercommunicating telephone systems will permit contact with various departments without causing confusion, interruptions or tying up the regular public telephones. These may be secured in different types: either the amplified or non-amplified, master selective-ringing common-talking, selective-ringing common-talking, selective-ringing selective-talking, manual switchboard and automatic dial.

The selection of such telephone systems depends upon the number of stations to be used, whether or not more than one conversation will be held at one time, whether the system is to be under the control and supervision of an individual or whether selectivity is to be obtained without the supervision of an attendant. Other features such as conference calls are also obtainable.

Elevator signals are most important for both passenger and freight elevators. These consist chiefly of "up" and "down" pushbuttons on every floor except on the extreme lower and upper floors, with associated annunciators in the elevator cabs.

All passenger elevators should be equipped with telephones for emergency purposes so that a conversation may be had with the starter on the main floor or the superintendent of the building. A dispatch signal system should also be included for starting the elevators and for signaling at points along the route.

Door signals are usually used between the front, rear and boiler room entrances, to such locations as the main lobby, elevator shafts, superintendent's office and boiler room. All exterior pushbuttons

Number of Microphone Cables in Conduit

NUMBER OF CABLES IN CONDUIT	REQUIRED SIZE OF CONDUIT* (INCHES)
1	½
2	½ or ¾
3	¾
4	¾ or 1
5	1
6	1 ¼
7	1 ½
8	1 ½
9	2

HIGH IMPEDANCE MICROPHONE CABLES — OUTSIDE DIAMETER = 0.245″

LOW IMPEDANCE MICROPHONE CABLES — OUTSIDE DIAMETER = 0.28″ OR 0.231″

*For runs up to 150 ft. with two 45° bends. Plastic outer jacket will pull easier than rubber. Data in the table is approximate; installer should use slightly larger conduit than may seem necessary. Where conduit is already installed and apparently too small, consider use of cables with 0.231″ O. D.

Number of Loudspeaker Cables in Conduit

SIZE OF WIRE IN SPEAKER CABLE (AWG)	REQUIRED SIZE OF CONDUIT (INCHES)										
	1 pr.	2 pr.	3 pr.	4 pr.	5 pr.	6 pr.	7 pr.	8 pr.	9 pr.	10 pr.	20 pr.
20	½	½	½	½	½	½	¾	¾	¾	1	1
18	½	½	½	½	¾	¾	1	1	1	1 ¼	1 ½
16	½	½	½	¾	¾	1	1	1	1	1 ¼	1 ½
14	½	½	¾	1	1	1 ¼	1 ¼	1 ¼	1 ¼	1 ½	2

NOTE: This table contains recommended sizes of conduit, based on the use of unshielded single twisted pairs of solid or stranded, rubber or plastic insulated conductors. This table is only an approximate guide; conduit length and number of bends should be carefully considered.

GENERAL INSTALLATION TIPS

1. Never use acid core solder. Rosin core solder is recommended.

2. Do not attempt to force too many cables through a conduit. Breaks, shorts, or intermittent operation may result.

3. Always ground amplifier, console or cabinet rack.

4. Do not run speaker and microphone lines in the same conduit. Never run either of these in the same conduit with power cables.

5. Label speaker cables before pulling through conduits so that identification of each twisted pair is simplified.

6. Do not use ac-type convenience outlets where specially designed microphone connectors are indicated.

7. When splicing shielded cable, make certain that shield is continuous and carefully soldered at the joints.

8. When soldering conductors with vinyl insulation (to connectors or lugs) avoid excessive heat.

9. Audio cables are specially designed and building wire should not be substituted.

10. Check with sound specialist from whom equipment is purchased when in doubt as to cable or connector to use.

11. When loudspeaker cables are run over very great distances, carefully determine required copper diameter of conductor.

Size of Wire for Loudspeaker Runs

AMPLIFIER OUTPUT TAPS FEEDING SPEAKER HOOKUP (1)	MAX. LENGTH OF SPEAKER CABLE-FEET (2)			
	#20 AWG PAIR	#18 AWG PAIR	#16 AWG PAIR	#14 AWG PAIR
500 ohm	1200	2000	3000	4000
250 ohm	700	1100	2000	3000
70 volts (10-watt amplifier)	1200	2000	3000	4000
70 volts (15-watt amplifier)	950	1600	2000	3000
70 volts (30-watt amplifier)	450	750	1200	2000
70 volts (50-watt amplifier)	290	450	750	1200
70 volts (100-watt amplifier)	150	230	360	560
140 volts (50-watt amplifier)	1100	1800	2800	4000
140 volts (100-watt amplifier)	590	950	1600	2000

(1) The taps to be used will be determined on the basis of the hookup of the line matching transformers for the loudspeakers.

(2) These maximum lengths are one-way distances from amplifier to line transformer. They are the maximum lengths speaker cables can be run without exceeding 10% power loss (an acceptable loss) in the line.

NOTE: In the table, the constant voltage amplifier taps are equivalent to impedance values as follows:

70-volt tap on	10-watt amplifier	= 500 ohms
" " "	15-watt "	= 333 "
" " "	30-watt "	= 167 "
" " "	50-watt "	= 100 "
" " "	100-watt "	= 50 "
140-volt " "	50-watt "	= 400 "
140-volt " "	100-watt "	= 200 "

Intercommunication System of Two-Way P.A. and FM Radio

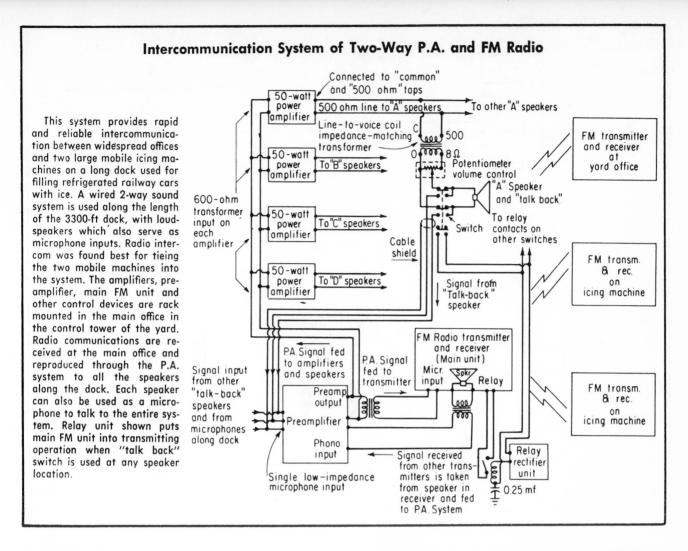

This system provides rapid and reliable intercommunication between widespread offices and two large mobile icing machines on a long dock used for filling refrigerated railway cars with ice. A wired 2-way sound system is used along the length of the 3300-ft dock, with loudspeakers which also serve as microphone inputs. Radio intercom was found best for tieing the two mobile machines into the system. The amplifiers, preamplifier, main FM unit and other control devices are rack mounted in the main office in the control tower of the yard. Radio communications are received at the main office and reproduced through the P.A. system to all the speakers along the dock. Each speaker can also be used as a microphone to talk to the entire system. Relay unit shown puts main FM unit into transmitting operation when "talk back" switch is used at any speaker location.

Schools

Safety is the prime consideration as schools are occupied in many cases by children of all ages. High schools, vocational schools and colleges, although occupied by students of a mature age, are equally in need of efficient and reliable protective systems, as such buildings are very large. In the case of many colleges, they are located in small towns where fire fighting apparatus is not always adequate.

In general there are several types of systems used in schools: manual fire alarm, automatic fire alarm, sprinkler alarm, clock, program, telephones, sound and radio distribution, lecture call, orchestra call and door call.

Fire alarms

Any fire signal should be distinctive from all other signals, and should be audible to everyone in the building. The apparatus for sounding the alarm should be generously distributed within the path of escape, and should be equipped for fire drill purposes. So-called fire-proof or fire-resistant buildings do not decrease the need for properly drilled students. Even a small fire may fill the corridors with smoke and may result in a panic.

Fire alarm systems for use in schools are usually

should be of the watertight type. All bells should be of the heavy-duty type.

of four types, having one common characteristic— they are all closed-circuit electrically supervised.

In small schools, either the non-coded or master coded type is frequently used. In the first system, non-coded break-glass stations operate vibrating bells or horns continuously. In the second system, non-coded break-glass stations operate an electrically tripped master movement on the control panel which in turn operates either single-stroke bells or horns, sounding a common coded signal such as 4-4.

In large schools and colleges, the coded types of system are used wherein every station transmits its own distinctive code to the sounding devices. Where a number of buildings are involved, the coded type systems may be modified and extended to a group system, wherein a fire in one building need not disturb students in other buildings. The operation, therefore, of a station in one building sounds all signals in the same building and only operates signals at certain other locations where supervisors and other members of the staff take command.

Auxiliarized systems, wherein the signal is also transmitted to the municipal fire department, may also be provided and is preferred in many communities. The stations used in this auxiliarized system are provided with a special lock which enables a fire drill to be made with assurance that the signal will not be transmitted outside the building.

Automatic fire detection systems may be included and interconnected with any of the manual fire

Wiring and Equipment for Sound Systems

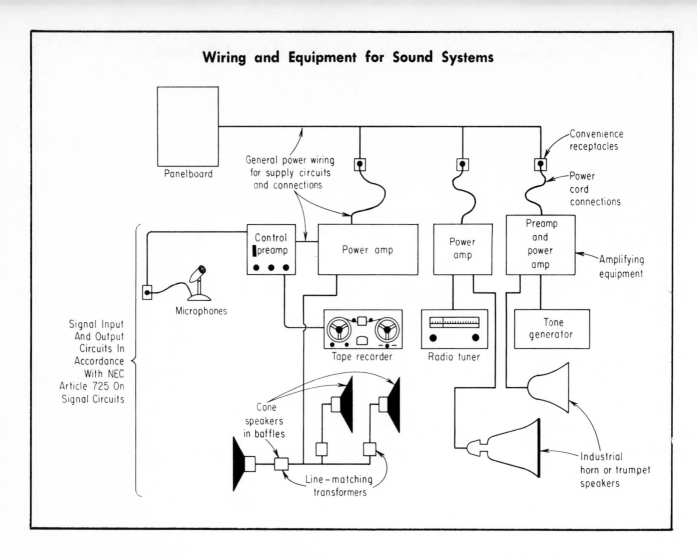

Panelboard

General power wiring for supply circuits and connections

Convenience receptacles

Power cord connections

Control preamp

Power amp

Power amp

Preamp and power amp

Amplifying equipment

Microphones

Signal Input And Output Circuits In Accordance With NEC Article 725 On Signal Circuits

Tape recorder

Radio tuner

Tone generator

Cone speakers in baffles

Line-matching transformers

Industrial horn or trumpet speakers

---

alarm systems mentioned above. The thermostatic detectors are generally located in the boiler room, kitchen and storerooms. In older schools having attics, this form of protection is very important.

Other systems

Sprinkler systems may be used in some areas in the school buildings where the fire hazard is considered great, such as in storerooms.

Clock and program systems provide the means of showing correct time throughout the premises, and to denote the different periods in a day's schedule. In grade schools, the programs are generally arranged to operate signals at the start of classes in the morning, morning recess, lunch period, afternoon recess, and afternoon dismissal. In high schools and colleges the changes in class periods and evening classes must also be considered in setting up the ringing schedules. Program instruments are provided for any minute interval over a 24-hour period.

The clock systems are available in different forms or types, namely, minute-impulse master control, synchronous-motored master control, dual synchronous-motored and electronic.

The minute-impulse system consists of a master clock and a number of secondary clocks and is operated on direct current through a rectifier. The master clock sends out electrical impulses every minute and in addition sends out correction impulses each hour to the secondary clocks.

The synchronous-motored master control system consists of a master clock and secondary clocks which are synchronous motored. The master clock corrects the secondary clocks each hour within specified limits.

The dual synchronous-motored system has no master clock as such but instead all clocks have two motors, one to operate the hands in a normal manner and speed, the other to operate at a much faster rate and which in turn is used to advance the clocks to correct time after an interruption in power.

The electronic system consists of a master clock or transmitter and a number of electronic secondary clocks which operate on a specified electrical frequency and are controlled once each hour by the master clock.

Program systems consist chiefly of a program instrument, a selective signal control board and the necessary audible signals such as bells or buzzers. In sound systems, the bells and buzzers are replaced by an oscillator and loudspeakers. The program instrument is composed of a calendar drum or device, a time drum, signal circuit relays, signal control switches, and program-circuit pushbuttons.

In a small system, the audible signals may be controlled directly from the program instrument. In the larger systems where selectivity is required, a signal control board is used having a pushbutton for each signal device and a set of program cross-connecting busbars with plugs, which permit the changing of program circuits.

Basic Layout of Audio-Video Nurse-Call and Patient Supervision System

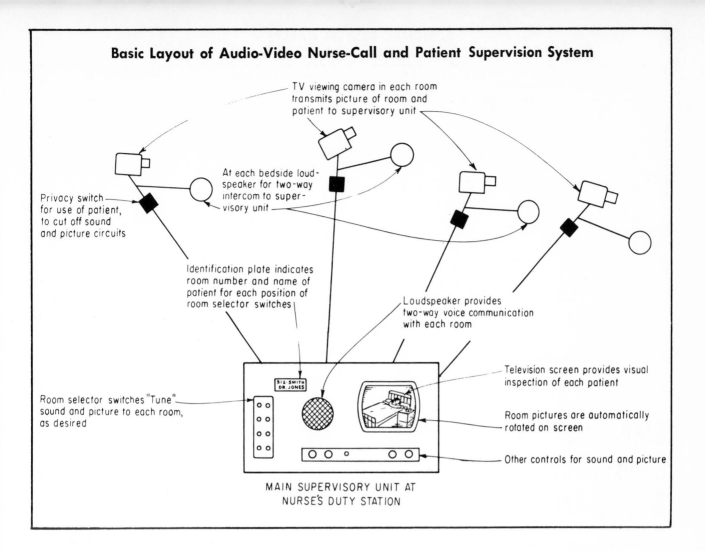

TV viewing camera in each room transmits picture of room and patient to supervisory unit

At each bedside loud-speaker for two-way intercom to super-visory unit

Privacy switch for use of patient, to cut off sound and picture circuits

Identification plate indicates room number and name of patient for each position of room selector switches

Loudspeaker provides two-way voice communication with each room

Television screen provides visual inspection of each patient

Room selector switches "Tune" sound and picture to each room, as desired

Room pictures are automatically rotated on screen

Other controls for sound and picture

312-SMITH DR. JONES

MAIN SUPERVISORY UNIT AT NURSE'S DUTY STATION

In systems incorporating telephones with the signal control board, a handphone is added to this board for communication from the main office to the classrooms and other locations having telephones. The pushbuttons on the signal control board are used for ringing the outlying telephones which actually use the program buzzers in the clock cases.

Elapsed-time clocks may be secured to indicate the time taken by various phases of experiments in laboratories, or the elapsed time in sports such as basketball, football, track, swimming, etc. These are connected individually and are not considered a part of the clock systems.

Telephones are used for intercommunication between the principal's office and the main office and the classrooms. This may be accomplished by means of a master system having a central telephone in which the pushbuttons are used to call the outlying telephones each of which has an audible signal enclosed within the instrument. Or the signal control board of the program system with a handphone and the associated control equipment may be used as the master, using standard outlying telephones with their enclosed signal or outlying telephones without a signal, in which case the program buzzer in the clock cases would be used as a signal.

The classroom telephones are usually of the wall mounted type, while those in the principal's and assistant principal's offices would be of the handphone-on-cradle type. In large high schools and colleges, a manual switchboard system or an auto-

matic dial type system is often used. In the former, the operator would have full control of the traffic between all points. With the automatic type, each person using the system may dial any telephone.

Sound and radio distribution systems are used in all types of schools. These systems consist chiefly of a control desk, microphones and loudspeakers. The control desk is composed of individual control switches for each outlying loudspeaker in classrooms, auditorium, gymnasium, athletic field, etc., together with monitor speaker, microphone, record turntable, radio receiver, amplifiers and other control devices. The microphones are located at the control desk, principal's office and stage with outlets at other points as selected. The loudspeakers are located in the classrooms, auditorium, gymnasium, corridors, cafeteria, athletic field, etc.

The system enables the distribution of radio programs, recordings, lectures and announcements to all points selectively or collectively. If desired, the talk-back feature may be included which will permit conversations to take place between the monitor speaker at the control desk and the loudspeakers in any classroom.

Lecture call systems are in reality return-call systems and are used between the stage in the auditorium and the projection booth. Most of these systems consist of a station on the stage, installed on the wall or in the floor. A long portable cord with a detachable plug and a pendant pushbutton is a

No. 18—1/64" RL*				No. 18—1/32" RL				No. 16—1/64" RL*				No. 16—1/32" RL			
Over. Diam.	Approx. Area Sq. In.	Thick Lead	Conduit Size	Over. Diam.	Approx. Area Sq. In.	Thick Lead	Conduit Size	Over. Diam.	Approx. Area Sq. In.	Thick Lead	Conduit Size	Over. Diam.	Approx. Area Sq. In.	Thick Lead	Conduit Size
0.56	0.243	4/64"	1"	0.69	0.377	4/64"	1¼"	0.61	0.292	4/64"	1"	0.73	0.416	4/64"	1¼"
0.70	0.385	4/64"	1¼"	0.90	0.636	5/64"	1½"	0.76	0.454	4/64"	1¼"	0.96	0.723	5/64"	1½"
0.82	0.528	4/64"	1¼"	1.05	0.864	5/64"	2"	0.92	0.665	5/64"	1½"	1.12	0.985	5/64"	2"
0.94	0.680	5/64"	1½"	1.17	1.076	5/64"	2"	1.02	0.817	5/64"	2"	1.28	1.288	6/64"	2"
1.03	0.833	5/64"	2"	1.32	1.367	6/64"	2½"	1.12	0.985	5/64"	2"	1.41	1.563	6/64"	2½"
1.10	0.950	5/64"	2"	1.41	1.563	6/64"	2½"	1.20	1.130	5/64"	2"	1.51	1.791	6/64"	2½"
1.21	1.147	5/64"	2"	1.55	1.885	6/64"	2½"	1.35	1.413	6/64"	2½"	1.66	2.168	6/64"	3"
1.29	1.304	6/64"	2"	1.61	2.035	6/64"	3"	1.40	1.539	6/64"	2½"	1.76	2.435	7/64"	3"
1.33	1.390	6/64"	2½"	1.68	2.199	6/64"	3"	1.46	1.673	6/64"	2½"	1.83	2.631	7/64"	3"
1.42	1.571	6/64"	2½"	1.82	2.592	7/64"	3"	1.55	1.885	6/64"	2½"	1.95	2.985	7/64"	3½"
1.54	1.885	6/64"	2½"	1.98	3.063	7/64"	3½"	1.69	2.246	6/64"	3"	2.12	3.526	7/64"	3½"
1.68	2.199	6/64"	3"	2.15	3.628	7/64"	3½"	1.86	2.717	7/64"	3"	2.34	4.304	8/64"	4"
1.82	2.592	7/64"	3"	2.33	4.265	8/64"	4"	1.99	3.110	7/64"	3½"	2.50	4.909	8/64"	4"
1.93	2.906	7/64"	3"	2.47	4.791	8/64"	4"	2.11	3.495	7/64"	3½"	2.66	5.553	8/64"	4½"

* Approved by special permission only.

Signal and Communication Wiring Data

Wire sizes, dimensions and raceway data for types of conductors commonly used on signal, alarm and communication systems. Systems operating at substantial voltages and currents derived from power or lighting circuits are subject to code rules. On low voltage circuits line drop may also become a critically important consideration.

SINGLE TELEPHONE CABLE

No. Cond.	Single No. 22 & 4 Single No. 18					
	Braided			Leaded		
	Over. Diam.	Approx. Area Sq. In.	Cond. Size	Over. Diam.	Approx. Area Sq. In.	Cond. Size
6	0.26	0.053	½"	0.30	0.071	½"
11	0.28	0.061	½"	0.33	0.086	½"
16	0.31	0.075	½"	0.36	0.102	½"
26	0.36	0.102	½"	0.40	0.126	¾"
35	0.40	0.126	¾"	0.45	0.159	¾"
45	0.44	0.152	¾"	0.48	0.181	¾"
55	0.46	0.165	¾"	0.51	0.204	¾"
65	0.51	0.204	¾"	0.55	0.236	1"
75	0.53	0.219	1"	0.59	0.255	1"
85	0.55	0.236	1"	0.60	0.283	1"
100	0.60	0.283	1"	0.64	0.322	1"

PAIR TELEPHONE CABLE

No. Pairs	Pairs No. 22 & 2 Pairs No. 18						Pairs No. 22 Only					
	Braided			Leaded			Braided			Leaded		
	Over. Diam.	Approx. Area Sq. In.	Cond. Size	Over. Diam.	Approx. Area Sq. In.	Cond. Size	Over. Diam.	Approx. Area Sq. In.	Cond. Size	Over. Diam.	Approx. Area Sq. In.	Cond. Size
6	0.36	0.102	½"	0.45	0.159	¾"	0.29	0.066	½"	0.33	0.086	½"
12	0.41	0.132	¾"	0.50	0.196	¾"	0.38	0.133	½"	0.42	0.139	¾"
16	0.50	0.196	¾"	0.59	0.273	1"	0.42	0.139	¾"	0.47	0.174	¾"
22	0.57	0.255	1"	0.66	0.342	1"	0.49	0.188	¾"	0.53	0.220	1"
32	0.62	0.302	1"	0.71	0.396	1¼"	0.57	0.253	1"	0.61	0.292	1"
41	0.74	0.430	1¼"	0.85	0.567	1¼"	0.61	0.292	1"	0.66	0.342	1"
51	0.88	0.608	1½"	0.97	0.739	1½"	0.70	0.385	1¼"	0.76	0.454	1¼"
65	0.92	0.665	1½"	1.01	0.802	2"	0.76	0.454	1¼"	0.83	0.541	1¼"
75	0.95	0.709	1½"	1.03	0.833	2"	0.82	0.528	1¼"	0.89	0.622	1½"
85	0.98	0.754	1½"	1.07	0.899	2"	0.86	0.581	1¼"	0.93	0.679	1½"
100	1.08	0.916	2"	1.16	1.057	2"	0.94	0.694	1½"	1.01	0.802	1½"
125	1.18	1.094	2"	1.26	1.247	2"	1.01	0.802	1½"	1.08	0.916	2"
150	1.27	1.254	2"	1.34	1.410	2½"	1.12	0.985	2"	1.18	1.094	2"
175	1.37	1.474	2½"	1.44	1.624	2½"	1.18	1.094	2"	1.25	1.227	2"
200	1.45	1.649	2½"	1.57	1.938	3"	1.27	1.254	2"	1.34	1.410	2½"

DUPLEX & TRIPLEX

Size AWG	Insulation Rubber Braid		Maximum Conductors in Conduit					
	Over. Diam.	Approx. Area Sq. In.	½ in. Int. Area .30 Sq. In.	¾ in. Int. Area .53 Sq. In.	1 in. Int. Area .86 Sq. In.	1¼ in. Int. Area 1.50 Sq. In.	1½ in. Int. Area 2.04 Sq. In.	2 in. Int. Area 3.36 Sq. In.
22*	.20	.031	6	12	20	36	50	84
22†	.22	.038	9	15	24	45	60	102
19*	.24	.045	4	8	14	24	34	68
19†	.26	.053	6	9	18	33	45	75

Note: * 2 Wire twisted.
† 3 Wire twisted.

part of this station and is used for calling the projection booth where a buzzer is sounded.

A buzzer is mounted on the wall of the stage and is controlled from the station in the projection booth which consists of a pushbutton mounted on the wall, ganged with the buzzer used for calling from the stage. A pilot light may be added to the projection booth station with a switch so that either the buzzer or the pilot light may be operated. Telephones may also be combined in these systems.

Orchestra call systems are usually return-call systems in which lamp annunciators with a buzzer and pushbuttons are used, and these are located in the orchestra pit.

Hospitals

There are several types of systems used in hospitals, namely visual and audio nurse-call, emergency calls, psychopathic alarms, paging, "In" and "Out," sprinkler alarms, intern, ambulance, clinic, inter-phone, nurses' home room-call, clocks, laboratory, fire alarm, watchman's report, elevator and dumbwaiter signals, door-calls and ground detector signals.

Nurse call

Nurse-call systems are used by the patients to call a nurse or attendant to the bedside. There are two general types of such systems—the visual and the audio. By pressing a portable button, lights are caused to be illuminated over the patient's door in the corridor, duty rooms, diet kitchens and the nurses' stations on a given floor or section thereof. In the case of a ward, a pilot light is included with the calling station or is mounted on the ceiling above the curtained cubicles to ascertain the origin of the call.

The lamp signal at the nurse's station may be a single common lamp for a floor, or a section thereof, or an annunciator with an indicating lamp for each room. The choice depends upon the number of rooms, shape and size of the floors, the number of nurses available, and the amount of efficiency desired. In addition to the lamp signals, a buzzer is located at each supervisory point such as duty rooms, diet kitchens and nurses' stations together with a cut-off switch permitting full control at all times.

Directional pilots are of assistance when used with nurse-call systems. They are used to direct attention to the nurses while enroute between patients' rooms and points of supervision. They indicate the general direction of a call without having to return to a supervisory point. These signals consist of door-lamp stations mounted on the ceiling of a corridor intersection and may be interconnected with other floors.

Nurse-call stations of the visual and audio type using locking buttons may be ganged with other outlets such as radio, public telephones, duplex convenience receptacles, night lights, etc. A barrier must be provided in the outlet box whenever a lighting circuit enters adjacent to a low-tension outlet. However, nurse-call stations of the visual and audio remote-reset type use momentary-contact buttons.

The audio or voice feature is used in conjunction with the visual nurse-call system and is a valuable adjunct since the nurses may converse with the patient and in that way can give better service and save considerable time and footsteps. In this system, the patient presses the pushbutton in the usual manner and all lights and buzzers operate as previously described. The chief change is at the nurse's station, where in a new installation the annunciator is omitted, since the lamps, the control and the audio equipment is enclosed in one unit. A loudspeaking unit is located in the wall at the head of the bed or on the night table alongside the patient's bed. When the patient presses the button, a lamp illuminates in the master unit at the nurse's station. A control key for that station or room is operated by the nurse and the circuit is completed for talking. All other lights in the corridor and supervisory points remain illuminated until the button is reset at the patient's bedside in the case of locking button systems, or reset at either the patient's bedside or at the nurse's station in the case of the momentary-contact button type.

Emergency call

An emergency feature may be added to any nurse-call system. This is, in most cases, used by the nurse to call assistance to a patient's room when the occasion requires. In the case of a locking button nurse-call system, the emergency button has the same contact mechanism as the portable button; but it is mounted directly on the gang plate. When this button is operated it illuminates separate and distinct lamps and audible signals. As an example, a red or green lamp is added to each corridor lamp station and to all supervisory stations. In addition a bell, which operates continuously, is used.

Psychopathic alarm systems are used as a protection in the event a nurse or attendant is attacked by a violent patient. Such a system consists of corridor-control stations, room-calling stations, corridor lamps and supervisory stations as for the regular nurse-call system.

When an attendant enters a room, the corridor control station is set by means of a key before going into the room. This immediately energizes the room stations within that room and lights a clear lamp in the corridor indicator and at the supervisory points. Should it become necessary to call for assistance, the room stations are operated by means of a pushbutton which lights colored lamps at all points described previously and operates a bell continuously at the nurse's station and at other points desired. The system is de-energized by resetting the corridor station.

Paging systems

Paging systems are used to locate doctors and other members of the staff throughout the building. There are three general types of systems used: visual, sound and coded.

The visual system uses lamp annunciators throughout but also incorporates an audible signal such as a buzzer or chime in the event an occasional selective signal is desired. In the visual type, three and as many as six persons may be paged at one time by setting up the combination of code numbers. Usually three-digit figures are used, although occasionally one, two, or four digits are used for other code number combinations.

The sound system consists of loudspeakers throughout the one or more hospital buildings. In the sound system, the name of the person is transmitted through microphone.

The coded system uses bells, buzzers, sounders or chimes throughout the hospital building. In the coded system each person is assigned a code number which is transmitted from a central point to all audible signals.

"In" and "Out" systems are used by the doctors and other members of the staff to designate whether or not they are present in the building. Generally, an entrance register, having a lamp and a switch for each person, is located near the main entrance of the building or in the doctors' cloak or lounge rooms. Another unit known as the office register and having the same capacity is located near the telephone switchboard operator. In the standard type system the office register does not require switches, but in the recall or message type system, a switch adjoins each lamp, the same as for the entrance register.

In the system using the entrance register and the regular office register, the doctor operates the switch alongside his name and thus causes the lamp to illuminate his name at the entrance register and at the office register. When he leaves the building he returns his switch to the original position in order to extinguish the lamps. In the message signal type, the operation of the switch in the office register by the telephone switchboard operator causes the connected lamp to flash in both units and indicate that such a person is wanted at the office to obtain a message, instructions or mail before leaving the building.

Other Systems

Intern-call systems generally consist of either a return-call system or a master telephone system between the interns' living quarters and the head nurse's or superintendent's office. In the return-call system a pushbutton board with a buzzer is located at the central point, and a return-call station consisting of a buzzer and pushbutton is located in each intern's room.

Sprinkler alarm systems are used where it is deemed necessary to deluge the contents of a room to insure against spread of fire from one point to another.

Ambulance calls may be kept separate but are often combined on an annunciator with other door signals. In most cases, however, the system is so arranged that a bell operates with the annunciator indicator as a distinctive signal when a pushbutton is operated from the ambulance entrance.

Clinic systems are generally composed of annunciator or buzzer call systems. In the case of examination and dressing rooms, a pushbutton plate is located in the former having a pushbutton for each dressing room. A buzzer is located in each dressing room. The signal designates that the doctor is waiting for a specific patient.

Interphones are used between the main kitchen and the floor diet kitchens and are usually located near the dumbwaiters. They may also be used between the offices, nurses' stations, supervisors, etc. For the kitchen service, a master system may be used wherein the master telephone may be located in the main kitchen equipped with a pushbutton for each outlying telephone. The outlying telephones are provided with a single pushbutton. In this system the master telephone can call any of the outlying telephones, but the outlying telephones can only call the master. For intercommunication between a small number of offices and various departments, a selective-ringing common-talking system may be used. In larger systems using more than 12 telephones a selective-ringing selective-talking system should be used.

Nurses'-home calling systems are composed of the same equipment as previously described under intern-call system. In very large nurses' homes, the central control unit should be of the plug and jack type wherein a telephone type jack is used for all rooms having the same last two digits in their room numbers.

Clock systems are very important in hospitals, both for keeping time and in administering anesthesia. Clocks are located in offices, corridors, nurses' stations, kitchens, laboratories, operating rooms, lounges, etc. Seconds-beat clocks should be installed in operating and delivery rooms.

Laboratory signal systems are used for various purposes. Contacts may be placed on the doors of cabinets which contain drugs, narcotics, etc., and the signals may be transmitted to an annunciator located in the office of the person in charge. An interlocking door control system may be provided on the doors leading to the darkroom for the development of X-ray films. This is so arranged that no one may enter such a room unless an inner or another entry door is closed to insure that bright light does not enter the developing room.

Fire alarm systems for use in hospitals are usually of the pre-signal type. In this type of system the first operation of the pull lever in the coded station only operates pilot bells at certain supervisory points such as the superintendent's office, chief nurse's office, engineer's office, elevator shafts, etc. Upon arrival at the point of the fire, if it is deemed necessary to vacate the building, the officer in charge inserts a plug in the station alarm jack and pulls the lever so that all bells throughout the building operate.

Watchman's report systems are used in hospitals to insure that the premises are covered properly at night. The types of systems described in other sections may be used for this purpose.

Sound and radio systems enable the patients to listen in, on one or more channels of radio programs, recordings, announcements, etc. Connection of the headphone or loudspeaker is made by plugging into the jack on the wall plate, usually ganged with the nurse-call station. Provision should also be made for television, the outlets being located in solariums, day rooms and lounges.

Elevator signals for passenger and freight are always provided, and are usually furnished by the manufacturers of these units. Signals are also required for dumb-waiters.

Index